BMC AUTOBOOK THREE

Workshop Manual for the
Austin Cambridge A40 1954-57
Austin Cambridge A50 1954-57
Austin Cambridge A55 Mk I 1957-58
Morris Oxford Series 2 1954-56
Morris Oxford Series 3 1956-59
MG Magnette ZA 1954-56
MG Magnette ZB 1956-59
Riley 1.5 1957-65
Wolseley 15/50 1956-58
Wolseley 1500 1957-65

by

Kenneth Ball G I Mech E

and the

Autopress team of Technical Writers

AUTOPRESS LTD   GOLDEN LANE   BRIGHTON   BN1 2QJ   ENGLAND

The AUTOBOOK series of Workshop Manuals covers the majority of British and Continental motor cars.

For a full list see the back of this manual.

CONTENTS

Acknowledgement

Introduction

ISBN 0 85147 147 1

First Edition 1967
Second Edition, fully revised 1968
Third Edition, fully revised 1969
Reprinted 1970
Reprinted 1971
Reprinted 1971

Printed in Brighton England for Autopress Ltd by G Beard & Son Ltd

ACKNOWLEDGEMENT

My thanks are due to The British Motor Corporation Ltd for their unstinted co-operation and also for supplying data and illustrations.

I am also grateful to a considerable number of owners who have discussed their cars at length and many of whose suggestions have been included in this manual.

Kenneth Ball G I Mech E
Associate Member Guild of Motoring Writers
Ditchling Sussex England.

INTRODUCTION

This do-it-yourself Workshop Manual has been specially written for the owner who wishes to maintain his car in first class condition and to carry out his own servicing and repairs. Considerable savings on garage charges can be made, and one can drive in safety and confidence knowing the work has been done properly.

Comprehensive step-by-step instructions and illustrations are given on all dismantling, overhauling and assembling operations. Certain assemblies require the use of expensive special tools, the purchase of which would be unjustified. In these cases information is included but the reader is recommended to hand the unit to the agent for attention.

Throughout the Manual hints and tips are included which will be found invaluable, and there is an easy to follow fault diagnosis at the end of each chapter.

Whilst every care has been taken to ensure correctness of information it is obviously not possible to guarantee complete freedom from errors or to accept liability arising from such errors or omissions.

Instructions may refer to the righthand or lefthand sides of the vehicle or the components. These are the same as the righthand or lefthand of an observer standing behind the car and looking forward.

CHAPTER ONE

THE ENGINE

Engine type   Overhauling methods   Removing engine   Dismantling head   Timing gear and camshaft
Servicing oil pump   Pistons and crankshaft   Oil filters   Reassembling engine
Crankshaft, pistons and rods   Fitting oil pump   Replacing head   Rocker adjustment   Valve timing
Replacing distributor drive   Fitting manifolds   Water pump and generator   Modifications
Fault diagnosis

All the BMC engines covered by this chapter are basically the same, even the difference between the 1200 cc engine of the 'A40' and the 1489 cc of the other cars being little more than one of capacity. There are, of course, changes which relate to the increased performance required from some of the engines. These would be twin carburetters, increased compression ratios and larger valves, but they make practically no difference to the servicing instructions. There might be small variations in such details as engine mountings which call for special instructions on removing the engine from the car. These will be found under appropriate sub-headings.

Engine type

The four cylinder, in-line engine has push-rod operated valves working vertically in a cast-iron detachable head. These parts can be seen in **FIG 1:1** and **1:2,** where the following features can also be identified. The valves have renewable guides, and the valve stems are fitted with seals to prevent excessive oil consumption. The push-rods and tappets are operated by a chain-driven camshaft on the left-hand side of the engine. The camshaft runs in three bearings which are fitted with white-metalled liners. On early engines the double-roller chain which

drives the camshaft is ingeniously tensioned and silenced by a synthetic rubber ring mounted between the large chain wheel sprocket teeth. Later engines have a self-adjusting chain tensioner. End thrust on the camshaft is taken by a plate bolted to the front of the cylinder block. An integral skew gear to the rear of the camshaft drives a transverse shaft which in turn drives a distributor on the right-hand side of the engine. The same camshaft gear also drives the oil pump. There is an eccentric on the camshaft for operating a mechanical fuel pump if one is fitted.

The forged steel crankshaft runs in three bearings. These have renewable shells with surfaces of different alloys selected to suit the loads imposed by varying power outputs. End float is restricted by thrust washers on each side of the centre main bearing.

The connecting rods have big-ends which are split diagonally so that they will pass upwards through the bores. The caps have machined lugs and dowel bolts for accurate location. The big-ends have renewable bearing shells, and like the main bearings, these have different alloy surfaces to cope with the various power outputs.

The split-skirt pistons have three compression rings and one oil-control ring each. The gudgeon pins are clamped in the small-ends of the connecting rods.

The oil pump is driven from the camshaft gear by a short vertical shaft which engages with the inner of a pair of rotors with specially shaped lobes. Oil is drawn through a gauze filter and delivered under pressure from the pump to a non-adjustable relief valve in the left-hand side of the cylinder block at the rear. This valve restricts oil pressure to a safe maximum when the oil is cold and thick, returning any overflow back to the sump. The oil then proceeds to a gallery along the right-hand side of the engine where, at the rear end, will be found an oil gauge union or an electrical pressure-operated switch which is connected to a warning light on the dash. If the engine is fitted with a full-flow oil filter there will also be a large-bore pipe leading forward to it. Both full-flow and by-pass types of oil filter are located just in front of the starter motor, the by-pass filter having no external feed pipe. The full-flow filter has a felt element which cleans all the oil and then passes it on to the main gallery feeding the bearings. If the element becomes clogged with dirt, a relief valve opens to allow unfiltered oil to by-pass the element and go to the bearings direct.

Early engines have a by-pass type of filter which takes only a small quantity of the oil from the main stream, cleans it thoroughly and passes it back to the sump. From the main oil gallery, drillings supply oil to the main, big-end and camshaft bearings. The connecting rods are drilled for jet lubrication of the cylinder walls. From the rear camshaft bearing oil passes upwards through a drilling in the block and the rear rocker shaft bracket to lubricate the rockers, returning to the sump via the push-rod holes. Oil from the centre camshaft bearing enters a gallery on the left-hand side of the engine and lubricates the tappets through individual drillings. A small hole in the camshaft thrust plate provides lubricating oil for the timing gear on early engines. On later engines it passes through a hole in the chain tensioner head.

Overhauling

Before tackling any operations on the engine, there are a few points which may be found useful. They are as follows:

No. 1 cylinder is at the front end of the engine. Reference to the right- or left-hand side of the engine means that it is viewed as from the driving seat looking forward.

It is good practice to clean away all accumulations of dirt from around joints which are to be broken, so that when they are parted no foreign matter can drop inside, perhaps into some inaccessible place.

When re-assembling, perfect cleanliness should be the rule. Wash the parts in paraffin and finish off with clean petrol. They can then be left to dry. If rag is used to clean any part it must certainly be of a non-fluffy type so that particles do not find their way into places like small oil jets.

When reassembling, lubricate working parts with clean engine oil unless otherwise specified.

On the mechanical side, scrape away all traces of old gaskets and jointing material. Then examine the joint faces for burrs, as they often cause persistent leakage. A light stroke with a fine file held flat will remove any high spots without actually touching the face. It is not good practice to use split pins and locking tab washers a second time, as the double bending may easily lead to

fracture. Any small piece of metal such as this is definitely out of place in an engine with close working clearances.

Finally, mark everything before dismantling to ensure that it is replaced correctly, but do not mark so heavily that working surfaces are damaged. As an example, a light scratch across the two edges of a flanged joint before splitting it will make it easy to settle upon the right position for reassembling.

Removing the engine

Given adequate lifting tackle it is not difficult to remove the power unit complete, or the gearbox can be left behind if desired. Generally, the instructions for removing the power unit will hold for all models, and are as follows. Any variations will be dealt with at the end of the section.

1 Detach the bonnet. Remove the windscreen washer bottle.
2 Drain the oil and cooling systems.
3 Remove the battery and all electrical leads to the engine.
4 Unclip the radiator hoses and heater hoses (if fitted). Remove the radiator.
5 Remove the air cleaner and carburetter, first detaching the controls and fuel pipe to the pump. Also detach all other pipes between the engine and the body, but not the one to the slave cylinder.
6 Unclip the exhaust pipe from the manifold and remove the down pipe and bracket by releasing the front end of the silencer.
7 In the case of remote control gear levers, work inside the car and remove the cover, the finisher and then the spring ring and lever. If a column change is fitted, detach the control rods from the levers on the side of the gearbox.
8 From below, take out the two clutch slave cylinder mounting bolts and tie the cylinder out of the way without disturbing the hydraulic pipe line.
9 Remove the speedometer drive cable from the gearbox and the wires to the reversing light switch if one is fitted.
10 Mark the two flanges of the rear universal joint, unscrew the four self-locking nuts and withdraw the propeller shaft from the gearbox.
11 At this stage, support the power unit with the lifting tackle, release the front engine mountings and remove the cross-member under the gearbox.
12 Making sure that everything between the power unit and the body has now been detached, the unit can be lifted forward and upward to remove it.
13 Replacement is the reverse of the procedure, not forgetting to refill the radiator, the engine and the gearbox.

Removing the power unit, 'A40', 'A50' and 'A55'

1 Experience has shown that it is much easier to remove the complete power unit than detach the engine by itself.
2 Proceed as in the previous section, but remove the battery tray as well as the battery.
3 Turn off the tap next to the fuel pump and disconnect the fuel pipe.
4 Remove the handbrake control rod bracket from the gearbox cross-member and unhook the pull-off spring.

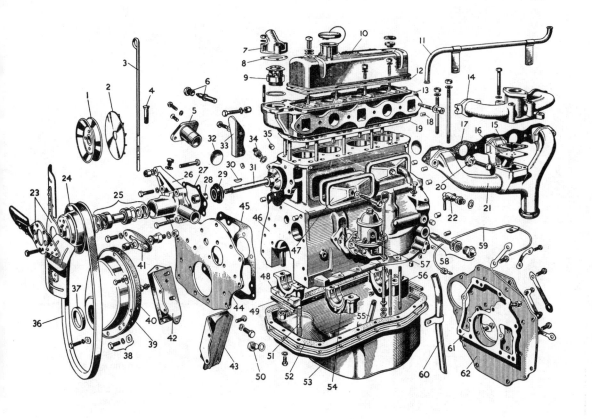

Fig 1:1 The cylinder block components.

Key to Fig 1:1   1 Generator pulley.   2 Generator fan.   3 Dipstick.   4 Dipstick guide.   5 Distributor housing.
6 Water temperature gauge element.   7 Thermostat housing.   8 Washer.   9 Thermostat.   10 Rocker cover.   11 Heater pipe.
12 Rocker cover joint washer.   13 Cylinder head.   14 Inlet manifold.   15 Hot spot joint washer.   16 Hot spot.
17 Inlet and exhaust manifold gasket.   18 Core plug.   19 Cylinder head gasket.   20 Manifold securing washer.   21 Exhaust manifold.
22 Cylinder block drain tap.   23 Fan blades.   24 Fan and water pump pulley.   25 Water pump bearings and seals.   26 Water pump.
27 Joint washer.   28 Distance piece.   29 Seal.   30 Water pump shaft key.   31 Shaft.   32 Welch plug.   33 Generator bracket.
34 Oil pressure gauge connection.   35 Core plug.   36 Fan belt.   37 Oil seal.   38 Timing cover set screw.   39 Timing cover.
40 Joint washer.   41 Generator swinging link.   42 Engine right hand front mounting.   43 Engine left hand front mounting.
44 Engine front plate.   45 Joint washer.   46 Crankcase and cylinder block.   47 Tappet cover.   48 Front main bearing cap.
49 Cork seal.   50 Sump drain plug.   51 Front main bearing stud.   52 Sump joint washer.   53 Sump.   54 Centre main bearing cap.
55 Oil return pipe.   56 Rear main bearing.   57 Fuel pump.   58 Oil release valve.   59 Vacuum ignition control pipe.   60 Breather pipe.
61 Joint washer.   62 Engine rear plate.

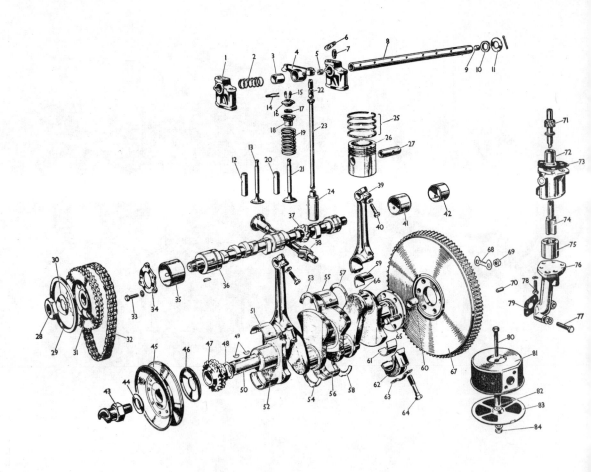

Fig 1:2   The camshaft and crankshaft components.

Key to Fig 1:2   1 Rocker standard.   2 Spring.   3 Rocker bush.   4 Rocker.   5 Rocker shaft end plug.   6 Locking plate.
7 Rocker shaft locating screw.   8 Rocker shaft.   9 Plug.   10 Spring washer.   11 Flat washer.   12 Exhaust valve guide.
13 Exhaust valve.   14 Valve circlip.   15 Collets.   16 Valve cap.   17 Oil seal.   18 Shroud.   19 Spring.   20 Inlet valve guide.   21 Inlet valve.
22 Rocker adjusting screw.   23 Push rod.   24 Tappet.   25 Piston rings.   26 Piston.   27 Gudgeon pin.   28 Camshaft gear nut.
29 Chain tensioner.   30 Lock washer.   31 Camshaft gear.   32 Timing chain.   33 Set screw.   34 Camshaft locating plate.
35 Camshaft front bearing.   36 Camshaft.   37 Distributor gear.   38 Distributor shaft.   39 Connecting rod.   40 Gudgeon pin clamping screw.
41 Camshaft centre bearing.   42 Camshaft rear bearing.   43 Starter dog nut.   44 Lock washer.   45 Crankshaft pulley.   46 Oil flinger.
47 Crankshaft gear.   48 Washer.   49 Keys.   50 Crankshaft.   51 Top half front main bearing shell.   52 Lower half front main bearing shell.
53 Front upper thrust washer.   54 Front lower thrust washer.   55 Top half centre main bearing shell.   56 Lower half centre
main bearing shell.   57 Rear upper thrust washer.   58 Rear lower thrust washer.   59 Big end upper half bearing shell.
60 First motion shaft bush.   61 Lower half big end bearing shell.   62 Big end bearing cap.   63 Lock washer.   64 Big end bolt.
65 Flywheel bolt.   66 Oil restriction nipple.   67 Flywheel.   68 Lock washer.   69 Flywheel bolt nut.   70 Dowel.   71 Oil pump gear.
72 Oil pump body.   73 Joint washer.   74 Inner rotor.   75 Outer rotor.   76 Oil pump bottom cover.   77 Set screw to strainer.
78 Bottom cover set screw.   79 Joint washer.   80 Strainer centre bolt.   81 Strainer.   82 Distance piece.   83 Strainer bottom cover.
84 Strainer centre bolt nut.

Taking out the radiator also entails removing the top cross-member. Unscrew the two bolts at each end, remove the distance pieces, and then unscrew the two set screws at the bottom of the centre stay. Detach the bonnet catch control wire and release the electrical harness from the clips.

It is not necessary to remove the front engine mounting brackets, but release the rubber mountings and slacken the setscrews holding the brackets to the frame. This allows the brackets to be tilted outwards enough to clear.

Sling the engine as in **FIG 1:3** so that it is at approximately 30° to the horizontal. Owing to the angle, it will be necessary to use a jack under the gearbox to take the weight before removing the cross-member. Once the weight of the complete unit is taken by the slings the jack can be removed.

Alternative method, 'A40', 'A50' and 'A55'

The engine and gearbox unit may also be removed downwards, complete with the front suspension. Having removed all the wires and controls which join the engine to the bodywork, proceed as follows.

Do not remove the radiator but take off the top and bottom hoses and the heater hoses if fitted.

Take off the distributor cap, the rotor, the generator and the fan belt.

Follow all the instructions in the previous section concerning the gearbox controls, the handbrake bracket and the propeller shaft.

4 Remove the front brake flexible pipe lines at the supporting bracket ends.
5 Remove the steering side tubes from the arms of the idler and the steering gearbox.
6 Use a trolley jack under the gearbox cross-member and take the weight. Release the cross-member from the body. The engine and front suspension can now be detached from the body by removing the four nuts, mounting plates and rubber seats, from the bolts to be found just above the lower wishbone bearings at the inner end. It will also be necessary to free the gear change cross shaft from its ball socket. Do this by levering it towards the engine.
7 Lift the body high enough to allow the engine and suspension unit to be wheeled away, taking care not to damage the exhaust outlet pipe at the rear. The spare wheel tray must also be retracted or it will foul the floor.
8 Reverse the process to reassemble the unit, carefully checking that all wires and controls have been reconnected. Fill the cooling system, the sump and the gearbox. Also the clutch and brake fluid reservoirs and bleed the brakes.

Removing the power unit, Wolseley '15/50'

Follow the general instructions up to paragraph 10. Then do the following:
1 Attach the lifting tackle and remove the four bolts securing the rear mounting to the body, also the nuts from the front engine mountings.
2 Raise the power unit as far as possible at an angle of 10° or 15° to the horizontal. Then raise the front of the engine and lift out vertically.

Removing the power unit, Wolseley '1500' and Riley '1.5'

Follow the general instructions up to the point where the lifting tackle has taken the weight of the power unit. Then proceed:

1 Remove the two bolts securing the engine control link front bracket to the gearbox extension. Remove the two nuts and washers securing the under side of the rear mounting rubbers to the rear cross-member.
2 Remove eight bolts and lower away the rear cross-member.
3 Manoeuvre the power unit from the chassis at a sharp angle, the front end being much higher than the rear.

Removing the power unit, 'Magnette'

Do not remove the bonnet as suggested in the general instructions, but detach the prop from the dash and tie up the bonnet clear of the windscreen. Follow the extra instructions given for the Wolseley '1500' and Riley '1.5', but after removing the radiator take out the four bolts to detach the valance tie-bar.

Removing the power unit, 'Oxford'

Having reached the stage in the general instructions where the lifting tackle has taken the weight of the unit, proceed as follows:
1 Remove the special bolts holding the rear tie-bar under the gearbox. Note that the engine must be at rest and the bar in an unstressed position when it is being reassembled.

2 Remove the bolts securing the rear gearbox cross-member to the underframe and those of the front engine mountings. Note that the front bottom bolt on each side of the cross-member bracket is larger than the others and also secures the master cylinder. The bolts pass through distance tubes inside the longitudinal frame members. When reassembling, the covers on the frame members must be removed so that it can be seen that the bolts and distance tubes are correctly replaced.

3 The power unit can then be lifted up and forwards at a slight angle.

To remove the engine alone, all models

1 Do not drain the gearbox.

2 Follow the general instructions for removing the complete power unit but do not disturb the gearbox fittings such as the slave cylinder for the clutch, the gear lever or other controls, and the rear mounting.

3 Take the weight of the gearbox on a jack and remove all the bolts from the clutch bell-housing flange. Pull the engine horizontally forward until it is clear of the gearbox first-motion shaft, and then lift away. It is of the greatest importance to ensure that no weight hangs on the first-motion shaft at any time. This point is also important when the engine and gearbox are being parted outside the frame.

Dismantling the engine

It would be useful at this stage to point out that many of the dismantling sequences can be followed with the engine still in the car. For instance, with the head off and the sump removed, the big-ends can be split and the pistons and connecting rods pushed upwards out of the bores. The tappets can be removed through the engine side-covers. With the radiator off, the water pump and timing gear can receive attention, and it is not even necessary to remove the radiator when dealing with the water pump on the 'Austins' and the 'Oxfords'.

The head, valves and rocker gear

The head can be seen lifted off the block in **FIG 1:1** and the rocker gear is shown exploded in **FIG 1:2**. If the engine is still in the car, do not attempt to remove the head until the cooling system has been drained. **IMPORTANT:** To remove the rocker assembly with the head remaining on the cylinder block, it is essential to drain the radiator and slacken all the cylinder head securing nuts, because four of the rocker shaft bracket nuts also hold down the head. If the seven external cylinder head fixing nuts are not slackened at the same time distortion may result, with subsequent water leakage. The correct order for slackening and tightening the cylinder head nuts is shown in **FIG 1:4**.

To take off the head, slacken the eleven holding-down nuts a little at a time. The smaller nuts on the right-hand side of the rocker shaft brackets do not prevent the head from being lifted, but if the valves are to be removed, the rocker gear might just as well be taken off now.

If the head sticks, do not drive a screwdriver between the joint faces but tap the sides of the head with light hammer blows on a piece of wood.

Alternatively the sparking plugs can be replaced and the engine turned over so that compression will lift the head.

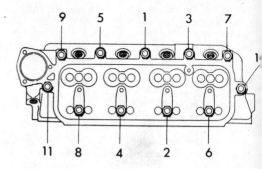

Fig 1:4 The order of loosening and tightening cylinder he nuts.

If decarbonizing is necessary, do most of the scrapi with the valves in place to avoid damaging the seats. T valves have 45° faces and a single spring with t exception of the Riley '1.5' and later 'Magnettes' whi are fitted with double springs for extra perfromanc **FIG 1:5** shows the oil-sealing ring above the valve ste This fits inside the shroud shown above the spring and of rectangular section on the earlier cars. Later cars ha the circular-sectioned ring shown in **FIG 1:6**.

Before dismantling working parts which are apparent identical, it is essential to have some storage ra available so that they can be kept in their correct orde A board drilled with holes is suitable for push-rods ar valves. This makes it possible to restore the parts to the original location, where they have run themselves in.

Fig 1:5 Early valve assembly showing oil seal above valv stem.

To remove the valves, pull off the hairpin circlip round the cotters and compress the valve spring with a suitable tool. Remove the cotters and release the spring. Separate the spring from the shroud and cap and check it for length against the dimension given in Technical Data to see whether it needs replacing. Examine the valve face and head seating for the excessive wear and deep pitting which cannot be removed by light grinding-in. The valve faces can be reground by a garage. A well-equipped garage can also re-cut the seats in the head, or if they have worn too far they can be machined out and inserts fitted.

Worn valve guides can be replaced by drifting out the old ones and driving in the new. **FIG 1:7** shows the type of drift required. When fitting the new guides, note that the exhaust guide is longer than the inlet. Press the guides in from the top, the inlets with the largest chamfer uppermost and the early exhaust guides with their counterbore at the bottom. The dimension 'B' is $\frac{5}{8}$ in above the machined spring seating. After fitting new guides the valve seatings in the head must be re-cut to ensure that they are concentric with the guide bores. The valves can then be ground-in with a rubber suction tool, using a semi-rotary motion and with a light spring under the head to lift the valve occasionally. The valve can be turned to a new position after each spell of grinding and this will help to prevent the grooving of the seats which is the result of a purely rotating motion. Wash away every trace of grinding compound afterwards.

When reassembling the valves on early engines, fit the oil-sealing ring with the chamfered face downwards in the shroud. Later engines which are fitted with the circular-sectioned ring shown in **FIG 1:6** have a different shroud. The ring is fitted by pressing it over the valve stem until it reaches the bottom of the cotter recess. If

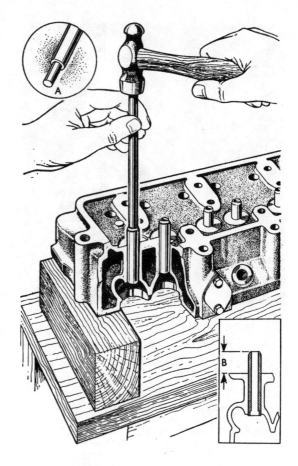

Fig 1:7   Using drift 'A' to fit a valve guide. 'B' is $\frac{5}{8}$ in.

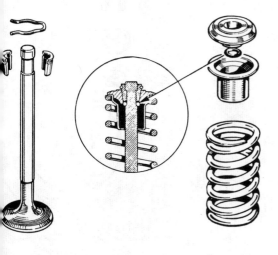

Fig 1:6   Later valve assembly showing correct fitting of oil seal.

both types of ring are soaked in clean engine oil for a short time they will be found easier to fit. It is most important to fit new sealing rings at every overhaul or there may be trouble with oil leaking down the valve stems.

To strip the rocker gear, unscrew the locating grub screw on top of the rear bracket. This is clearly shown in **FIG 1:8**. Note the locking plate. By removing the split pins, flat washers and spring washers from each end of the rocker shaft it will be possible to slide off the rockers, brackets and springs, having marked them so that they can be correctly assembled. The oilways in the shaft can be cleaned out by unscrewing the plug from the front end. When reassembling, start with the rear bracket, securing it with the locating grub screw, and do not forget the locking plate when replacing the rocker assembly on the head. Tightening the bracket nuts will also clamp the rocker shaft.

Fig 1:8   Rocker-shaft location in rear bracket.

Key to Fig 1:8   1 Locking plate.   2 Locating screw.

The push-rods should be checked for straightness and for wear of the ends. The bottom ball-end locates in a barrel tappet. To remove the tappets release the breather pipe and take off the tappet covers 47 in **FIG 1:1**. The tappets 24 in **FIG 1:2** can be lifted out by turning the camshaft until each one is raised. Keep them in their correct order. New tappets should be fitted by selective assembly so that they just fall into the guides under their own weight when lubricated.

Removing the timing gear

If the engine is in the car, drain the cooling system and remove the radiator. When dealing with the 'Magnette', also remove the front engine mounting nuts and lift the front of the engine to allow the fan pulley to clear the cross-member. Then carry out the following operations on all models:

1 Slacken the generator bolts and remove the belt.
2 Bend back the tab on the lock washer 44 in **FIG 1:2** and unscrew the starting dog 43 anti-clockwise. Pull off the pulley 45.
3 Remove the nine timing cover bolts, spring washers and elongated flat washers. Note the varying bolt lengths and positions.
4 Draw off the timing cover, taking care not to damage the gasket. Behind the cover and on the crankshaft will be found the oil thrower 46 with its concave face to the front.
5 Unlock and remove the camshaft chain wheel nut 28 and lock washer 30. The two chain wheels, together with the chain, can now be eased off a fraction at a time using small levers. Look out for the packing washers 48 behind the crankshaft wheel.

On those engines which are fitted with the chain tensioner shown on the left-hand side of **FIG 1:9**, it is not necessary to remove the device to withdraw the timing chain and wheels. Simply unscrew the bottom plug from the tensioner body and insert a $\frac{1}{8}$ in Allen key to engage the cylinder. These parts can be seen in **FIG 1:10**. Turn the key clockwise between a half and a full turn until the rubber slipper is free from spring pressure. Early engines have a synthetic rubber ring 29 fitted between the teeth of the large chain wheel to act as a chain silencer and tensioner. This should be replaced if the chain is noisy.

If it is decided to replace either of the chain wheels with a new part it will be necessary to check the alignment to determine the thickness of the packing washers 48. Place a straightedge across the sides of the camshaft wheel teeth, and using a feeler gauge, measure the gap between the straightedge and the sides of the teeth on the crankshaft chain wheel. Subtract .005 in from the feeler gauge reading and fit the resultant thickness of packing washers 48.

Replacing the timing gear

To replace the timing chain and wheels, set the crankshaft key at tdc and the camshaft key at one o'clock when seen from the front. Assemble the wheels into the chain with the timing dimples opposite each other as shown in **FIG 1:9**. Engage the crankshaft wheel with its key, then turn the camshaft slightly until the camshaft wheel will engage the camshaft key. Push the gear home and secure the camshaft wheel with nut and lock washer. If a tensioner is fitted, it can be released for operation by inserting the Allen key and turning it anticlockwise until the slipper head moves forward under spring pressure against the chain.

Note: Do not use force when turning anti-clockwise or push the slipper head into the chain by external pressure.

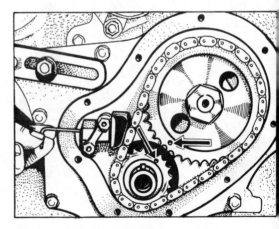

Fig 1:9   Timing gear assembly marks. Also shows Allen key releasing chain tensioner.

Before replacing the timing cover, fit the oil thrower 46 with its concave face forward. Oil leakage past the seal 37 in **FIG 1:1** can be cured by renewing the seal, lubricating it well with engine oil. The seal must be carefully centred when fitting the timing cover. Assemble the fan pulley into the seal in the cover with a rotating motion. Press the pulley on to the crankshaft, complete with timing cover and line up the holes for the cover fixing bolts. Secure the cover by tightening the bolts evenly and a little at a time. The starting dog and locking washer can then be replaced.

Servicing the chain tensioner

1 Unlock and remove the two securing bolts, enabling the assembly and the backplate to be lifted away from the engine.
2 Withdraw the plunger assembly from the body and insert the Allen key into the base of the plunger. Turn the key anti-clockwise, holding both key and plunger securely until the cylinder and spring are released. The parts can be identified in **FIG 1:10**.
3 If the slipper head is worn, replace both head and cylinder assembly, provided that they will be fitted into a body bore that is not more than .003 in oval. If the bore is worn beyond this, then the whole assembly must be renewed.
4 Clean all the components and pay particular attention to the inlet oil hole in the spigot and the small outlet oil hole in the slipper face. These provide lubricant for the timing chain.
5 To reassemble, insert the spring in the plunger and place the cylinder on the other end of the spring.
6 Compress the spring until the cylinder enters the plunger bore, engaging the helical slot with the peg in the plunger. Hold the assembly compressed and fit the Allen key. Turn the cylinder clockwise until its end is below the peg, holding the spring compressed. Withdraw the key and insert the plunger assembly into the body.
7 Replace the back plate and fit the assembly to the cylinder block. Check the slipper head for freedom of movement, and ensure that it does not bind on the back plate.
8 When the timing chain is fitted, release the tensioner as instructed in the previous section. Make sure that the two bolts and the plug are securely locked.

Removing the camshaft

This is an operation best performed with the engine out of the car and detached from the gearbox.

1 Remove the inlet and exhaust manifold assembly, the push-rods and tappets and the timing gear.
2 Disconnect the vacuum pipe and low-tension lead from the distributor.
3 Take out the two bolts and flat washers securing the distributor to its housing. Do not slacken the clamping plate bolt or the ignition timing will be lost. Withdraw the distributor.
4 Take out the securing screw and withdraw the distributor housing 5 in **FIG 1:1**. Then take a bolt with a $\frac{5}{16}$ in UNF thread and screw it into the tapped end of the drive spindle 38 in **FIG 1:2**. This can be withdrawn as shown in **FIG 1:11**.
5 Remove the sump, the oil pump and the oil pump drive shaft as detailed later in this chapter. Then remove the timing cover and gear.
6 Behind the camshaft chain wheel is a triangular thrust plate secured by three screws, (item 34 in **FIG 1:2**). By removing this and the mechanical fuel pump, if one is fitted, the camshaft can be withdrawn. Make a careful note of the exact location of the thrust plate. On earleir engines without the self-adjusting chain tensioner, the plate is drilled for an oil jet which lubricates the timing chain. The later-type of plate has no jet and is different in shape. The plate also controls end-float of the camshaft. If the figure exceeds .007 in the thrust plate must be replaced with a new one.

Now check the camshaft bearing journals for wear and scoring, the diameters and clearances being given in Technical Data. The white-metalled bearing liners in the block should also be examined for wear or pitting. These liners can be renewed, but the final operation is to line-ream them with a special tool. This is a highly skilled job and must be entrusted to a garage with the necessary equipment.

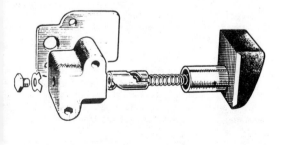

Fig 1:10 Timing chain tensioner components.

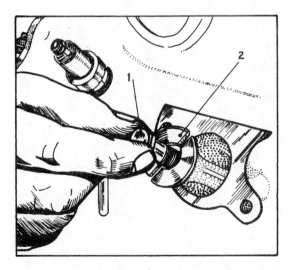

Fig 1:11 Removing distributor drive shaft 2, using bolt 1.

After examining the cams and distributor drive gear for excessive wear the camshaft can be replaced in the reverse order of dismantling.

Removing the sump and oil strainer

The following instructions apply to all the cars with the exception of the 'Magnette' and Wolseley '15/50'. On these last two it is necessary to disconnect the front engine mountings, drain the cooling system, disconnect the radiator hoses and lift the front of the engine as far as possible. It is then possible to remove the sump as on all the other models.

1 Drain the sump and replace the drain plug.

2 Remove the nineteen set-screws and shakeproof washers from the sump flange. It may also be necessary to remove the two lowest bolts from the rear engine mounting plate and bell housing. Drop the sump away, taking great care of the gaskets and the cork strips 49 in **FIG 1:1**, at each end.

3 Remove the gauze oil strainer on early models by undoing the union connecting the oil pick-up pipe to the pump and unscrewing the four bolts securing it to the crankcase. On later models, simply remove the two bolts securing it to the pump cover 76 in **FIG 1:2**.

4 Dismantle the strainer by removing the centre nut, bolt and distance piece. On models with four bracket bolts, also remove the two delivery pipe flange bolts.

5 Clean the sump and strainer with a stiff brush and paraffin. Never use a piece of rag. Dry thoroughly and start to reassemble.

6 Replace the strainer centre bolt and distance tube, then the cover. Note the locating tongue on the cover and replace it correctly.

7 If the sump gasket is undamaged and has not been leaking it may be used again although it is advisable to fit a new one. To fit a new gasket, remove all traces of the old one. Smear the faces of the crankcase joint with grease and fit the gasket. Refit the sump, taking particular care of the cork sealing strips mentioned in paragraph 2. Tighten the bolts diagonally and evenly.

Removing and dismantling the oil pump

With the sump and strainer removed as explained in the previous section, the oil pump can be detached.

1 Two bolts secure the oil pump bottom cover 76 in **FIG 1:2**. Three studs and nuts secure the oil pump to crankcase. Unscrew the stud nuts and remove the pump, followed by the drive shaft and gear 71.

2 Remove the bottom cover and extract the rotors 74 and 75. Examine the body and rotors and renew worn parts.

3 When reassembling the pump, insert the outer rotor with the chamfered end first. Follow with the inner rotor and replace the cover. After tightening the two cover bolts, try the pump to see that it revolves freely. Replace the drive gear and the pump. Do not forget to prime the pump by pouring oil into the priming plug orifice above the oil release valve 58 in **FIG 1:1**. This is closed by a set screw and washer.

On later engines, the oil pump has an aluminium body and the rotor spindle bearing is extended to the pump bottom cover, which is dowelled to the pump body. The body spigot diameter is increased, the crankcase altered to suit the new pump body and a new joint washer used. The new driving spindle is drilled to feed oil to the driving gears and the cylinder block is drilled to supply oil to the spindle. This second-type spindle may be used to service the earlier undrilled type, but never the other way round, as the earlier undrilled spindle would blank off the oil supply to the gear. When fitting a new joint washer to the first type of pump it should be cut away between the two large holes as shown on the right in **FIG 1:12**. Engines with the early-type pump have a 12 or 15 cast on the right-hand side of the cylinder block. With the introduction of the new pump, the number was changed either to 1200 or 1500 and repositioned.

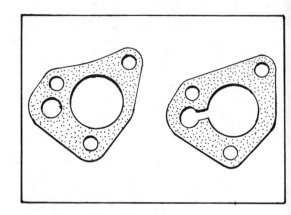

Fig 1:12 Early oil pump joint washer correctly cut on right.

Removing the clutch and flywheel

With the gearbox parted from the engine, the clutch and flywheel can be taken off.

1 Remove the clutch by unscrewing the six bolts and spring washers which secure it to the flywheel. To avoid distortion of the clutch cover, release the bolts a turn at a time. Two dowels locate the clutch cover to the flywheel.

2 Unlock and remove the nuts which hold the flywheel to the crankshaft. Draw the flywheel off the crankshaft spigot.

When refitting the flywheel, ensure that pistons 1 and 4 are at tdc when the flywheel mark 1/4 is uppermost.

Fitting a new starter ring

To remove the old starter ring from the flywheel, saw partly through the ring and then split the cut open with a cold chisel, taking care not to damage the flywheel register on which the ring fits. Check that the new ring gear and the flywheel surfaces are clean and free from burrs.

Heat the new ring all round to an even light blue surface colour which is equivalent to a temperature of 300° to 400°C, (575° to 752°F). Do not overheat or the hardness of the teeth will be impaired. Place the heated ring on the flywheel with the cut-away on the gear teeth uppermost. The expanded ring can be lightly tapped into place on the flywheel register and allowed to cool naturally. The ring will then be a permanent shrink fit and immovable.

The connecting rods

These may be removed complete with pistons without taking the engine out of the car, providing the sump and cylinder head have been taken off. The big-end bearings can be removed and replaced from below, with the sump dropped down out of the way.

The parts can be readily identified in **FIG 1:2.** Before attempting to split any of the big-ends it is essential to mark adjacent surfaces on each rod and cap with the number of the bore from which they will be removed. Start with No. 1 at the front. This will ensure that the caps will be returned to the correct rods and fitted the right way round.

To remove the big-ends:

1 Unlock the bolts 64, unscrew a few turns and tap lightly. The cap will then come away from the rod, the bolts can be completely removed and the cap and rod lifted away from the crankshaft.

2 Remove the bearing shells by hand. Observe the locating tags and notches. No attempt should be made to adjust the bearings. If they are worn, pitted, scored or breaking up, they must be renewed. The steel-backed shells have alloy bearing surfaces which are selected to suit the power output of the engine concerned. Refer to Technical Data at the back of this manual for details of the correct type to use, and never mix different alloys in one engine.

IMPORTANT: The bearing shells are precision machined and do not require bedding in. Never try to carry out adjustments by filing the rods, caps or shells, as they at once become non-standard and will not be accepted for new rods on an exchange basis.

Removing rods and pistons

With the cylinder head off, and the big-ends split, remove any carbon at the top of the cylinder bores, then the rods and pistons can be pushed upwards and out. At this stage it is a good idea to replace the caps and bolts on their respective rods to avoid confusion. **FIG 1:13** shows the assembly.

Pistons

These are of the split-skirt, aluminium alloy type with the gudgeon pin clamped in the small-end of the connecting rod. To separate the pistons from the rods, unscrew the gudgeon pin clamping screw 9 in **FIG 1:13.** It must be completely removed so that the groove in the pin is clear, enabling the pin to be pushed out.

The piston has four rings, three at the top for compression sealing and one at the bottom for oil-control. The top ring is plain. The second and third are taper, and these must be fitted with the narrow side uppermost. They may also be found to be marked with a 'T'. Oil control rings can be fitted either way up.

Piston rings must always be removed and replaced over the top of the piston. Use a narrow piece of thin steel inserted under one end of the ring and rotate it gently, applying slight upward pressure on the ring so that it begins to rest on the land above the ring groove,

until the whole ring is out of the groove. Before replacing rings, clean out the grooves free from carbon using a piece of broken ring, but do not remove metal in the process. When in place in the bore the ring gap should be between .008 and .013 in. This can be measured with a feeler gauge by pushing the ring well down the bore on top of a piston to ensure that it is square with the bore.

When fitting new rings, remove any 'lip' which may have formed at the top of the cylinder bores. This is the limit of travel of the top ring and may lead to noisy operation or a fractured ring, if new rings are fitted.

In production, pistons are fitted by selective assembly, because of very small variations in size. The grade is indicated by a figure stamped inside a diamond on the piston crown, and if it is for example a '2', the piston must be replaced in a bore marked with the same number. Oversize pistons are marked with the actual oversize dimension enclosed in an ellipse. After a rebore, this size must always be stamped on the cylinder block adjacent to the bore. The piston crown is also stamped 'FRONT' to show which way round it should be fitted.

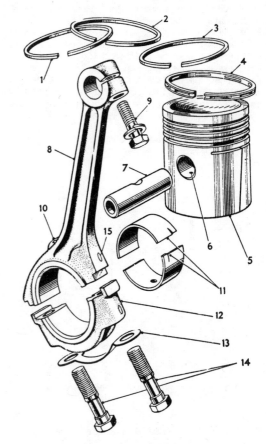

Fig 1:13   Piston and connecting-rod assembly.

Key to Fig 1:13   1, 2 and 3 Compression rings.   4 Oil control ring.   5 Piston.   6 Oil hole.   7 Gudgeon pin.   8 Connecting-rod.   9 Clamping screw.   10 Oil hole.   11 Bearing shells.   12 Bearing cap.   13 Locking plate.   14 Bolts.   15 Identification marking.

If the piston clearances given in Technical Data are exceeded, a rebore is necessary. Oversize pistons and rings are available in +.010 in, +.020 in, +.030 in and +.040 in sizes, and suitable bore sizes for these are given in Technical Data.

If excessive wear makes it necessary to fit cylinder bore liners, this can only be done by experts with precision machinery. After the liners are fitted they are finished to the standard bore size.

It is important to bear the following points in mind when reassembling pistons and connecting rods.

1 When fitting new gudgeon pins use selective assembly until a pin is found which is a double thumb push fit for three-quarters of the way at room temperature. Finally tap home with a soft-faced mallet.

2 Check that the gudgeon pin is positioned in the connecting rod so that its groove is in line with the clamp screw hole.

3 Ensure that the clamp screw spring washer has sufficient tension.

4 The clamp screw must not be bent. It should pass readily into its hole and screw freely into the threaded portion of the little end so that it will firmly compress the spring washer.

5 Fit the connecting rod with the gudgeon pin clamp screw on the slotted side of the piston.

When replacing the piston and rod assembly in the correct bore, set the piston ring gaps at 180° to each other. The gudgeon pin clamp screw should be on the same side as the split skirt, and both screw and split skirt should be on the camshaft side of the engine. The word 'FRONT' on the piston crown should now be in the correct position.

Note that the big-ends are offset, with the narrow part facing the main bearing nearest to it. This is clearly shown in **FIG 1:14**.

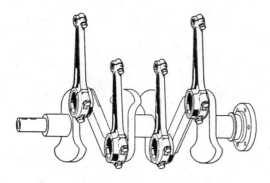

Fig 1:14   Correct assembly of connecting-rod offsets.

Removing the crankshaft and main bearings

This is done with the engine out of the car.

1 Remove the flywheel and clutch, the timing chain, the sump and strainer and the rear engine mounting plate 62 in **FIG 1:1**. Remove the two bolts passing through the front mounting plate 44 into the front bearing cap 48.

2 Check the crankshaft end float to see that it lies between the limits given in Technical Data. The end float is controlled by thrust washers on either side of the centre main bearing. If the end float is excessive the thrust washers need renewal.

3 Mark each bearing cap and the crankcase so that there is no doubt about the exact location when the cap is replaced. Remove the self-locking nuts and spring washers. Lift off the caps. Note the thrust washers 53, 54, 57 and 58 in **FIG 1:2**. The half washers with lugs are located in the bearing cap.

4 Lift out the crankshaft. This will give access to the top halves of the thrust washers and the bearing shells.

Inspect the crankshaft journals and big-end pins for scoring and ovality, comparing the diameters with those given in Technical Data. If worn outside the limits, the crankshaft can be reground, the undersizes being −.010 in, −.020 in, −.030 in and −.040 in for both journals and pins. Bearing shells are available for these undersizes. The shells have alloy-metal linings and are machined to give the correct running clearance, no fitting being necessary. Bearing material varies with the model and the correct specifications will be found in Technical Data.

IMPORTANT: Never file the caps to take up wear or reduce running clearances.

When the lining-metal of the bearing has 'run' it is essential to clean out all oilways in the crankshaft and block to remove every particle of metal. This is done by forcing paraffin under pressure through the oilways, following up with clean engine oil. It is also necessary to clean the oil pump, the sump and sump strainer.

Examine the bearing shells and thrust washers and renew them if they are scored, pitted or breaking away.

When the crankshaft is replaced, the thrust washers must have their oil grooves facing outwards and the main bearing shells fitted into the caps and crankcase housings with their tags located in the appropriate notches. The rear main bearing cap horizontal surfaces should be thoroughly cleaned and lightly coated with 'Wel-Seal' or similar jointing compound, so that there will be an oil-tight seal when the cap is fitted to the block.

Oil pressure relief valve

The component parts of this valve are shown as item 58 in **FIG 1:1**. The function of the valve is to provide an extra return passage for oil back to the sump if pressure becomes excessive. This may happen when the oil is cold and thick. Lifting pressure is determined by a spring which is positioned by two fibre washers and a domed screw plug. There is no provision for adjustment.

Check the length of the spring against the figure given in Technical Data, which also gives the correct relief pressure. The spring must be renewed if it is not the right length.

Examine the valve seating for wear. If not excessive, the valve can be ground in using a little fine compound, removing every trace of it after the operation.

External oil filters

These are of two types, the early by-pass one shown in **FIG 1:15**, and the later full-flow filter as depicted in **FIG 1:16**. It may be found that recent full-flow filters have a different head fitting which enables the bowl to be removed without disturbing the external feed pipe.

The by-pass filter has an element 2 which is thrown away when it is clogged. To replace the element, unscrew the centre bolt and remove the bowl, taking care of the sealing ring 3. Wash out and dry the bowl before fitting the new element. Washer 8 fits on the centre bolt before it is inserted in the bowl. When the assembly is ready to refit, fill the bowl with clean engine oil and offer up into position.

The full-flow filter is fitted with a felt element which should be renewed every 6000 miles.

1 Place a container below the filter to catch oil which may drain from the feed pipe and the bowl.
2 Release the banjo connection on the filter bowl unless it is the type with no connection to the bowl.
3 Unscrew the centre bolt and remove the bowl from the engine, keeping an eye open for the sealing ring 2 in **FIG 1:16**. This may stay in position in the head casting or it may come away with the bowl.
4 Pull out the relief valve assembly and remove the old element.
5 Draw the centre bolt out of the bowl. This will free the bottom plate, spring, washers and circlip. Clean the bowl and all the parts and dry thoroughly.

To reassemble the filter

1 Using **FIG 1:16** for reference, fit the washer 9 to the centre bolt 10 and insert the bolt in the bowl.
2 Place the parts 12, 13, 14 and 15 over the bolt in that order, followed by circlip 16 which is pushed down to the raised surface of plate 15.
3 Place the element in the bowl, which can now be half-filled with engine oil. Insert the relief valve assembly and refit the filter bowl, making sure that sealing ring 2 is not twisted and fits correctly in the head casting.

On the full-flow filter without the feed pipe to the bowl, it is simply a matter of unscrewing the centre bolt to remove the bowl. The feed pipe, which is attached to the filter head, need not be disturbed.

In every case, after fitting a new filter element of any type, run the engine for a few minutes and top up the sump if necessary.

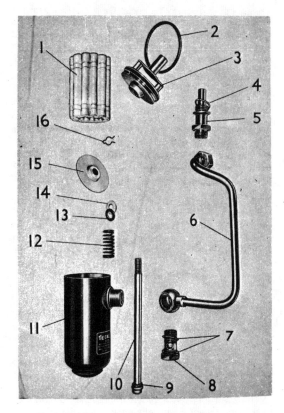

Fig 1:16 Components of early full-flow oil filter.

Key to Fig 1:16 1 Element. 2 Sealing ring. 3 Relief valve assembly. 4 Copper washer. 5 Pipe connection. 6 Filter feed pipe. 7 Copper washers. 8 Banjo bolt. 9 Rubber washer. 10 Centre bolt. 11 Bowl. 12 Bottom plate spring. 13 Steel washer. 14 Felt washer. 15 Bottom plate. 16 Circlip.

Reassembling a dismantled engine

Before starting operations it is advisable to stock up with a complete set of new gaskets. Clean every joint face free from old gasket material and jointing compound, examining the faces for burrs which may have given rise to oil leakage. If the cylinder block has been rebored, pay particular attention to the crevices behind the crankcase webs, where swarf is likely to lodge. Clean out all oil passages with a powerful jet of cleaning fluid followed by engine oil. If the auxiliaries such as the water pump, distributor and mechanical fuel pump are in good condition, or have been overhauled according to the instructions given in the appropriate chapters, the work of reassembling the engine can proceed.

Stand the cylinder block upside down and fit the top halves of the main bearing shells, locating the tags properly in their notches. Also fit the top halves of the thrust washers which are without tags. The oil grooves face outwards.

Lower the crankshaft into place after oiling the working surfaces liberally. Put the bottom bearing shells in the caps, fit the caps and tighten the fixing nuts to the torque

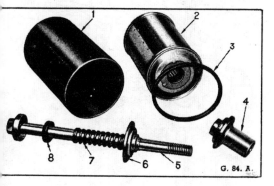

Fig 1:15 Components of by-pass oil filter.

Key to Fig 1:15 1 Bowl. 2 Element. 3 Sealing ring. 4 Distance piece. 5 Centre bolt. 6 Collar. 7 Spring. 8 Rubber washer.

wrench figure given in Techncial Data, starting with the centre bearing. As each cap is tightened, check that the crankshaft will turn freely. If it does not, remove the last cap to be tightened and look for burrs or dirt under the bearing shells. Coat the horizontal surfaces of the rear cap with jointing compound.

Fitting the pistons and connecting rods

Oil the bores and fit the pistons from the top, using a ring compressor. The correct position for the gudgeon pin clamping bolt and the split in the skirt of the piston have been given in the section dealing with pistons and connecting rods. Press the pistons down the bore until the top bearing shell can be fitted to each connecting rod, locating the tag in the machined notch. Oil the big-end pins, fit the bottom shells into the caps and refit the caps. After checking that the identifying marks on each cap and rod tally, fit the bolts and locking plates. Tighten the bolts to the correct torque figure, checking the freedom of the crankshaft to turn before moving on to the next rod. Finally, lock the bolt heads.

Replacing the flywheel and clutch

Check the mating surfaces of the crankshaft and flywheel for burrs, fit the flywheel and tighten the nuts to the required torque figure. Lock the nuts. The 1 and 4 mark on the periphery of the flywheel must be in line with, and on the same side as the first and fourth throws of the crankshaft.

When bolting the clutch to the flywheel, the clutch plate must be centralized by using the special arbor described in the Clutch chapter. This is most important, as it might otherwise prove impossible to enter the first-motion shaft when refitting the gearbox.

Line up the dowels with the clutch cover plate, fit the fixing bolts and tighten them diagonally, a turn at a time, to prevent distortion of the cover.

Replacing the camshaft and timing gear

Oil the camshaft and slide it into the crankcase. Refit the camshaft locating plate 34 in **FIG 1:2**. With the engine the right way up, the oil jet hole is at approximately two o'clock when viewed from the front. Replace the packing washers 48 on the crankshaft.

The rest of the assembly operation will now follow the instructions given earlier for removing and replacing the timing gear and the chain tensioner, if one is fitted to the engine in question.

Replacing the oil pump and the sump

Before fitting the early-type oil pump, check the gasket 73 in **FIG 1:2** to see that it conforms with the correct shape illustrated in **FIG 1:12**. Drop the drive gear into place and press the pump over the three fixing studs inside the crankcase. Tighten the securing nuts and then replace the strainer. On early models this also entails replacing the four bracket bolts to the crankcase and the oil pick-up pipe. Fit the sump, paying particular attention to the gasket and the cork sealing strips mentioned in the section covering the oil pump and the sump. Do not over-tighten the sump screws as this may result in distortion of the pressed steel flanges and later trouble with leakage. The oil pump can now be primed as previously instructed.

Replacing the cylinder head

The cylinder block must be standing the right way up so that the tappets can be inserted. Oil them liberally and drop them into their correct bores. Do not fit the tappet covers 47 in **FIG 1:1** until after the push-rods have been fitted, as it is important to see that the lower ends of the rods are properly located in the tappets.

The cylinder head gasket is pressed gently over the holding-down studs. Do not use jointing compound. The gasket is marked 'TOP' and 'FRONT' so that it can be positioned correctly. The head can now be lowered squarely into place and the seven cylinder head securing nuts fitted finger tight. Insert the push-rods, replacing them in the positions from which they were taken and entering the bottom ends into their respective tappets. Before replacing the rocker gear, slacken all the tappet adjusting screws and unscrew them two or three turns. Drop the rocker assembly over the head studs, locating each push-rod under its own tappet screw. Fit the locking plate 6 in **FIG 1:2** to the rear rocker bracket and screw on the stud nuts finger tight. The small rocker bracket nuts are paired off with the cylinder head nuts 2, 4, 6 and 8 in **FIG 1:4**. Tighten all fifteen nuts evenly a little at a time, using a torque wrench set to the figure given in Technical Data. Note that the torque is less for the small rocker bracket nuts.

Turn the crankshaft to see that all is well and then adjust the rocker clearances.

Valve rocker adjustment

If the engine is to give its best performance, and the valves retain their maximum useful life, then the correct rocker clearance is essential. These engines have been designed to run with a clearance of .015 in hot or .016 in cold. This is measured by feeler gauge between the rocker face and the end of the valve stem as shown in **FIG 1:17**.

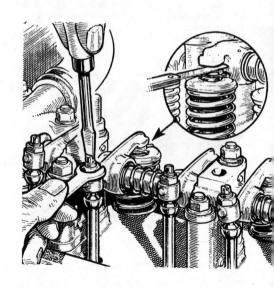

Fig 1:17   Adjusting rocker clearance. Inset shows feeler gauge

When adjusting the clearance, the valve must be fully closed, with the tappet on the back of the cam, opposite the peak. This can be done by observing the following sequence:

Adjust No. 1 rocker with No. 8 valve fully open
Adjust No. 3 rocker with No. 6 valve fully open
Adjust No. 5 rocker with No. 4 valve fully open
Adjust No. 2 rocker with No. 7 valve fully open
Adjust No. 8 rocker with No. 1 valve fully open
Adjust No. 6 rocker with No. 3 valve fully open
Adjust No. 4 rocker with No. 5 valve fully open
Adjust No. 7 rocker with No. 2 valve fully open

Notice that the numbers in each line add up to nine. Remembering this, it is easy to go on checking without constant reference to the table. Slacken the locknut just enough to allow the adjustment screw to be turned with a screwdriver until the feeler gauge is very slightly nipped.

Always maintain pressure with the screwdriver on the adjusting screw so that the film of oil in the push-rod cup is dispersed, otherwise the actual clearance may be greater than the feeler gauge indicates. Tighten the locknut and check the clearance to be certain that the adjustment was not disturbed in the process. It must be pointed out that it will be impossible to obtain accurate clearances if the end of the valve stem is worn out of square, or the rocker arm is pitted with wear.

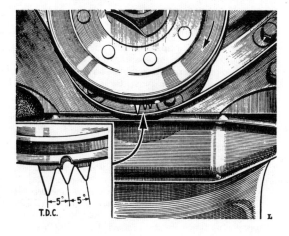

Fig 1:18 Pulley notch and timing pointers. Notch coincides with long pointer at tdc.

Valve timing

There are two ways of checking tdc, early engines having a small hole in the rear flange of the crankshaft pulley and a pointer stamped on the timing cover. Later engines have the arrangement seen in **FIG 1:18** where not only tdc, but five and ten degrees btdc can be set.

To check the timing on engines with the hole in pulley and single pointer arrangement, with the inlet valve opening at 5° btdc.

1 Set No. 1 cylinder inlet valve to .026 in clearance when cold, and turn the crankshaft until the valve is about to open.

2 Check that the small hole in the pulley flange is now opposite the pointer on the timing cover, which indicates that the piston of cylinder No. 1 is at tdc.

3 If correct, the inlet valve clearance can be restored to the normal running position of .015 in when hot.

NOTE: The valve timing given in Technical Data is that which would result from an inlet valve clearance of .021 in. As an accurate setting of 5° btdc is not easily made, the clearance is increased to .026 in at tdc, which gives the same actual timing.

To check the timing on engines with the pointers shown in **FIG 1:18** repeat the above instructions but check that the notch in the pulley comes opposite the long pointer marked tdc with the valve clearance at .026 in. Do not forget to restore the clearance to .015 in afterwards.

On the later Wolseley '1500' and Riley '1.5' engines, the setting is such that the inlet valve will be about to open when the pulley notch and pointer indicate tdc and the clearance is .021 in. After checking, restore the correct running clearance. Technical Data gives the commencing engine numbers of the 'Wolseley's' and 'Riley's' concerned.

Replacing the rocker cover and thermostat

Fit the rocker cover with the filler cap to the front. The rubber bushes go on the fixing studs first, followed by the cup washers and then the domed nuts with plain washers. On some engines there will be lifting brackets which take the place of the two plain washers. It is a good plan not to fit a new cover gasket at this stage but to wait until after the engine has been run and the rocker clearances finally checked.

The thermostat 9 in **FIG 1:1** is replaced at the front end of the head, assuming that it is in good condition or has been checked according to the notes in the Cooling chapter. Drop the narrow ring gasket into the head recess, follow up with the thermostat, then the triangular joint washer and lastly the housing 7 facing to the right.

Replacing the distributor and drive

Use a tappet cover bolt or any long $\frac{5}{16}$ in UNF bolt and screw it into the tapped end of the distributor drive shaft 38 in **FIG 1:2**. Insert it into the right hand side of the cylinder block after reading the instructions for this operation in the Ignition chapter. Check that the driving slot finishes up in the correct position or the ignition timing will be out. Then remove the bolt.

Fit the distributor housing 5 in **FIG 1:1** using the special bolt and lock washer. It is important that the bolt head does not protrude above the face of the housing. Refit the distributor into the housing. If the split clamp has been disturbed, refer to the Ignition chapter for details of how to re-set the timing.

The fuel pump

If a mechanical fuel pump is fitted to the engine, this can now be replaced. Use a good joint washer and feed the rocker arm in carefully so that it is correctly positioned against the eccentric on the camshaft and does not lie to one side of it.

The inlet and exhaust manifolds

On cars with a single carburetter, the manifolds would be removed as a unit. If necessary, it is possible to part the manifolds by undoing the four long bolts holding them together. This will give access to the hot spot. Some engines are not fitted with the part numbered 16 in **FIG 1:1**. Renew the gasket between the joint faces if it is damaged, bolt the two manifolds together but leave the bolts finger tight until the manifolds have been fitted to the engine. Renew the manifold gasket and replace the manifolds. The two outside studs have nuts and washers, the remaining four bolts being fitted with the large washers 20, which bridge both manifold flanges. After tightening the manifold nuts and bolts, tighten the four hot spot bolts. Do not fit the carburetter(s) until the engine has been replaced in the car. Remember to fit the heater pipe 11.

The water pump and generator

These are serviced by referring to the chapters on Cooling and Electrical Equipment, and if satisfactory they can be replaced. Use a new paper washer between the pump body and the cylinder block.

Refit the generator, leaving the pivot and link bolts finger tight until the belt is put on the pulleys. With the belt in place, lift the generator by using a gentle hand pull only and tighten the three fixing bolts and the link set screw. The belt must not be tight nor so loose that it slips. It should be possible to move it laterally about an inch in the middle of the longest run.

Final assembly

It now remains to check that all the accessories are in place. These include the filter, the breather pipe 60, the relief valve 58, the ignition vacuum pipe 59, the temperature gauge element 6 and such items as the drain cock and oil gauge connection.

When the engine has been replaced in the car, the carburetter(s) can be fitted but leave off the air cleaner until the engine has been run up to working temperature and the rocker clearance checked. After checking all the hose connections and drain plugs, put water in the radiator, oil in the sump, and also oil in the gearbox if it was drained. Make sure that all the electrical connections have been restored correctly and connect the sparking plug leads so that the firing order is 1, 3, 4, 2. After running the car for 100 miles, remove the rocker cover, tighten the cylinder head nuts and again check the rocker clearance.

Modifications
Pistons

There have been many changes to pistons and piston rings. New types can only be fitted in place of old ones in sets. Quote the engine number when ordering spare parts.

Oil pump and strainer

On later engines a modified oil pump 1H1191 and oil strainer 1H1192 were fitted. The suction pipe was moved forward to prevent oil starvation. New units are interchangeable with the old type as complete units. To do this involves fitting longer oil pump to crankcase studs to accommodate the increased thickness of the oil pump cover. Part number of the longer stud is 51 K267.

Cylinder head gasket

On later Wolseley '1500' and Riley '1.5' engines the gasket has thinner asbestos and thicker copper and steel, with different ferrules. The new type is interchangeable with the old.

On the Magnette from engine number 3978, a copper-steel-asbestos gasket replaces the earlier all-steel type. The new type should be fitted if the old type gives trouble. Also, a new cylinder head was introduced to improve output. The compression ratio was increased and the valve ports modified, necessitating a new exhaust valve 1H686 and a new inlet guide 1G2882.

Tappets and push-rods

On later engines the ball ends of the push-rods and the seats in the tappets are increased in spherical diameter. The new tappets 11G240 and push-rods 11G241 are interchangeable in sets only.
Commencing engine numbers:
'Oxford' 71265, 'Magnette' 16614—16710, and 16747 onwards.

Valve shrouds and oil seals

The introduction of the modified shroud and an oil seal of circular section has been mentioned in this chapter and illustrated in **FIG 1:6**. On the Riley '1.5' a modified spring shroud, bottom collar and valve spring cup were introduced at Engine number 15RB-U-H872. These are interchangeable with earlier types in sets. The new parts are identified by a turned groove in the top face of the valve spring cup and a notch in the flange of the shroud. The new circular-sectioned oil seals can be fitted in earlier engines providing they are used with shrouds which have no oil seal retainers inside.

Engine rear stabilizer

On the 'Oxfords' from car No. 211534 a re-designed rear stabilizer is fitted in place of the original tie-rod assembly to prevent gear lever vibration and jumping out of gear. This stabilizer must be correctly adjusted, especially after refitting an engine. Refer to **FIG 1:19** and proceed as follows:
1 See that the pivot bracket assembly ACH 5883 is fitted with the pivot higher than the two mounting holes as shown at A.
2 Assemble as shown at B but leave the bracket bolts and rear engine mounting bolts loose, so that the assembly is firm but free to slide in the bolt slots.
3 Adjust the clearance 'B' to $\frac{1}{4}$ in and tighten the bracket pin nut FNZ 108 until the large plain washers PWZ 208 do not rotate, then lock the nut. There should be no appreciable pinch on the rubbers ACH 5882 and the pivot pin should lie centrally in the hole in the engine bracket.
4 Tighten the pivot bracket bolts and the rear engine mounting nuts, taking care that clearance 'B' does not alter.

The adjustment must be made on level ground, and when completed there must be no undue pinch on the rubber bushes.
'Oxford' cars fitted with the original tie-rod may be modified according to **FIG 1:20**.
1 Remove the pin securing the engine steady rod to the gearbox. Undo the steady rod nut and lock nut and remove the rod, rubber buffers, buffer plates and distance tube.
2 Remove the rubber bushes from the gearbox extension lug and ream out the hole in the lug to .781 in. Press in the Tufnol bushes ACC 5979.

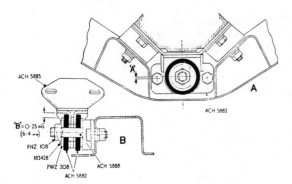

Fig 1:19   Modified 'Oxford' stabilizer assembly.

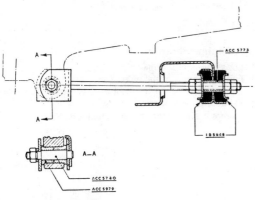

Fig 1:20   'Oxford' steady rod modified.

3 Reassemble the rod using the new parts illustrated. The steady rod and bushes should be in neither tension nor compression. The new parts are:

Steady rod buffers (2)	...	...	1B 5848
Steady rod distance tube	...	...	ACC 5773
Steady rod to engine pin	...	...	ACC 5780
Tufnol bushes (2)	...	...	ACC 5979

Valve guides

Shorter exhaust valve guides with a plain bore are fitted to later engines. The new guides are interchangeable with the old and must be fitted from the top of the cylinder head with the large chamfer uppermost. $\frac{5}{8}$ in of the guide must project above the machined spring seating.

Timing chain tensioner

The self-adjusting chain tensioner cannot be fitted to engines equipped with the early tensioner which consisted of a rubber ring between the large chain wheel teeth.

Oil filter

On later full-flow oil filters the element is removable without disconnecting the oil feed pipe. This pipe enters the filter bowl on earlier full-flow filters. The filter can be either Tecalemit or Purolator and the elements are interchangeable, the Part No. being BMC 8G683.

FAULT DIAGNOSIS

(a)   Engine will not start

1 Defective coil
2 Faulty distributor condenser
3 Dirty, pitted or incorrectly set contact breaker points
4 Ignition wires loose or insulation faulty
5 Water on sparking plug leads
6 Corrosion of battery terminals or discharged condition
7 Faulty or jammed starter
8 Sparking plug leads wrongly connected
9 Vapour lock in fuel pipes
10 Defective fuel pump
11 Over-choking
12 Under-choking
13 Blocked petrol filter or carburetter jets
14 Leaking valves
15 Sticking valves
16 Valve timing incorrect
17 Ignition timing incorrect

(b)   Engine stalls

Check 1, 2, 3, 4, 10, 11, 12, 13, 14 and 15 in (a)
1 Sparking plugs defective or gap incorrect
2 Retarded ignition
3 Mixture too weak
4 Water in fuel system
5 Petrol tank breather choked
6 Incorrect valve clearance

(c)   Engine idles badly

Check 1 and 6 in (b)
1 Air leak at manifold joints
2 Slow running jet blocked or out of adjustment
3 Air leak in carburetter
4 Over-rich mixture
5 Worn piston rings
6 Worn valve stems or guides
7 Weak exhaust valve springs

(d)   Engine misfires

Check 1, 2, 3, 4, 5, 8, 10, 13, 14, 15, 16, 17 in (a) and 1, 2, 3 and 6 in (b)
1 Weak or broken valve springs

(e)   Engine overheats, see Chapter 4

(f)   Compression low

Check 14 and 15 in (a), 5 and 6 in (c), and 1 in (d)
1 Worn piston ring grooves
2 Scored or worn cylinder bores

(g)   Engine lacks power

Check 3, 10, 11, 13, 14, 15 and 16 in (a), 1, 2, 3 and 6 in (b), 5 and 6 in (c) and 1 in (d). Also check (e) and (f).
1 Leaking joint washers
2 Fouled sparking plugs
3 Automatic advance not operating

(h)   Burnt valves or seats

Check 14 and 15 in (a), 6 in (b) and 1 in (d). Also check (e)
1 Excessive carbon around valve seat and head

(j) Sticking valves

Check 1 in (d)
1 Bent valve stem
2 Scored valve stem or guide
3 Incorrect valve clearance

(k) Excessive cylinder wear

Check 11 in (a) and check Chapter 4
1 lack of oil
2 Dirty oil
3 Piston rings gummed up or broken
4 Badly fitting piston rings
5 Connecting rods bent

(l) Excessive oil consumption

Check 5 and 6 in (c) and check (k)
1 Ring gap too wide
2 Oil return holes in piston choked with carbon
3 Scored cylinders
4 Oil level too high
5 External oil leaks
6 Ineffective valve stem oil seal

(m) Crankshaft and connecting rod bearing failure

Check 1 in (k)
1 Restricted oilways
2 Worn journals or crank pins

3 Loose bearing caps
4 Extremely low oil pressure
5 Bent connecting rod

(n) Internal water leakage

See Chapter 4

(o) Poor circulation

See Chapter 4

(p) Corrosion

See Chapter 4

(q) High fuel consumption

See Chapter 2

(r) Engine vibration

1 Loose generator bolts
2 Fan blades out of balance
3 Incorrect clearance for front engine mounting rubbers
4 Exhaust pipe mounting too tight
5 Incorrect adjustment of rear stabilizer

CHAPTER TWO

CARBURETTERS AND FUEL SYSTEMS

Mechanical fuel pump   Operation   Servicing   Testing   Electric fuel pumps   Operation   Servicing   Testing   Zenith carburetter   Operation   Servicing   Adjustment   SU carburetters   Operation   Servicing   Adjustment   Air cleaners   Modifications   Fault diagnosis

Austin cars 'A40', '50' and '55' are fitted with Zenith carburetters and AC-Sphynx mechanical fuel pumps. 'Wolseley', 'Riley', 'Magnette' and 'Oxford' cars have SU carburetters and SU electric fuel pumps.

The mechanical fuel pump

This is an AC-Sphynx type 'U', operated by an eccentric on the engine camshaft. It will be found just behind the left-hand front engine mounting. The external priming lever 15 in **FIG 2:1** is for pumping fuel by hand. An exploded view of the pump is shown in **FIG 2:2.**

Operation—see FIG 2:1

As the engine camshaft 8 revolves, eccentric 9 lifts rocker arm 10 which pivots at 11. Rod 14 and diaphragm 5 are pulled down by the rocker arm against pressure from spring 6. Suction produced in chamber 16 sucks fuel through inlet 20 and filter 1. The fuel passes valve 19 and goes into the chamber. On the return stroke the pressure of spring 6 pushes the diaphragm upwards, forcing fuel out of the chamber through delivery valve 4. It leaves the pump by outlet port 3 which is connected by pipe to the carburetter. When the carburetter float chamber is full and the float needle shut, there can be no flow of fuel from the pump until the level in the float chamber drops and the needle valve opens again.

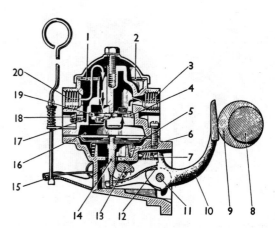

Fig 2:1   Sectional view of the AC-Sphynx mechanical fuel pump.

Key to Fig 2:1   1 Gauze filter.   2 Cork sealing washer. 3 Delivery union.   4 Delivery valve.   5 Diaphragm.   6 Diaphragm spring.   7 Anti-rattle spring.   8 Camshaft.   9 Camshaft eccentric.   10 Rocker arm.   11 Rocker arm pivot. 12 Connecting link.   13 Priming lever cam.   14 Diaphragm pull rod.   15 Priming lever.   16 Pump chamber.   17 Sediment chamber.   18 Sediment drain plug.   19 Suction valve. 20 Inlet union.

The pump chamber 16 thus remains full, the diaphragm is depressed and the connecting link 12 is out of contact with the abutment on rocker arm 10. The rocker arm will then reciprocate idly until a renewed demand for fuel in the float chamber causes the diaphragm to rise. Spring 7 keeps the rocker arm always in contact with the camshaft eccentric to eliminate noise.

Routine servicing

Refer to **FIG 2:2** and remove the top cover by undoing screw 1. Lift out the gauze filter 5 and clean it with petrol and a brush, or with an air jet. Also clean out the sediment chamber in the top of item 8.

Refit the parts, using a new cork washer 4 if the old one is broken or hard. The fibre washer 2 must also be in good condition. Tighten the top screw enough to make a leak-tight joint, but beware of excessive tightening.

The pump can be checked by disconnecting the fuel outlet pipe at the carburetter float chamber end. Turn the engine by hand, when there should be a well-defined squirt of fuel every two revolutions.

Dismantling

Clean the outside of the pump and make a file mark across the two flanges of parts 8 and 16 in **FIG 2:2**. This will ensure correct assembly.

1 Unscrew bolt 1 and remove cover 3.
2 Lift out filter 5 and sealing washer 4.
3 Unscrew the five securing screws 6 and separate the pump halves 8 and 16.
4 Remove the screws 12. This will release the valve securing plate 11, the valves 10 and the valve joint washer 9.
5 Turn the diaphragm assembly 24 through 90°, which will release it from rocker link 22. Spring 23 can then be removed.

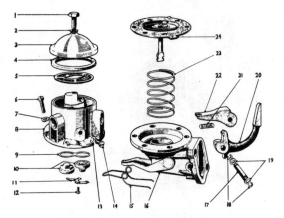

Fig 2:2 Component parts of the AC mechanical fuel pump.

Key to Fig 2:2 1 Top cover screw. 2 Cover screw washer. 3 Pump top cover. 4 Cork sealing washer. 5 Filter gauze. 6 Upper chamber securing screw. 7 Washer for securing screw. 8 Upper chamber. 9 Valve joint washer. 10 Valves. 11 Valve securing plate. 12 Valve plate screw. 13 Drain plug washer. 14 Drain plug. 15 Priming lever spring. 16 Lower casting. 17 Rocker arm pin. 18 Rocker arm pin clips. 19 Rocker arm washers. 20 Rocker arm. 21 Anti-rattle spring. 22 Rocker link. 23 Diaphragm spring. 24 Diaphragm.

6 Remove the two circlips 18 from the rocker arm pivot pin 17 and push out the pin. This will release the rocker arm 20, the rocker link 22, the washers 19 and the spring 21.

Do not try to separate the four diaphragm layers from the pull-rod. This is an assembly which is permanently riveted together. Renew it if the diaphragm is cracked or hard.

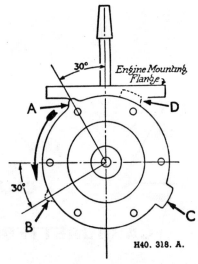

H40. 318. A.

Fig 2:3 Fitting the diaphragm. Engage pull-rod then grip tab C and move to D.

Reassembling

Clean all parts thoroughly. Wash the valves in a separate container of clean paraffin as this helps to improve their sealing.

1 Place the valve joint washer 9 in the body 8, followed by the valves 10. The suction valve is located below the passage from the upper filter chamber, with its spring underneath. The delivery valve will have its spring on top. Secure the valves with plate 11 and screws 12.
2 Replace filter 5, washer 4 and cover 3, tightening screw 1 moderately.
3 In lower casting 16 assemble the link 22, washers 19, rocker arm 20 and spring 21. This can be simplified by using a piece of .240 in diameter rod. This is inserted in one side of the body 16 to engage all the internal parts. The pivot pin 17 is then pushed through from the other side, gradually displacing the temporary pin. Pin 17 should be a tap fit in the body. If the holes are slightly worn they can be burred over on the outside. Replace circlips 18.
4 Place the diaphragm spring 23 in position in the lower casting. If it is a new part, it must be the same strength as the old one. Check the identification colour with the original. Place the diaphragm assembly 24 over the spring with the pull-rod downwards. Centre the upper end of the spring in the flanged diaphragm protector washer. Refer to **FIG 2:3** and set the diaphragm tab A at eleven o'clock. Press down on the diaphragm and turn it by means of tab C until it reaches position D.

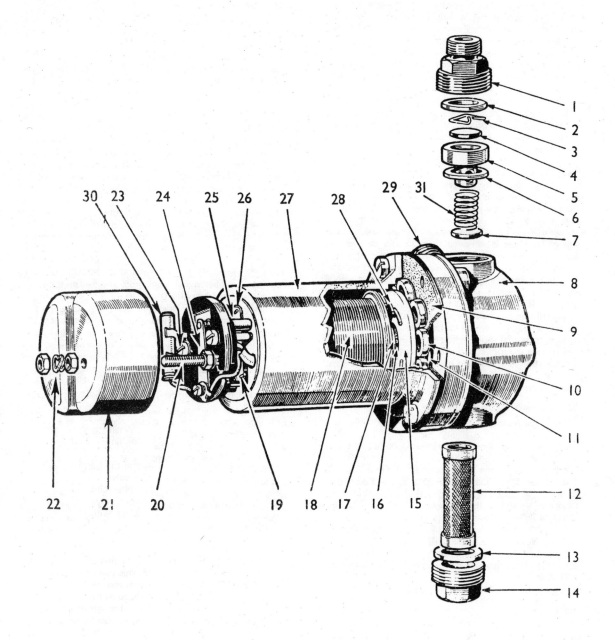

Fig 2:4   The SU fuel pump, type HP.

Key to Fig 2:4   1 Outlet union.   2 Fibre washer (thick orange).   3 Spring clip.   4 Delivery valve disc.   5 Valve cage.
6 Fibre washer.   7 Suction valve disc.   8 Pump body.   9 Diaphragm assembly.   10 Armature guide rollers.   11 Retaining plate.
12 Filter.   13 Fibre washer (thick orange).   14 Filter plug.   15 Steel armature.   16 Push-rod.   17 Magnet iron core.   18 Magnet coil.
19 Rocker hinge pin.   20 Terminal screw.   21 Cover.   22 Cover and terminal nuts.   23 Earth terminal screw.   24 Spring blade.
25 Inner rocker.   26 Outer rocker.   27 Magnet housing.   28 Volute spring.   29 Inlet union.   30 Condenser.   31 Suction valve spring.

This will result in tab A finishing up at eight o'clock at B. This should place the pull-rod in correct engagement with rocker link 22 and bring the diaphragm holes in line with those in the body flanges.

5 Push the rocker arm 20 towards the pump until the diaphragm is level with the body flange. Place the upper half of the pump in position, lining up the marks made before dismantling. Install the screws 6 and lock washers 7, doing them up until the washers are only just engaged. By pushing the rocker arm away from the pump, the diaphragm will be held at the top of its stroke. While so held, tighten the screws 6 diagonally and securely.

Testing

Flush the pump by immersing it in clean paraffin and working the rocker arm a few times. Empty it by repeating the process with the pump held clear of the paraffin. Do not immerse again, but place a finger over the union socket marked 'IN' and work the rocker arm several times. When the finger is removed there should be a distinct sucking sound. The finger is now placed over the outlet union and the rocker arm pressed inwards and released. This will compress air drawn into the pump chamber, where the pressure should be held for two or three seconds. Repeat the operation with the pump immersed in paraffin and watch the diaphragm clamping flanges for the air bubbles which will denote a leak.

Care is needed when refitting the pump to the engine. Ensure that the rocker arm is correctly positioned against the camshaft eccentric and not to one side or underneath. Run the engine and check for leaks at the pipe unions and pump flanges.

The SU electric fuel pumps

There are four types of SU pump to be covered in this section, the HP, SP, AUF and PD.

The first three operate on the same principle, but the PD is an exception and is fitted only to the later Wolseley '15/50's' after engine numbers 8538 (H) and 7301 (L). The HP which is illustrated in FIG 2:4 is fitted to the 'Oxfords' 11 and 111, the early Wolseley '1500's' and Riley '1.5's', and to the Wolseley '15/50' up to engine numbers 8538 (H) and 7301 (L).

Type SP is illustrated in FIG 2:6 and 2:7, and is fitted to later Wolseley '1500's' and Riley '1.5's'.

The AUF is a newer pump fitted to more recent Wolseley '1500' and Riley '1.5' cars. It is illustrated in FIG 2:8.

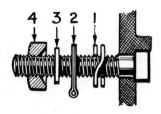

Fig 2:5 Correct assembly of SU terminal screw.

Operation

To describe the principles of the HP, SP and AUF pumps it is proposed to use the sectioned drawing in FIG 2:6 as a typical example. The pump is shown at rest, with the diaphragm 10 pressed away from the solenoid core 13 by the spring 12. The armature spindle 29 has pulled the inner rocker 27 so that spring toggle 17 forces the outer rocker 18 in the opposite direction, thus closing the contacts 21. The rockers are mounted on a common hinge pin 28. The outer contact is fixed to a spring blade 22. The electrical circuit is then through the terminal screw 24 to the coil winding 15 back to the outer spring contact. With the contacts closed, current can then pass by way of the outer rocker arm and a braided copper wire, through the coil housing 14 and so to earth. With the pump switched on, the solenoid winding 15 is energized and the core 13 pulls the armature 31 and diaphragm 10 towards it. The armature assembly is centralized by a ring of brass rollers 32 of which allow movement to and fro. The partial vacuum now created below the diaphragm causes fuel to be drawn into the pumping chamber by way of inlet valve 3. Feed nozzle 1 is connected to the fuel tank. The movement of the armature and spindle 29 makes the inner rocker move away from the housing, causing toggle spring 17 to flick the outer rocker towards the coil housing and so open the contacts 21. This break in the electrical circuit de-energizes the coil, the pressure of feed spring 12 forces the diaphragm downwards and fuel is pushed out through delivery valve 6 to the outlet connection 9. This movement again operates the rockers, the contacts are closed and the cycle is repeated.

Routine maintenance – HP, SP and AUF pumps

The gauze filter on the inlet side of the pump should be cleaned with a brush and petrol and not with a piece of rag. To remove the filter proceed as follows:

On the HP pump remove plug 14 in FIG 2:4.

On the SP pump unscrew feed nozzle 1 in FIG 2:6.

On the AUF pump remove the clamp plate 2 in FIG 2:8, take off the inlet nozzle 4 and the filter disc 6 will be found between the sealing washers 5. The contact breaker points can be cleaned by drawing a strip of paper between them while holding them lightly together.

Check all the electrical connections for tightness.

Dismantling HP pump

1 Remove the filter plug 14 and filter 12 in FIG 2:4.
2 Unscrew the outlet union 1, which will allow the removal of the washer 2, the valve cage 5 complete with valve disc 4 and spring clip 3. Below these will be found another fibre washer 6, a valve spring 31 and the suction valve 7.
3 Undo the six screws in the flange of magnet housing 27, making a scratch across the flanges of the housing and the body to ensure correct assembly.
4 Unscrew the diaphragm 9 by turning it anti-clockwise, holding the housing over a box to catch the brass rollers 10.
5 Remove the cover 21 and unscrew the last nut on the terminal screw 20. Beneath this nut will be found a lead washer which has been squeezed into the terminal thread. Cut it away and push the terminal screw inwards until the coil tag is free.

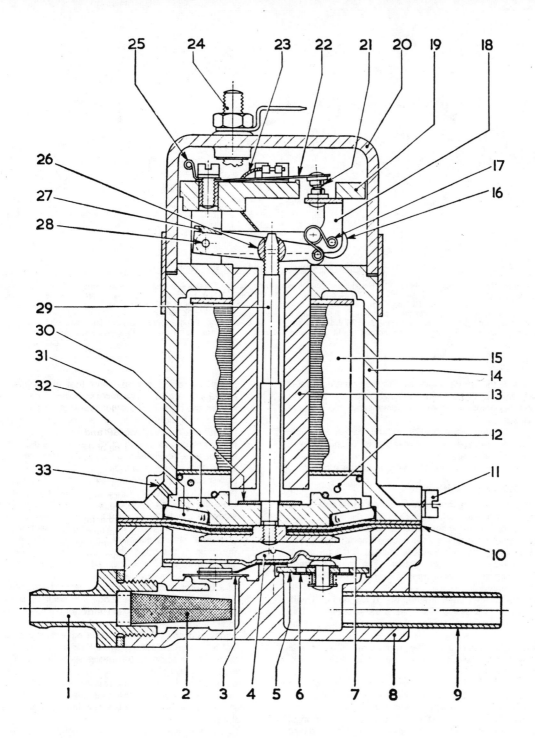

Fig 2:6 Section of SU fuel pump, type SP.

Key to Fig 2:6 1 Feed nozzle. 2 Filter. 3 Inlet valve. 4 Screw—valve retainer. 5 Carrier plate. 6 Delivery valve. 7 Valve retainer.
8 Body. 9 Outlet connection. 10 Diaphragm. 11 Earth screw. 12 Feed spring. 13 Solenoid core. 14 Coil housing. 15 Coil.
16 Fibre rollers. 17 Toggle spring. 18 Outer rocker. 19 Pedestal. 20 End cap. 21 Contact points. 22 Spring blade.
23 Braided earth wire. 24 Terminal screw. 25 Coil lead tag. 26 Trunnion. 27 Inner rocker. 28 Rocker hinge pin.
29 Armature spindle. 30 Impact washer. 31 Armature. 32 Brass rollers. 33 Air vent.

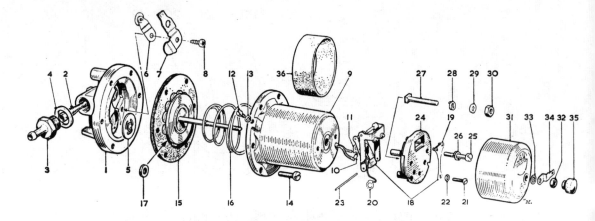

Fig 2:7 Component parts of SP fuel pump.

Key to Fig 2:7 1 Body.   2 Filter.   3 Nozzle inlet.   4 Washer for nozzle.   5 Valve—outlet.   6 Valve—inlet.   7 Retainer—valve.
8 Screw for retainer.   9 Housing—coil.   10 Tag—4 B.A. terminal.   11 Tag—2 B.A. terminal.   12 Screw—earth.   13 Washer—spring.
14 Screw—housing to body.   15 Diaphragm assembly.   16 Spring.   17 Roller.   18 Rocker and blade.   19 Blade.   20 Tag—2 B.A. terminal.
21 Screw for blade.   22 Washer—dished.   23 Spindle for contact breaker.   24 Pedestal.   25 Screw—pedestal to housing.
26 Washer—spring.   27 Screw for terminal.   28 Washer—spring.   29 Washer—lead—for screw.   30 Nut for screw.   31 Cover—end.
32 Nut for cover.   33 Washer—shakeproof.   54 Connector—Lucar.   35 Knob—terminal.   36 Sleeve—rubber.

6 Remove the contact blade 24 and the two long screws which hold the bakelite pedestal in place. Ease the coil tag over the terminal screw and the contact breaker can be taken away.

7 Push out the hinge pin 19 and the rocker assembly will be released. This assembly is supplied as a complete unit only.

Do not attempt to disturb the core of the magnet.

Reassembling the HP pump

All parts must be thoroughly cleaned and a new set of fibre washers provided.

1 Fit valve 7 with the smooth side downwards, followed by spring 31. Replace valve 4, also smooth side down, with spring circlip 3 correctly located in the groove in the valve cage 5. Fibre washer 6 is thin and hard. Replace the thick fibre washer 2, and screw down the outlet union 1.

2 Fit the contact breaker assembly to the pedestal with hinge pin 19. **Note:** This pin is case-hardened. Use only a genuine SU spare part as soft wire will be useless.

Check the rockers for free movement without side play, setting the outer rocker with a pair of thin-nosed pliers if tight.

3 Fit the terminal screw 20 to the pedestal. Refer to **FIG 2:5** and fit the spring washer 1, short wire from coil 2, new lead washer 3 and nut 4.

4 Slip the braided earth lead from the outer rocker on to one of the long pedestal securing screws, followed by a spring washer. Fit the pedestal using both screws.

5 Fit the remaining coil lead to the spring blade screw and replace the blade 24. The blade must bear against the small rib along the inner edge of the rectangular hole in the pedestal. The points should make firm contact, the outer one being a little above the rocker point.

Move the rocker arm to check that the points wipe over the centre line of each other. If the blade does not rest on the rib with the outer rocker depressed, take it off and set it slightly, but only just enough, as excessive pressure will restrict rocker travel.

6 Now swing the spring blade to one side. Fit the impact washer in the recess in the armature 15 and screw the armature spindle into the trunnion of the rocker assembly. Place the eleven rollers 10 in position. **Note:** Do not put jointing compound on the diaphragm.

7 Hold the housing 27 in the left hand horizontally and screw in the armature until the rocker gear ceases to throw over. Then turn it back gradually a sixth of a turn at a time. This is the same as turning the diaphragm one hole at the edge. Press the armature firmly and slowly until a point is reached when the rocker will throw over. Unscrew the armature a further two-thirds of a turn, or four holes at the edge of the diaphragm.

8 Place the housing 27 and body 8 in position, with the drain hole in the housing at the bottom, in line with the filter plug. Make sure that the rollers are in the armature groove. Fit the six securing screws but do not tighten down until the diaphragm is stretched. Do this by first re-positioning the spring blade 24 and placing a matchstick behind one of the white rollers on the outer rocker. Pass current through the pump to energize the coil and magnet. This will pull the armature and diaphragm forward, in which position the six screws should be tightened.

9 Check the action of the contact breaker. Hold the spring blade 24 against the pedestal without bending the tip. It should now be possible to insert a .030 in feeler between the white rollers on the outer rocker and the face of the magnet housing 27. If necessary, the tip of the blade may be set to give the correct clearance.

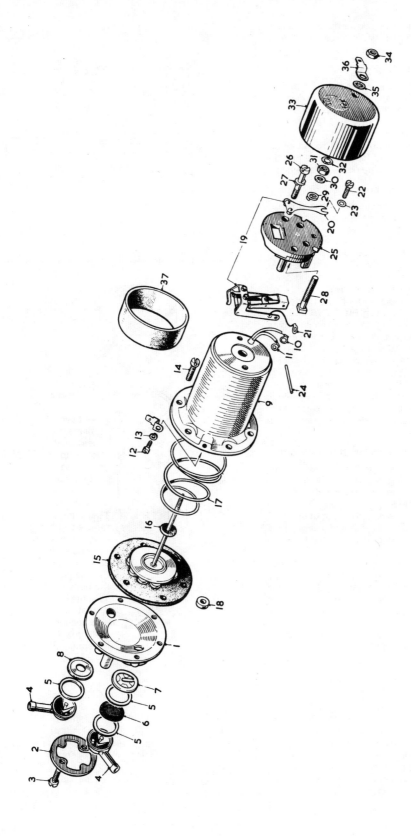

Fig 2 : 8 Component parts of SU fuel pump, type AUF

Key to Fig 2 : 8   1 Body.   2 Clamp plate.   3 Screw for clamp plate.   4 Nozzle—inlet/outlet.   5 Washer—sealing.   6 Filter.   7 Valve—inlet.   8 Valve—outlet.
9 Housing—coil.   10 Tag—4 B.A. terminal.   11 Tag—2 B.A. terminal.   12 Screw—earth.   13 Spring washer for screw.   14 Screw—housing to body.
15 Diaphragm assembly.   16 Washer—impact.   17 Spring—armature.   18 Roller—diaphragm.   19 Rocker mechanism and contact blade.   20 Contact blade.
21 Tag—2 B.A. terminal.   22 Screw for blade.   23 Washer for blade.   24 Pivot pin.   25 Pedestal.   26 Screw—pedestal to housing.   27 Washer—spring—for screw.
28 Terminal screw.   29 Washer—spring—for terminal.   30 Washer—lead—for terminal.   31 Nut for screw.   32 Spacer—nut to cover.   33 Cover—end.
34 Nut for cover.   35 Washer—shakeproof.   36 Connector—Lucar.

When testing a pump without a cover fitted, remember that it is the cover which prevents the hinge pin 19 from falling out.

Dismantling SP and AUF pumps

The procedure is much the same as that outlined for the HP pump, the differences being mainly concerned with the valves. Those on the SP pump are readily removed by taking out screw 8 in **FIG 2:7**. This will release inlet valve 6 and outlet valve 5.

The valves on the AUF pump will be found under the inlet and outlet nozzles 4 in **FIG 2:8**. Note that the contact breakers on both these pumps have twin contacts.

Reassembling SP and AUF pumps

On the SP pump, reach the point where the armature spindle has been screwed into the rocker trunnion on the HP pump. Then proceed as follows:

1 Screw in the spindle until firm steady pressure on the armature just fails to make the outer rocker snap over. Then unscrew the diaphragm seven holes at the edge. Position the brass rollers, fit the housing and body together and secure with the six screws. There is no need to stretch the diaphragm. The correct assembly of the valves is clearly shown in **FIGS 2:6** and **2:7**. On the AUF pump the previous instructions will cover fitting the armature and diaphragm. To fit the valves and set the rocker mechanism, follow these instructions.

1 Check the tongues on the valve cages. They should allow the valve to lift $\frac{1}{16}$ in. Fit the inlet valve 7 in **FIG 2:8** with the tongue entering the recess first. Then fit a sealing washer 5, the filter 6 and another washer 5. The outlet valve has its tongue facing outwards. After fitting the sealing washer 5 the inlet and outlet nozzles can be replaced.

To set the rocker mechanism on the AUF pump

1 Check that the top of the inner rocker 4 is touching the end face of the coil housing, see **FIG 2:9**. If there is a gap, the six body screws are slackened and re-tightened until this condition is reached. The spring contact blade which was previously swung to one side, is now replaced and adjusted so that one pair of points wipes over the other pair on the centre line and symmetrically.

2 When the outer rocker is pressed back to the coil housing face 6, the spring blade 2 must rest on the narrow ridge on the pedestal moulding 1. The gap between the points should then be .030 in. When the outer rocker is released, the spring blade should be deflected away from the ridge. If necessary the blade and the rocker fingers can be set to achieve this by following the data given in **FIG 2:9**.

Testing all pumps

With the pump fitted and the fuel pipes connected, switch on. If the pump is noisy and operates rapidly, an air leak is probable. Check by disconnecting the fuel pipe from the carburetter and turning the pipe down into a jar. Keeping the end submerged with the pump switched on, the emission of continuous bubbles will confirm an air leak. Check that the inlet union to the pump is tight and that all connections from the tank to the pump are in good order. Check also that the coil housing screws round the diaphragm flanges are evenly tightened.

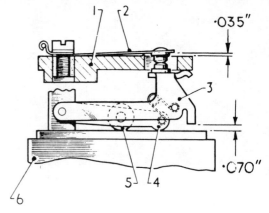

Fig 2:9   Rocker finger settings on AUF pump.

Key to Fig 2:9   1 Pedestal.   2 Contact blade.   3 Outer rocker.   4 Inner rocker.   5 Trunnion.   6 Coil.

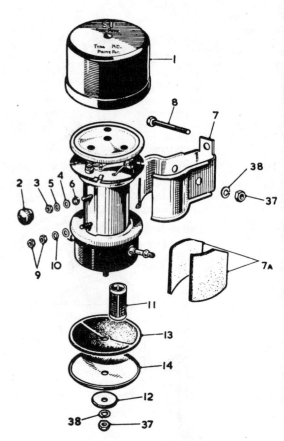

Fig 2:10   Parts which can be serviced on SU fuel pump, type PD.

Key to Fig 2:10   1 Cover—top.   2 Knob—terminal.   3 Nut —terminal.   4 Washer—plain.   5 Washer—lead.   6 Collar —insulating.   7 Bracket—holding.   7A Bracket—packing. 8 Bolt—clamp.   9 Nut—terminal—earth.   10 Washer— terminal—earth.   11 Filter.   12 Washer—dished.   13 Gasket —cork.   14 Cover-plate.   37 Nut.   38 Washer—spring.

If the pump operates without delivering fuel, check for a serious air leak on the suction side, or foreign matter under the valves, particularly the inlet. Remove the valves for cleaning.

If the pump works initially but the carburetter float chamber does not fill, look for an obstructed float needle. Disconnect the fuel pipe from the carburetter, switch on and check the flow from the open pipe. If it diminishes rapidly and the pump slows down, check the petrol tank venting by removing the filler cap. Blocked or inadequate venting causes a slow power stroke of the pump and burning of the contact points. If the reduced flow is accompanied by slow operation of the pump, check for a clogged filter at the pump inlet. If the pump operates rapidly, check for air leaks, dirt under the valves or faulty valve sealing washers where fitted.

If there is no flow, check the electrical supply. If satisfactory, check the contact breaker points. With the main supply lead connected, short across the contacts with a piece of bare wire. If the pump makes a stroke the fault is due to dirt, corrosion or mal-adjustment of the contacts. If the pump will only operate with the inlet pipe disconnected, there may be a restriction in the pipe between the pump and the tank. If compressed air is used to clear a pipe line, never pass it through the pump as the valves will be damaged.

If all these checks fail to locate the trouble, suspect a stiffening of the diaphragm material, or abnormal friction in the rocker mechanism. Remove the coil housing and flex the diaphragm a few times, taking care not to lose the eleven rollers under it. Assemble the diaphragm as instructed and use a little thin oil on the throw-over spring spindles where they pivot in the brass contact-breaker rockers.

Renew the solenoid coil assembly if there is excessive sparking at the contact points. Do not try to cure leakage at the diaphragm joint by using jointing compound.

The PD pump fitted to later Wolseley '15/50's'

This pump was fitted to cars after number 40088 if they were non-Manumatic. The Part No. is AUA 100 and the pump is illustrated in **FIG 2:10**.

It differs from earlier designs because the diaphragm is operated magnetically through a hydrostatic medium instead of the mechanical connection previously used. The pumping diaphragm is only slightly flexed, which makes it possible to use a terylene film instead of the synthetic rubber one in former use.

Servicing the PD pump

The main part of the pump is hermetically sealed, so that only those parts shown in **FIG 2:10** are accessible or capable of being serviced separately. If the contact points become dirty, remove the cover 1 and draw a piece of clean paper or card between them. Take care not to overstress the blades.

Rapid operation and diminished fuel supply indicates a leakage of air into the suction side of the pump. Detect this by disconnecting the fuel delivery pipe at the carburetter and allowing the fuel to discharge into an open jar, the end of the pipe being submerged. Should a quantity of air bubbles be observed, check the cover plate cork gasket 13 and renew it if necessary. The rubber connections at each end of the suction pipe line should also be examined and renewed if they show signs of damage.

Note: It is a peculiarity of the PD pump that it will continue to 'tick' even when the ignition is switched on, the engine is not running and the carburetter float chamber is full.

The Zenith carburetter fitted to the Austin 'A40', '50' and '55'

This is the type 30.VIG–10 which incorporates an accelerating pump, an economy device and an automatic strangler connected to the throttle for starting purposes.

Operating principle

Refer to **FIGS 2:11** and **2:12** for details of the parts mentioned. When starting from cold the strangler control is pulled to close the flap 1 in **FIG 2:12**. The lever 63 and interconnecting link assembly 16 will also open the throttle slightly. When the engine fires and its speed increases, the greater suction on the spring-loaded strangler flap causes it to open progressively to admit

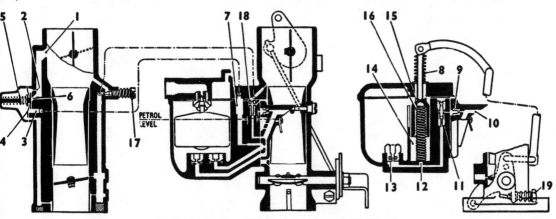

Fig 2:11   Sections of Zenith carburetter, type 30. VIG-10.

Key to Fig 2:11   1 Air bleed   2 Air restrictor   3 Economy air bleed   4 Diaphragm valve   5 Spring   6 Main air drilling   7 Capacity well   8 Accelerator pump rod   9 Accelerator pump jet   10 Emulsion block beak   11 Ball valve   12 Accelerator pump outlet   13 Non-return valve   14 Accelerator pump well   15 Accelerator piston   16 Spring   17 Air adjustment screw   18 Slow-running jet   19 Slow-running adjustment screw

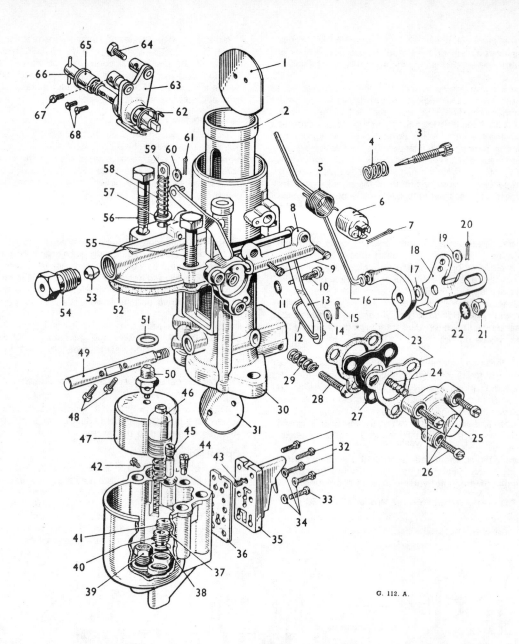

Fig 2:12 Exploded view of Zenith carburetter fitted to Austins A40, 50 and 55.

Key to Fig 2:12 1 Strangler flap. 2 Choke tube. 3 Air regulating screw. 4 Air regulating screw spring.
5 Spring, (automatic). 6 Spring carrier. 7 Split pin. 8 Bearing plate for pump control. 9 Bearing plate screw. 10 Choke tube screw.
11 Serrated washer. 12 Pump control link. 13 Pump control lever. 14 Washer for link. 15 Split pin for link.
16 Interconnecting link assembly. 17 Washer for throttle spindle. 18 Throttle lever. 19 Link washer. 20 Link split pin.
21 Throttle spindle nut. 22 Shakeproof washer. 23 Economy diaphragm gaskets. 24 Diaphragm spring. 25 Economy valve cover.
26 Cover screws. 27 Economy diaphragm. 28 Throttle stop screw. 29 Throttle stop screw spring. 30 Carburetter body.
31 Throttle. 32 Emulsion block screws (short). 33 Emulsion block screw (long). 34 Washers for emulsion block lower screw.
35 Emulsion block. 36 Emulsion block gasket. 37 Main jet washer. 38 Compensating washer. 39 Non-return valve.
40 Compensating jet. 41 Main jet. 42 Piston stop screw. 43 Pump jet. 44 Slow running jet. 45 Ball valve. 46 Pump piston.
47 Float. 48 Throttle fixing screws. 49 Throttle spindle. 50 Needle and seating. 51 Needle and seating washer.
52 Carburetter bowl gasket. 53 Petrol connection compression washer. 54 Petrol pipe connection. 55 Carburetter bowl screw (plain).
56 Bowl screw (squared end). 57 Pump spring washer. 58 Pump spring. 59 Pump rod. 60 Washer for pump rod pivot.
61 Pump rod pivot split pin. 62 Strangler spring. 63 Strangler lever. 64 Screw for strangler wire. 65 Strangler spindle bearing.
66 Strangler spindle. 67 Interconnection swivel screw. 68 Strangler flap screws.

re air and weaken the mixture. With the strangler con-
pushed in, the engine will idle on mixture supplied by
slow-running jet 18 in **FIG 2:11.** The fuel from this
mixes with air admitted by a regulating screw 17.
is is used to adjust the idling mixture. Further opening
the throttle causes suction to be concentrated on the
zzle of the emulsion block 35 in **FIG 2:12.** Fuel is then
wn eventually from the main and compensating jets
and 41 in the base of the float chamber.

The economy device is shown exploded by the parts
24, 25, 26 and 27. The valve in the centre of the dia-
ragm assembly 27 is kept on its seating by spring 24.
en cruising along with a high depression in the in-
ction system, the diaphragm is lifted off its seating, so
t air is released to weaken the depression on the main
s, thus reducing their output of fuel and giving greater
onomy. The diaphragm can also be seen as part 4 in
3 2:11.

The accelerating pump system is shown in section to
right of **FIG 2:11.** It supplies the extra fuel needed
en the throttle is opened suddenly, giving smooth and
tantaneous engine response. The pump piston 15 is
used in the float chamber and operated by the throttle
er through links and a push-rod 8. Fuel enters the
mp cylinder 14 through a non-return valve 13, so that
en the pump piston is suddenly depressed by a rapid
ening of the throttle it forces fuel out through a ball-
ve 11 and jet 9 to reach the emulsion block and be
cted as a fine spray which will enrich the mixture.

smantling the Zenith 30.VIG–10, see FIG 2:12

Remove the float chamber by undoing screws 55 and
56. Ensure that gasket 52 is undamaged. Screw 56
has a squared end which can be used to remove the
ets 40 and 41. Note the washers 37 and 38.

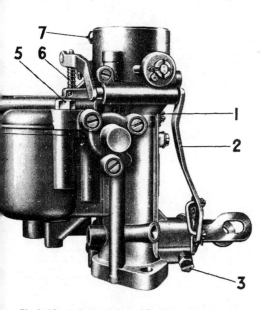

Fig 2:13   Left-hand view of Zenith carburetter.

y to Fig 2:13   1 Air regulating screw.   2 Pump control
er.   3 Throttle stop screw.   4 Fuel inlet.   5 Bowl screw.
ump rod spring.   7 Strangler wire screw.

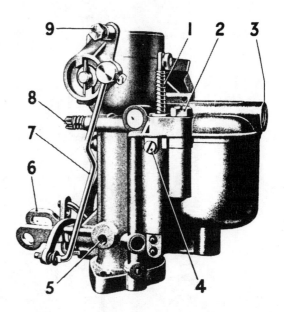

Fig 2:14   Right-hand view of Zenith carburetter.

Key to Fig 2:14 1 Pump rod spring.   2 Bowl screw.
3 Fuel inlet.   4 Piston stop screw.   5 Vacuum control pipe
connection.   6 Accelerator connection.   7 Interconnecting
link.   8 Air regulating screw.   9 Strangler wire screw.

2 Remove screw 42 to release the pump piston 46. The
   pump non-return valve 39 should be examined for
   clogging which will make it inoperative. Pump ball-
   valve 45 can be unscrewed and slow-running jet 44
   checked for blockage.

3 Remove the emulsion block 35, taking great care of
   the gasket 36. Check the pump jet 43. When replacing
   the emulsion block fit the bottom screw first and tighten
   all five evenly.

4 Remove the economy valve cover 25 and examine the
   diaphragm 27 for signs of damage leading to air leaks.

5 Unscrew the slow-running air regulating screw 3 and
   check all passages for cleanliness and freedom from
   fluff and sediment.

Do not clean the jets with wire, but use an air jet. A
bicycle pump is quite effective. Afterwards, wash in clean
petrol. The higher the jet number, the larger the jet.

If there has been flooding, check the needle and seating
50, and the float 47 for a puncture. Immerse the float in
very hot water, when bubbles will rise and indicate the
smallest hole. When the petrol inside the float has been
evaporated in this way, seal the puncture with a tiny spot
of solder. Too much solder will affect the fuel level in the
float chamber, and a new float is the best cure.

Reassembling

This can be readily followed by referring to **FIG 2:12.**
Absolute cleanliness is needed, and there must be no air
leaks through defective gaskets.

Adjustment

The stop screw 3 in **FIG 2:13** controls the speed of
slow-running. Turn clockwise to increase the speed.

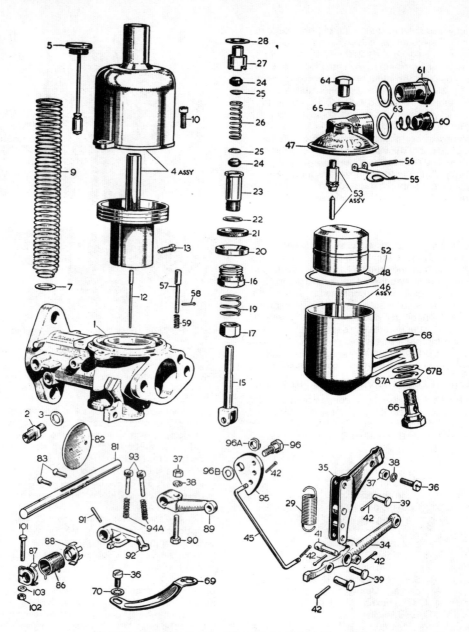

Fig 2:15 SU carburetter, type H2, as fitted to Oxfords 11 and 111.

Key to Fig 2:15 1 Body. 2 Auto ignition union. 3 Auto ignition union washer. 4 Suction chamber and piston assemb
5 Oil cap assembly. 7 Thrust washer. 9 Piston spring. 10 Suction chamber securing screw. 12 Jet needle. 13 Jet needle locking screw
15 Jet with head. 16 Jet screw. 17 Jet adjusting nut. 19 Jet adjusting lock spring. 20 Jet sealing ring—bras
21 Jet sealing ring—cork. 22 Jet copper washer—bottom half. 23 Jet bearing—bottom half. 24 Jet gland washer—cor
25 Jet gland washer—brass. 26 Jet gland spring. 27 Jet bearing—top half. 28 Jet copper washer—top ha
29 Return spring—jet lever. 34 Jet lever. 35 Jet link. 36 2 B.A. screw—support arm. 37 2 B.A. nut—jet lin
38 2 B.A. spring washer—jet link. 39 Pivot pin—short—jet link. 41 Pivot pin—long—jet link. 42 Split pin ($\frac{1}{16}$ in
45 Link rod—intermediate jet and throttle. 46 Float-chamber with stud. 47 Float-chamber lid. 48 Oakenstrong washer—li
52 Float. 53 Float needle and seat. 55 Float hinged lever. 56 Float hinged lever pin. 57 Tickler pin. 58 Tickler split pi
59 Tickler pin spring. 60 Filter. 61 Banjo bolt. 63 Banjo bolt fibre washer. 64 Cap inlet—brass. 65 Cover ca
66 Holding-up bolt—float-chamber. 67A Brass skid washer—holding-up bolt. 67B Fibre washer—holding-up bo
68 Fibre washer—holding-up bolt. 69 Float-chamber support arm. 70 Shakeproof washer. 81 Throttle spindle. 82 Throttle dis
83 Throttle disc screw. 86 Return spring—throttle. 87 Retainer clip. 88 Anchor plate—throttle return sprin
89 Lever—throttle spindle. 90 Bolt—throttle lever (2 B.A.). 91 Taper pin—stop lever. 92 Stop lever—interconnecting jet and throttl
93 Stop adjusting screw—long. 94A Stop adjusting spring—long. 95 Cam. 96 Pivot bolt—intermediate jet and throttl
96A Pivot bolt washer. 96B Aluminium washer—cam. 101 Bolt (4 B.A.). 102 4 B.A. nut. 103 4 B.A. washer.

he richness of the slow-running mixture is controlled
the air-regulating screw 8 in **FIG 2:14.** If the engine
ses to tick over for any length of time or stalls on
eleration, the slow-running jet may be choked and
uld be cleaned. Afterwards, reset the stop screw and
egulating screw. If the engine is inclined to hunt when
ning slowly, weaken the mixture by turning the screw
nti-clockwise. Probably the best position will be
und three turns open from the fully-closed position.
ed up the engine and shut the throttle suddenly. If the
ine stalls the idling speed should be increased to a
t where the sudden release of the throttle allows the
ine to tick over evenly. Remember that a new engine
ne with tight bearings or a re-bore will not idle evenly
l it is free.

he standard jet sizes are given in Technical Data.

cleaner for Zenith carburetter

his is the oil-wetted type. It is removed by discon-
ting the breather pipe and slackening the clamp bolt.
an the wire mesh element in petrol and allow to dry.
 not detachable. When all the petrol has evaporated,
rate the element with engine oil and allow this to
n off.

carburetters

he earlier type of SU carburetter fitted to the 'Oxfords',
first 'Magnettes' and early Wolseleys, is the H2. In
er form, as the H4, it was fitted to the later 'Magnettes'
 the Riley '1.5's'. This is illustrated in **FIG 2:15.** The
r type with a different jet construction is known as the
2 and is fitted to the more recent Wolseleys. It is shown
xploded form by **FIG 2:16.** All these types have the
e working principle.

eration

Jsing **FIG 2:15** as a guide, the SU carburetter action
 be followed. The body 1 is fitted with the usual butter-
hrottle valve 82. On the air intake side of this valve is a
able choke aperture in the body which is formed by
on 4 rising and falling inside the top chamber 4. This
on is automatic, depending upon throttle opening and
ine load. This variable volume of air needs a varying
 of fuel and this is governed by the tapered needle 12
ured to the piston by screw 13. The needle rises and
 inside a fixed jet aperture in item 15, giving the greatest
 when the piston is at the top of its travel. Rapid
tuations of the piston are damped out by an hydraulic
per 5. To obtain a rich mixture for starting, the jet 15
ulled downwards to a smaller diameter of the needle
This increases the size of the annulus and the flow of
. Spring 9 is fitted to help gravity to return the falling
on. Link 45, cam 95 and stop lever 92 are arranged to
 a small throttle opening when the choke or mixture
trol is pulled out.

moving

 single-carburetter installations:
Remove the air cleaner and support rod if one is fitted.
Disconnect the fuel pipe from the carburetter, and the
hrottle cable from the carburetter lever. In the case of
he Wolseley '15/50' disconnect the throttle control
od instead, and also the throttle return spring.

3 Unscrew the union nut connecting the vacuum pipe
to the body. This is the pipe which goes to the
distributor.
4 Disconnect the mixture control wire from the lever at
the bottom of the carburetter, and release the outer
cable from its bracket.
5 Remove the carburetter flange nuts and take away the
carburetter and air intake as an assembly.
Replacement is the reverse of this procedure. Twist the
mixture control wire clockwise through half a turn before
re-locking.

Removing twin carburetters

On the 'Magnette'
1 Release the breather hose and then the air cleaner.
2 Unscrew the set screw holding the intake pipe to the
manifold bracket.
3 Disconnect the fuel pipe from the rear carburetter and
the throttle rod at the ball joint. Disconnect the vacuum
pipe from the rear carburetter.
4 Remove the float chamber drain tubes from the crankcase bracket.
5 Disconnect the mixture control wire from the common
mixture levers below the jets, and detach the outer cable
from its bracket.
6 Remove the four carburetter flange nuts and remove the
carburetter and intake pipe assembly. Replace in the
reverse order.

On the Riley '1.5'

1 Release the breather hose, the air cleaner brackets and
clip. Lift off the air cleaner.
2 Detach the throttle return spring from the peg at the
rear end of the intake manifold. Remove the manifold
from the carburetters.
3 Remove the split pin and disconnect the accelerator
cable from the back of the rear carburetter.
4 Slacken the pinch bolt and release the mixture control
cable from the front carburetter lever. Remove the
clevis pin and disconnect the mixture lever link rod
from the front carburetter lever. Pull off the main fuel
pipe.
5 Unscrew the four carburetter flange bolts and withdraw
the carburetters together. Note the heat washers and
gaskets at each flange. To separate the carburetters,
remove the rubber connecting pipe and disconnect one
of the throttle rod clamps.
On some earlier Riley's the throttle return spring is
connected to an abutment bracket, and the mixture control
cable is connected to a lever between the carburetters.
When replacing the carburetters in the reverse order,
make sure that the gaskets on each side of the heat
washers fitted to the manifold flanges, are in good condition.

Dismantling the H2

First mark the relative positions of the throttle and
control levers, and scratch a line across the body and
piston chamber flanges so that they can be correctly
located on assembly. Refer to **FIG 2:15.**
1 Remove the damper 5 and invert the carburetter to pour
off the thin oil inside. Remove screws 10 and lift off the
piston and chamber assembly 4. Spring 9 will be
found inside the chamber. Note the washer 7.

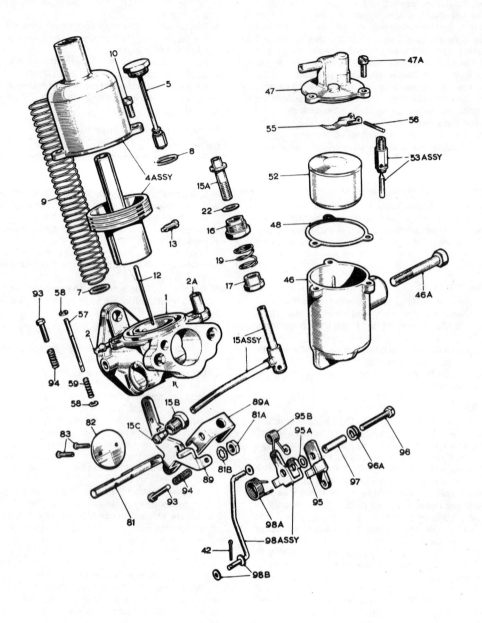

Fig 2:16 SU carburetter, type HS2, as fitted to the later Wolseley 15/50's and 1500's.

Key to Fig 2:16 1 Body. 2 Automatic ignition tube. 2A Tube—choke guide. 4 Suction chamber and piston assem̄
5 Oil cap damper assembly. 7 Washer—thrust—piston ring. 8 Washer—fibre. 9 Spring—piston. 10 Screw—suction cham
12 Needle—jet. 13 Screw—locking. 15 Jet assembly. 15A Bearing—jet. 15B Nut—gland. 15C Nipple. 16 Screw fo
17 Screw—jet adjusting. 19 Spring—jet adjusting. 22 Washer—brass. 42 Pin—cotter. 46 Float-chamber. 46A Bolt—secur
47 Lid. 47A Screw for lid. 48 Gasket for lid. 52 Float. 53 Needle and seat assembly. 55 Lever—hinged. 56 Pin—le
57 Pin—piston lifting. 58 Circlip for pin. 59 Spring for pin. 81 Spindle—throttle. 81A Nut for spindle. 81B Washer—shakepr
82 Disc—throttle. 83 Screw for disc. 89 Lever—throttle. 89A Adaptor—lever. 93 Screw—adjusting. 94 Spring for sc
95 Lever—cam. 95A Washer for lever. 95B Spring for lever. 96 Bolt—pivot. 96A Washer—spring. 97 Tube—p
98 Lever and link rod assembly. 98A Spring—return. 98B Washer—plain.

The piston and chamber assembly is a piece of precision engineering and must be treated with the greatest care.

Remove the float chamber lid 47. The needle in assembly 53 is loose and will drop out if hinge pin 56 is removed. Unhook spring 29, remove the split pins and clevis pins through lever 34 which will enable jet 15 to be pulled out. Nut 17 is the jet stop and is used for mixture adjustment. Do not disturb the larger nut 16 unless there has been trouble with leakage round the jet. This is cured by attention to the gland washers 24, but dismantling of all the parts drawn out above nut 16 will mean that the jet will need re-centring. Instructions for this will be given later in the chapter.

Piston lifting pin 57 is used when tuning the carburetter. With the damper still removed, check that the piston is quite free in the piston chamber. Clean carefully if there is any sign of sticking. Use thin oil on the piston rod and nowhere else. There must be no metallic contact between the piston rim and the inner bore of the piston chamber. Slacken screw 13 to change the needle 12. Correct needle numbers are given in Technical Data. Insert the new needle so that its shoulder is flush with the bottom face of the piston, see **FIG 2:17**.

The fuel level in the jet and the float chamber is controlled by the position of the float 52 and lever 55. The correct setting can be verified by reference to **FIG 2:18**. Use a piece of round bar $\frac{7}{16}$ in in diameter placed between the forked lever and the lip of the float chamber lid. The prongs of the lever should just rest on the bar. Correct by bending at the point indicated. Check the float for a puncture by following the Zenith instructions.

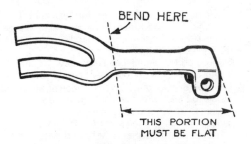

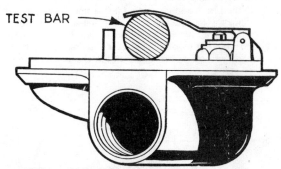

Fig 2:18 Checking float lever (metal float). Use $\frac{7}{16}$ in dia bar for H2 and H4 carburetters, $\frac{5}{16}$ in dia for HS2.

To centre the jet of the H2

Refer to **FIG 2:15**, and **FIG 2:19** for a section of the assembly.

1 Withdraw the jet, adjusting nut 17 and spring 19. Replace the nut without the spring and screw it right home. Then press the jet fully home against the nut.

2 Remove the piston damper. Slacken the jet screw 16 and manipulate the parts projecting below it. They must be slightly loose and this will allow the piston and needle to rise and fall quite freely, as the needle is able to move the jet into the required central position. Tighten screw 16 and check that the piston is still free. Repeat the operation if it is not. When satisfied, replace the spring above the adjusting nut.

Dismantling the HS2

The instructions given for the H2 can be followed in general, but it will be seen from **FIG 2:16** that the jet is of a different construction and there are changes in the float chamber assembly. The simplified jet assembly consists of a metal tube 15 sliding in a single bearing bush 15A. Fuel is fed to it by a nylon tube from the base of the float chamber. The tube can be detached from the chamber by unscrewing the nipple nut 15B. This will make it possible to remove the jet. If the jet screw 16 is disturbed or a new needle fitted, it will be necessary to re-centre the jet.

Jet centring on the HS2

When the suction piston 4 is lifted by the pin 57, it should fall freely and hit the inside jet bridge in the body with a soft metallic click. The jet adjusting nut 17 should be in its top position. If there is no audible click then, but it can be heard when the jet is fully lowered, the jet unit needs re-centring.

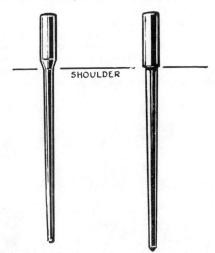

SHOULDER

Fig 2:17 Fitting SU needles. Shoulder must be flush with face of piston.

Reassembly of the H2

Follow the dismantling process in reverse. Be careful to position the piston keyway over the key in the body. Before replacing the damper, pour in thin oil to within $\frac{1}{2}$ in of the top of the piston rod. Check the piston for free movement. It should drop with a smart click. If it does not do so the trouble may be a sticking piston or a badly-centred jet.

1 Disconnect the rod 98, the nylon feed tube from the float chamber, and withdraw the jet and tube together.
2 Remove the jet adjusting nut 17 and spring 19. Replace the jet and feed tube.
3 Slacken off the large jet locking screw 16 until the jet bearing is just free to rotate by finger pressure.
4 With the damper removed, use a pencil on top of the piston rod and press the piston gently down to the jet bridge in the body. The needle should now have centred the jet, and the jet screw 16 can be tightened. It is important that the jet head and tube are in their correct positions.
5 Lift the piston and check that it falls freely and evenly, hitting the jet bridge with a soft metallic click. Fully lower the jet and check again to see if there is any difference in the sound of impact. If there is, repeat the operation until successful. Replace the adjusting nut and spring.

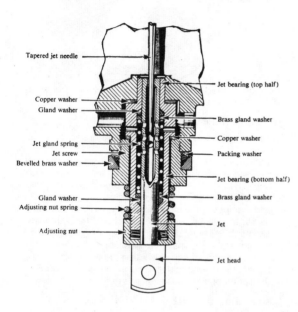

Tapered jet needle

Jet bearing (top half)

Copper washer
Gland washer

Brass gland washer

Copper washer

Jet gland spring
Jet screw
Bevelled brass washer

Packing washer

Jet bearing (bottom half)

Gland washer
Adjusting nut spring

Brass gland washer

Jet

Adjusting nut

Jet head

Fig 2:19   Section through early jet assembly, type H2 and H4.

Float setting on the HS2

Refer to **FIG 2:18** but substitute a $\frac{5}{16}$ in bar for the larger one used when setting the H2 float lever. Otherwise follow the H2 instructions.

Nylon float

This is fitted to later models of the HS2 carburetter and the float position is checked by referring to **FIG 2:20**. Hold the lid upside down and place a $\frac{1}{8}$ in to $\frac{3}{16}$ in diameter bar centrally across the lip of the lid and parallel to the float lever hinge pin. The face of the float lever should just rest on the bar when the float needle is fully on its seating. If this is not so, carefully reset the angle at the point C, until the correct position is obtained. Do not bend the straight part of the float lever.

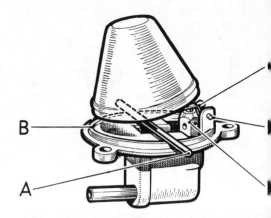

Fig 2:20   Checking and adjusting float lever (nylon float)

Key to Fig 2:20 A $\frac{1}{8}$ to $\frac{3}{16}$ in dia bar.   B Machined l
C Float lever resetting point.   D Needle valve assemb
E Hinge pin.

Servicing the H4 carburetter

The instructions given for working on the H2 carburett can be followed when dealing with the H4 as it is simil in design. It is a larger model and is fitted to the lat 'Magnettes' and to all the Riley '1.5's'.

Carburetter adjustment on the H2

Tuning the SU carburetter is based on the fact that t jet aperture can be increased by lowering the jet ar decreased by raising it.

It must be stressed that it is not possible to tune carburetter properly if other components of the engin are out of adjustment. If an owner is satisfied with h ignition setting, the condition of the valve gear and t performance of his sparking plugs he will be more certai of getting good results from his tuning.

Fig 2:21   Arrow indicates slow-running screw. Fast-idlin screw to right of arrow.

The first part of the operation is to run the engine up to working temperature and then set the throttle stop screw for fast idling as shown in **FIG 2:21**. With the jet head firmly in contact with the jet adjusting nut, turn the nut up or down until the engine runs smoothly. This operation is shown in **FIG 2:22**. Check the setting by raising the piston $\frac{1}{32}$ in with a penknife blade, or by the piston lifting pin 57 to be found below the suction chamber. If the engine stops, the mixture is too weak. If the speed of the engine continues to increase with the piston raised as much as $\frac{1}{4}$ in the mixture is too rich. If the lift of $\frac{1}{32}$ in gives a slight momentary increase in engine speed, the mixture is correct. The throttle stop screw can now be set to give the desired slow running. The fast-idling screw is seen to the right of the arrow in **FIG 2:21**. Set this by pulling the choke or mixture control knob on the dash until the linkage under the carburetter(s) is about to move the jet(s). This will probably be a pull of about $\frac{1}{4}$ in. Adjust the fast-idling screw to give an engine speed of 1000 rpm when hot.

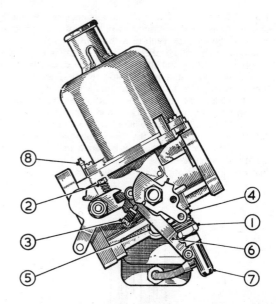

Fig 2:23   Controls and other features of the HS2 carburetter.

Key to Fig 2:23   1 Jet adjusting nut.   2 Throttle stop screw. 3 Choke or fast idling screw.   4 Jet locking nut.   5 Float chamber securing nut.   6 Jet link.   7 Jet head.   8 Vacuum ignition take-off.

2 Slacken one of the coupling clips on the throttle interconnecting shaft, disconnect the mixture control cable and the link between the two jet adjusting levers.
3 Unscrew both throttle stop screws until the throttles are completely closed. Turn the rear screw about one turn to set the throttle for fast idling and lift the piston of the front carburetter $\frac{1}{2}$ in to put it out of action.
4 Set the rear adjusting nut for smooth running in the manner described for the H2. Then reverse the proceedings for tuning the front carburetter.
5 When both carburetters are correctly adjusted set the throttle stop screws to give the required slow running. Adjust the link between the jet levers so that each one is moved the same amount when the mixture control is used.

Synchronization

Listen at each carburetter air intake with about two feet of rubber tubing, placing one end to the ear and the other just touching the intake. The hiss of ingoing air will be heard, and any variation in the sound entails an alteration to the throttle stop screws until both sounds are of the same intensity. Having achieved this, tighten the throttle shaft coupling clip so that the throttles move together. The characteristics of two carburetters working together may vary a little from those of each carburetter working separately. Check the mixture strength again, by lifting each piston in turn, following the method used when adjusting the jets. Do this to balance the mixture strength and to ensure that it is not too rich.

Carburetter troubles

Difficult starting may be due to a sticking piston. Remove the intake pipe and try lifting the piston. It should

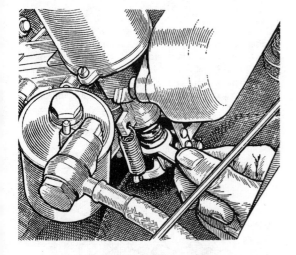

Fig 2:22   Turning the jet adjusting nut.

Adjusting the HS2

The procedure is much the same as that just detailed for the H2, but disconnect the mixture control cable after running the engine up to working temperature. Unscrew the throttle stop screw until the throttle is completely closed, and then turn the screw in a clockwise direction about one turn to set the throttle for fast idling. The adjustments to the jet nut are then the same as those given for the H2. Reference to **FIGS 2:23** and **2:24** will help when identifying the parts.

Adjusting Riley and 'Magnette' twin carburetters

The throttles are interconnected by a coupling shaft and spring clips, so that slackening off one clip enables the throttles to be independently adjusted. The mixture controls are also interconnected by an adjustable link. To adjust the jets:
1 Run the engine up to working temperature and take off the aircleaner and intake pipe.

rise and fall freely but with slight resistance due to the damper. Removing the damper will allow the piston to fall with a smart click. With or without the damper there should be no sticking. If there is, it will be caused by dirt in the piston and suction chamber assembly, or by a badly centred jet. Never stretch the piston return spring in an attempt to improve the rate of return. A blocked jet can often be cleared by opening the throttle with the engine running, and momentarily blocking the air intake. With the throttle still open, remove the hand and the engine should start to race, which shows that the jet has been cleared.

Steady leakage round the jet is generally due to defective gland washers in the jet bearing. Flooding of the float chamber and dripping from the drain pipe is often caused by grit between the float chamber needle and its guide. The needle is removed by withdrawing the float pivot pin. If the tapered end of the needle is deeply grooved, replace both the needle and its seating, which is screwed into the float chamber lid.

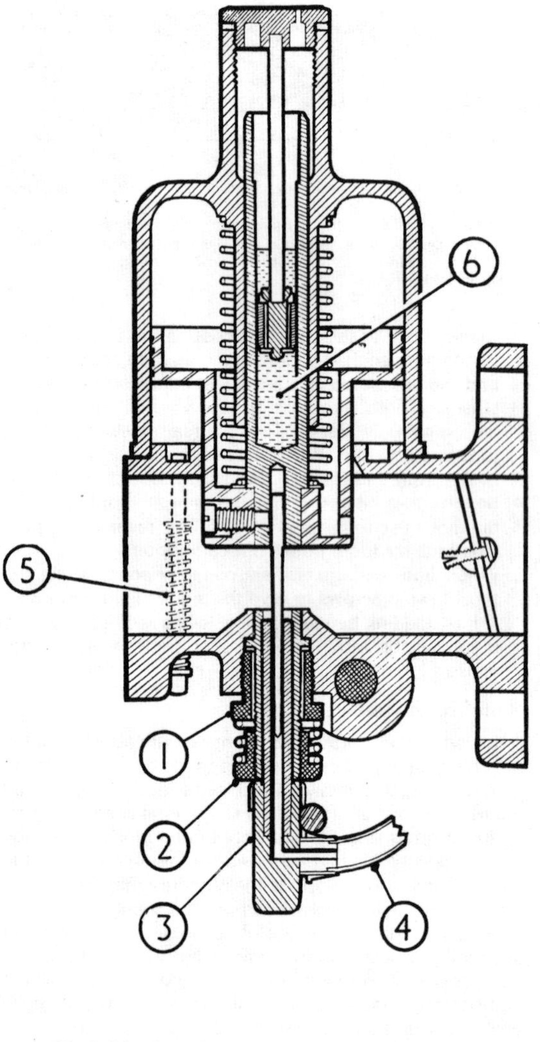

If there is fuel in the tank and the pump is working, yet there seems to be no fuel in the float chamber, the cause may be a sticking float needle. Disconnect the fuel feed pipe from the carburetter. Switch on the ignition and if there are regular spurts of fuel from the open pipe then the diagnosis is almost certainly correct.

No attempt at tuning will overcome the effects of air leaks at the carburetter flanges, or past a badly worn throttle spindle. The worn spindle must be replaced by a new one. It may also be necessary to renew the body if the spindle bearings are worn. It will be impossible to adjust or centre the jet if the needle is bent.

Air cleaners for SU carburetters

Some Wolseley '1500's' have the dry-type air filter. Remove it and dismantle by detaching the spring clip on the underside, so that the base can be lifted off. Blow away all dust and renew the element if the mileage has reached the recommended figure. The original dry-type cleaner has been superseded by an AC-Delco assembly with fixing stays, (Part No. 12H 161) or a Tecalemit assembly with stays, (Part No. 12H 187). The two makes of element are not interchangeable, but the complete assemblies can be interchanged provided the appropriate fixing stays are also fitted.

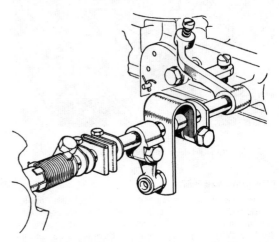

Fig 2:25 Modified coupling between Magnette carburetters.

The oil-wetted type

This is fitted to early 'Oxfords' and 'Magnettes'. To service it at the recommended intervals of 3000 miles, remove the central nut and lift out the cover-element assembly. Wash this well in petrol and leave to drain. When dry, re-oil with engine oil and allow to drain before replacing.

The oil-bath type

In this type of cleaner, most of the dirt in the incoming air is precipitated into the oil-bath when the air changes direction on its way up into the woven wire-mesh element.

Fig 2:24 A sectional view of the HS2 carburetter.

Key to Fig 2:24 1 Jet locking nut. 2 Jet adjusting nut. 3 Jet head. 4 Feed tube from float-chamber. 5 Piston lifting pin. 6 Oil damper reservoir.

At this point the air picks up drops of oil which wet the wire mesh and the remaining dirt adheres to it. As the oil drains back into the oil-bath it takes the dirt with it.

Inspect the oil-bath container every 1000 miles to see if it has accumulated any sludge. To remove the cleaner, slacken the clip securing it to the air intake pipe and detach the breather pipe. Lift off the assembly, withdrawing the support spigot from its rubber mounting on the engine bracket. Keep the cleaner upright and remove the central retaining bolt. The top cover with element is lifted out first, followed by the oil-bath container. If there is no sludge in the bottom of the container top up the oil to the level shown by the arrow on the side of the bowl. Replace the parts, making sure that the cork sealing washer up inside the element centre tube is in good condition.

If there is sludge, empty out the old oil and scrape away the accumulation. Wash in paraffin and dry, then fill to the mark with clean engine oil. Wash the element in paraffin, allow it to drain and then dry thoroughly. It is not necessary to oil it afterwards. Reassemble, keeping the filter assembly upright to avoid spilling the oil.

Modifications

On the 'Magnette', beginning at car No. ZB22701, the carburetters are fitted with a modified coupling to provide a delayed opening of the forward carburetter. This is to ease the take-off from a standstill. The new coupling is shown in **FIG 2:25**.

To set the coupling, slacken the clamping bolt of the brass throttle lever and tighten the mating pressed steel lever in the downward-pointing or six o'clock position shown. The throttles should be held in their closed or slow-running position by their closing springs. Now tighten the brass lever clamping bolt so that its driving pin is just touching the far side of the clearance hole in the pressed steel lever.

Note: The carburetters are interchangeable with the older type only as complete units.

Fault diagnosis

(a) Leakage or insufficient fuel delivered

1 Air vent in tank restricted.
2 Fuel pipes blocked.
3 Air leaks at pipe connections.
4 Pump or carburetter filters clogged.
5 Pump gaskets faulty.
6 Pump diaphragm damaged.
7 Pump valves sticking or seating badly.
8 Fuel vapourizing in pipe lines due to heat.

(b) Excessive fuel consumption

1 Carburetters need adjusting.
2 Fuel leakage or float chamber flooding.
3 Strangler flap partially closed.
4 Dirty air cleaner.
5 High engine working temperature.
6 Brakes binding.
7 Tyres under-inflated.
8 Incorrect jets or needle.

(c) Idling speed too high

1 Rich fuel mixture.
2 Carburetter controls sticking.
3 Slow-running screws badly adjusted.
4 Worn carburetter butterfly valve.

(d) Noisy fuel pump

1 Loose pump mountings.
2 Air leaks on suction side or at diaphragm.
3 Obstruction in fuel pipe.
4 Clogged pump filter.

(e) No fuel delivery

1 Float needle stuck.
2 Vent in tank blocked.
3 Electric pump connections faulty
4 Electric pump contacts dirty.
5 Pipe line blocked.
6 Pump diaphragm stiff or damaged.
7 Inlet valve in pump stuck open.
8 Bad air leak on suction side of pump.

CHAPTER THREE

THE IGNITION SYSTEM

Operation   Routine maintenance   Removing distributor   Dismantling   Servicing   Assembling
Installing   Driving spindle   Timing   Faulty performance   Testing   Sparking plugs   Modifications
Fault diagnosis

This chapter deals with distributors which differ very little in their working principles, but have design differences which are mainly concerned with the contact breaker mounting. The early type DM2 is shown in exploded form in **FIG 3:1** and it can be seen from **FIG 3:3** that the fixed contact plate is held down by two screws. The later distributors are of the type shown in **FIG 3:2** and a glance at **FIG 3:4** will show that there is a single fixing screw and two notches for adjustment of the points.

To show the parts which require routine maintenance we have used illustrations which are typical of the distributor mounting. The angle of mounting may vary, particularly in the case of the 'Magnette', but this will not affect servicing instructions, except those to do with ignition timing. These will be dealt with in the appropriate section.

Operation

All the distributors incorporate automatic ignition timing by centrifugal mechanism and by a vacuum control. The centrifugal device has weights which fly out against the tension of small springs as the engine speed rises. This movement advances the contact breaker cams relative to the distributor driving shaft, giving advanced ignition. The vacuum control is a diaphragm which is deflected by the depression in the inlet manifold, to which it is connected by a small-bore pipe. At small throttle openings, with no load on the engine, there is a high degree of vacuum in the manifold, causing the unit on the distributor to advance the ignition. When hill-climbing on large throttle openings, the degree of vacuum is much reduced and the unit will then retard the ignition. The centrifugal timing control and the vacuum unit can be seen in **FIG 3:1**.

Routine maintenance every 3000 miles

Pull off the rotor, see **FIG 3:1**. Do not remove the screw from the end of the shaft but squirt a few drops of thin machine oil into the recess. This will make its way past the screw and downwards to lubricate the cam bearing and the distributor shaft. When refitting the rotor, turn it about until its key engages with the shaft keyway and then press it right home.

Give the cam a light smear of grease and apply a slight trace of oil to the top of the contact breaker lever pivot pin shown in **FIG 3:5**. Squirt a few drops of engine oil through the gap between the cams and the contact breaker base plate, taking care that no oil gets on the plate or near the contact points. This operation will lubricate the centrifugal timing control.

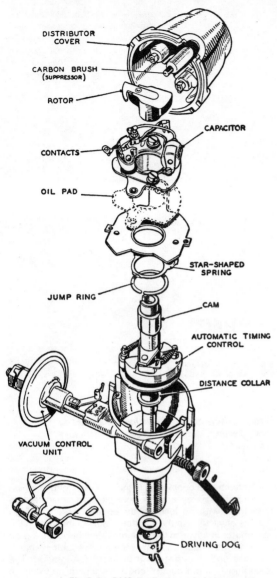

Fig 3:1   DM2 distributor exploded.

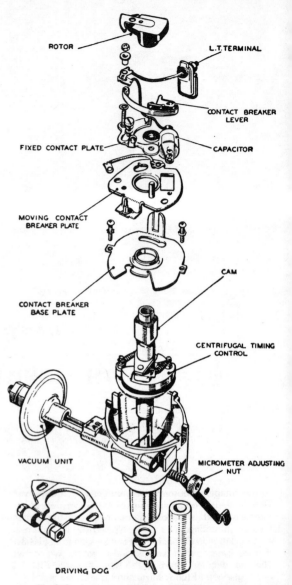

Fig 3:2   Later type distributor DM2 P4 exploded.

Check the contact breaker gap by turning the engine by hand until the points are fully opened by one of the cams. The position is clearly shown in **FIG 3:3**, for the early distributor, and in **FIG 3:4** for the later type. The gap is correct if a feeler gauge having a thickness between .014 in and .016 in is a sliding fit between the points. Do not alter the setting unless the gap varies considerably from the gauge thickness. To adjust the gap on the early type, slacken both securing screws and manipulate the plate until the setting is correct, then tighten the two screws. On the later type, refer to **FIG 3:4** and slacken the single screw. Place a screwdriver between the notches indicated by the right-hand arrow and turn clockwise to reduce, or anti-clockwise to increase the gap. When satisfied with the adjustment, tighten the securing screw.

Removing the distributor

The distributor can be removed and replaced without interfering with the ignition timing, provided the clamp bolt shown in **FIG 3:6** is not disturbed.

1 Turn the engine over until the rotor arm is pointing to No. 1 plug lead segment in the distributor cap. Note also the position of the vacuum unit as this will simplify connecting the vacuum pipe during reassembly.
2 In the case of the 'Magnette', remove the windshield washer container.
3 Remove the distributor cap, the low-tension lead from the terminal on the side of the distributor and the suction pipe from the union on the vacuum control unit.

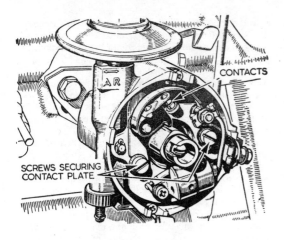

Fig 3:3   Two screws secure the DM2 fixed contact plate.

Dismantling

With both types of distributor the procedure is much the same.

1 To remove the contact breaker assembly complete, lift off the rotor, slacken the low-tension terminal nuts and withdraw the slotted connector to be seen top right in **FIG 3:2**. On early models take out the spring clip securing the suction unit link to the contact plate. On the later type of distributor the flexible actuating link is simply unhooked from the plate. The plate assembly is released from the distributor body by removing the two fixing screws.

2 The plate can be dismantled completely, either in or out of the distributor body. Remove the nut and washer from the pin which anchors the moving contact spring. The pin and its associated parts are shown exploded in **FIG 3:2** just below the rotor. Withdraw the insulating sleeve from the capacitor (condenser) lead connector and low-tension lead connector, noting the order in which they are fitted. Lift the moving contact from its pivot pin and the insulating washers from both pins.

3 The fixed contact plate is secured by two screws on the early distributor and one screw on the later type. Each screw has a spring and a flat washer. Remove the screw(s) and take away the plate.

4 Take out the securing screw and remove the capacitor. Note that the earthing lead, which is attached to the same screw, passes under the capacitor to keep clear of the cams.

5 With the suction unit link detached, remove the two fixing screws which hold the base plate to the distributor body and lift out the plate. One of the screws also takes the earthing lead.

Important: Before carrying out the next operation, note the relative positions of the rotor arm drive slot at the top of the cam spindle, and the offset driving dog at the bottom of the drive spindle. These details can be seen in **FIGS 3:1** and **3:2**. This will ensure that

the timing is not 180 deg out when the cam spindle is engaged with the centrifugal weights on assembly.

6 Now take out the cam retaining screw to be found in the recess in the top end and remove the cam spindle.

7 Take out the centrifugal weights. These may be lifted off as two assemblies, each complete with a spring and a toggle.

8 Release the suction unit by removing the circlip from the threaded end, then the adjusting nut and spring. Take care not to lose the special locking clip behind the adjusting nut.

9 Remove the offset drive dog from the bottom end of the driving spindle by punching out the parallel pin. The spindle can then be withdrawn from the body. Note the position of any thrust washers.

Servicing

Examine the distributor cap for cracks or signs of 'tracking'. The latter can be seen as a thin black line between the brass segments inside the cap. There is no cure for this, and the cap must be renewed. The carbon brush indicated in **FIG 3:7** should protrude slightly and move freely when pressed. It is composite in construction, the top part being of a resistive compound to give some degree of suppression against radio interference. For this reason it must never be replaced with the short, non-resistive type of brush. Clean the inner and outer surfaces of the cap with a dry cloth.

Renew the rotor if the metal electrode is loose or badly eroded. The faces of the contact breaker points should be clean and flat, with a greyish frosted look. If they are not too deeply burned or pitted, they can be polished by using a fine stone with a rotary motion. It is essential to maintain the faces in a flat and square condition, so that they will meet perfectly when fitted. After working on them, wipe them clean with a petrol-moistened cloth.

Check that the moving arm of the contact breaker is free on its pivot. If tight or sluggish, remove the arm and polish the pivot pin with a strip of fine emery cloth. Afterwards, remove every trace of emery dust and apply a drop of engine oil to the top of the pin.

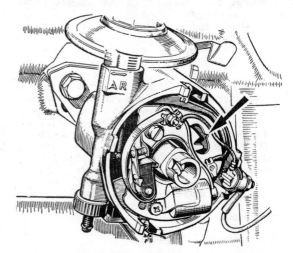

Fig 3:4   Adjustment notches for contact points on DM2 P4 distributor.

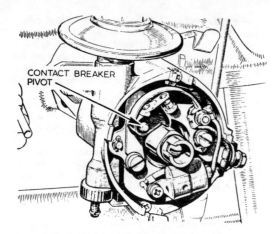

Fig 3:5 Location of contact breaker pivot.

If the centrifugal timing weights and pivot pins are worn it will be necessary to renew the weights and the cam assembly. Also check the fit of the cam spindle in the drive shaft. Slackness here will cause cam wear, and lead to erratic opening of the contact points. The drive shaft runs in bushes in the body, and these can be renewed if the shaft has excessive clearance.

Assembling

1 Using thin engine oil, lubricate the parts of the centrifugal advance mechanism, the drive shaft and the part of the top shaft where the cam fits.
2 Assemble the two shafts together, making sure that the cam driving pins engage with the centrifugal weights in the original position. When viewed from above, the offset of the driving dog must lie in the correct relative position to the driving slot for the rotor arm, as checked when dismantling.
3 When replacing the vacuum control unit, turn the adjusting nut to the half-way position.
4 After assembling the contact breaker, adjust the points to the correct gap.

Installing

1 Insert the distributor into the crankcase housing until the driving dog rests on the inner drive shaft. Turn the rotor arm until the driving dogs engage. As they are offset, there is only one place where they can do this.
2 Align the clamping plate holes and place the vacuum control unit in the position it occupied before dismantling. Fit the two bolts and tighten them.
3 Fit the distributor cap and the vacuum control pipe.
   Note: If the engine has not been turned since the distributor was removed, the rotor arm should be opposite the segment in the cap which leads to No. 1 sparking plug. If correct, the high-tension leads can be replaced on the plugs in the firing order 1, 3, 4, 2. The rotor arm moves anti-clockwise when viewed from above, and No. 1 cylinder is at the front.

Setting the driving spindle

The distributor is driven by a spindle which engages with a skew gear on the camshaft. It is shown as part 38 in **FIG 1:2** in the Engine chapter. If this spindle has been removed during an overhaul, it must be correctly replaced or the ignition timing will be wrong. The following replacement procedure is correct for all the cars except the Austins 'A40', '50' and '55'. The instructions for the latter will be given at the end of this section.

1 Turn the crankshaft until No. 1 piston is at tdc on the compression stroke. Valves 7 and 8 on No. 4 cylinder should then be just 'rocking', that is the exhaust valve will be just closing and the inlet just opening. No. 4 cylinder is at the rear of the engine.
2 When dealing with early engines, look at **FIG 3:9**; and use **FIG 3:10** for later engines. Taking the early type of setting, turn the crankshaft slightly until the hole in the pulley and the arrow on the timing cover are exactly in line. At this point the piston of No. 1 cylinder will be precisely at the top of its stroke. Now determine the correct ignition timing from Technical Data. It will be given as so many degrees before top dead centre (btdc). To arrive at a point before top dead centre the crankshaft must be turned backwards. The distance in degrees can be estimated by the fact that an angular movement of four degrees of the crankshaft is the same as turning the rim of the pulley $\frac{3}{16}$ in backwards from the pointer. Thus, an 8 deg advance btdc would require a movement of $\frac{3}{8}$ in on the pulley rim.

   To find the correct setting on later engines it is assumed that the piston of No. 1 cylinder is already at tdc on its compression stroke. Using **FIG 3:10** as a guide, turn the crankshaft until the notch in the pulley is in line with the longest pointer below the timing cover. This will then put No. 1 piston exactly at tdc. Turning the pulley backwards will enable the notch to be lined up with either of the two short pointers. The inset in the illustration shows the position for the angular setting of 5 deg btdc. The short pointer to the right would be the setting for 10 deg btdc. Angular settings between these figures can be estimated.
3 Into the end of the driving spindle, screw a length of $\frac{5}{16}$ in BSF rod, or one of the tappet cover bolts. Push the spindle into the crankcase housing with the right-hand end of its slot just below the horizontal and the large segment uppermost, as shown in **FIG 3:8**. As the gears engage, the slot will move anti-clockwise until it finishes at approximately the one o'clock position. Remove the bolt.

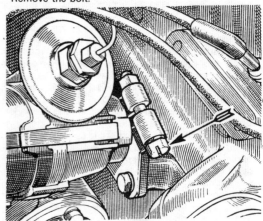

Fig 3:6 Distributor clamping bolt.

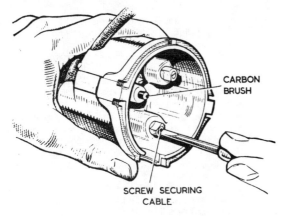

CARBON
BRUSH

SCREW SECURING
CABLE

Fig 3:7   Securing cables in distributor cap.

4 Insert the flanged distributor housing, securing it with
the special bolt. It is essential that this bolt should not
project above the face of the housing. Refit the distributor. If the clamp plate has been disturbed it will
be necessary to retime the ignition, an operation which
will be described in the next section.

To insert the driving spindle on the Austins 'A40', '50'
and '55', adopt the following method after setting the
crankshaft at the correct angular position according to
the previous notes.

On the 'A40' up to car No. GS5 131885 and the 'A50' up
to car No. HS5 124482, hold the spindle with the slot
vertical and the slot offset to the rear. When the gears
engage, the slot will turn anti-clockwise until it finishes at
approximately eleven o'clock. After the car numbers
quoted, and on the 'A55', the distributor is fitted with a
modified cap which is turned clockwise through 90 deg
compared with the earlier models. This means a change in
the position for entering the driving spindle. Set it so that
the slot is horizontal with the large segment at the bottom.
As the gears engage, the slot will turn anti-clockwise to
the 2 o'clock position.

Timing the ignition

Read the previous section and set the piston of No. 1
cylinder to the correct position for the required degrees of
ignition advance given in Technical Data. This will be
done by using the timing marks on the crankshaft pulley
and the timing cover.

1 Set the contact breaker points to the correct gap as
given in Technical Data. Remove the vacuum pipe.
2 Slacken the distributor clamping bolt indicated in
FIG 3:6 and turn the distributor until the rotor arm is
pointing to the segment and plug lead in the cap which
are correct for No. 1 cylinder. Generally, this will be
with the vacuum unit to the rear and almost vertical.
On the 'Magnette' it will be on top with the pipe union
at two o'clock, and the Austins will also have it on top
at about one o'clock.
3 Rotate the distributor body anti-clockwise until the
points are fully closed. Then slowly turn the body until
the points just begin to open. An accurate setting is
best achieved by using the electrical method of finding
the position where the points begin to break.

Do this by turning on the ignition switch and making
sure that the low-tension lead is connected to the
terminal on the body of the distributor. Connect a
12-volt lamp in parallel with the contact breaker points,
which means placing one lead on the low-tension
terminal and the other to earth. Now turn the distributor
body until the lamp lights, which will show that the
points have just opened.

4 Tighten the clamp bolt, check that the rotor is opposite
No. 1 plug lead segment in the cap, refit the cap and the
vacuum pipe. Check on the road, making small adjustments by using the micrometer nut shown in **FIG 3:11**.
The scale indicated by the top arrow is useful as a
datum.

Timing with a stroboscopic lamp

1 Disconnect the vacuum pipe.
2 Keep the engine speed below 600 rev/min so that the
centrifugal advance weights do not operate.

Faulty performance

Examine the sparking plug leads and the one to the
ignition coil if there is trouble with misfiring or difficult
starting. The insulation may be cracked, perished or
damaged, in which case the leads must be renewed. The
connection to the coil is made by slipping the knurled
terminal nut over the new cable first. Then bare about $\frac{1}{4}$ in
of the inner wire and thread this through the brass washer
taken off the old lead. Bend back the wire strands fanwise
over the washer and then replace the assembly in the coil
socket. Fit new cables to the distributor cap by following
the method shown in **FIG 3:7**. Slacken the screws inside
the cap until the old cables can be pulled clear. If Silicone
grease is available it will waterproof the cables if the
sockets in the cap are filled with it before pushing the
new ones into place. Press the cables home and secure
them by tightening the pointed screws inside the cap.
The ring of Silicone grease round the cables will form a
water-tight seal.

Before replacing the cap, press the central carbon
brush to check that it moves freely.

Start the engine, and if misfiring persists, short each
plug in turn by using a screwdriver with an insulated
handle, placing the blade between the plug top and the

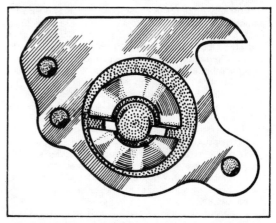

Fig 3:8   Replacing the 'Oxford' distributor drive spindle. The
large segment is uppermost.

Fig 3:9 Timing marks on early engines. Note hole in rear flange of pulley.

cylinder head. There will be no difference in performance when shorting a defective plug, but shorting good ones will make uneven running more pronounced. Having located the faulty cylinder, stop the engine and remove the lead from the plug in question. Start up again and hold the end of the lead about $\frac{3}{16}$ in away from the cylinder head. If the spark is strong and regular the fault is most probably in the sparking plug. Clean and adjust the plug or fit a new one. If the spark is weak and irregular, suspect the distributor or the low-tension circuit. If the plug leads are not at fault, examine the distributor cap for dirty surfaces, for cracks or signs of 'tracking'.

Testing the low-tension circuit

1 Remove the cap and rotor. Check the contact breaker points for cleanliness and correct gapping.
2 Disconnect the cable from the CB terminal on the coil and from the low-tension terminal on the side of the distributor. Connect a test lamp between these terminals. If the lamp lights when the contacts close and goes out when they open, the low-tension circuit is in order.

If there is a fault, switch on the ignition and turn the engine until the contact breaker points are fully open. Refer to the appropriate wiring diagram in Technical Data and check the circuit with a 20-volt instrument. If the circuit is in order the voltmeter will read about 12 volts.

1 Check battery to starter switch cable. Connect voltmeter to starter switch terminal and to earth. No reading indicates a faulty cable or connection.
2 Connect to ammeter terminal A and to earth. No reading indicates a faulty cable or connection. Repeat on the other ammeter terminal. No reading indicates a faulty ammeter.
3 Connect to control box terminal A and earth. No reading indicates a faulty cable or connection.
4 Connect to control box terminal A1 and to earth. No reading indicates a fault in the series winding in the control box.
5 Connect to lighting switch terminal which takes wire from control box terminal A1, and to earth. No reading indicates a faulty cable or connection.

6 Connect to ignition switch terminal which is wired to lighting switch, and to earth. No reading indicates a faulty cable or connection.
7 Connect to the other ignition switch terminal and earth. No reading indicates a faulty ignition switch.
8 Connect to fuse unit terminal A3 and to earth. No reading indicates a faulty cable or loose connections in wiring from ignition switch to A3.
9 Connect to ignition coil terminal SW and to earth. No reading indicates a fault in the connection between fuse unit terminal A3 and terminal SW.
10 Connect between ignition coil terminal CB and earth. No reading indicates a faulty primary winding and the coil must be renewed.
11 Connect to distributor low-tension terminal and earth. No reading indicates faulty wire or connections to ignition coil terminal CB.
12 Connect across the breaker points. No reading indicates a faulty capacitor.

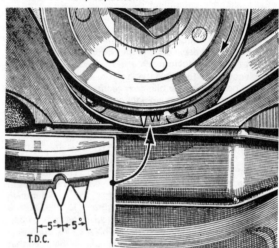

Fig 3:10 Timing marks on later engines. Note notch in rear flange of pulley.

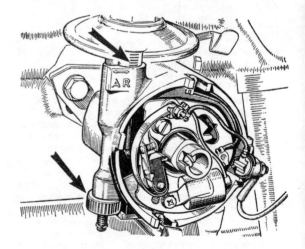

Fig 3:11 Micrometer adjusting knob and scale.

Test the capacitor by substitution, connecting a new one between the low-tension terminal and earth. If possible, fit a new capacitor complete with bracket. If it is necessary to use the old bracket, unsolder it and fix it to the new capacitor using as little heat as possible. The capacity is 0.2 microfarads.

There is one final test which can be made in the event of trouble. Remove the high-tension lead from the centre of the distributor cap. This is the lead which goes to the coil. Hold the free end about $\frac{3}{16}$ in away from the cylinder block and flick the contact points open from the closed position with the ignition switched on. If there is a strong spark the ignition coil is in good order, but if there is no spark then the coil is faulty.

Sparking plugs

Examine, clean and test the sparking plugs every 3000 miles and replace them with new ones every 12,000 miles.

The conditions under which a plug has been working can be readily determined by the deposits on the firing end. Normal working would include a mixed period of both low and high speed driving. This leaves a deposit which is brown or greyish tan in colour. A white or yellowish powdery deposit indicates a long spell of constant-speed driving or much low-speed city driving. Neither of these deposits will affect performance if the plugs are cleaned in a blasting machine and the gaps set correctly. File the sparking surfaces to reveal bright metal.

If the deposits are black and wet they are due to oil fouling. This can be traced to cylinder bore wear, worn pistons and rings, or oil finding its way down the valve stems.

Dry, fluffy black deposits are caused by rich mixture or misfiring. Excessive idling or running at slow speeds will also keep plug temperatures so low that normal deposits are not burned off.

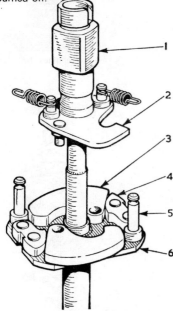

Fig 3:12 Rolling weight centrifugal advance mechanism.

Key to Fig 3:12 1 Cam. 2 Cam foot. 3 Rolling weight.
4 Action cam. 5 Spring pillar. 6 Action plate.

A white blistered appearance of the insulator nose, and badly eroded electrodes are a sign of overheating. This can be caused by weak mixture, poor cooling, incorrect timing or sustained high speed driving and heavy loads. Cleaning the plugs should also include attention to the threads. If these are clean they will help to dissipate heat through the head casting. They will also make it easier to screw in the plugs. If there is trouble with thread binding, run a tap down the holes in the head or use an old plug with cross cuts down the threads.

Set the electrode gap to the figure given in Technical Data, fit a new gasket and tighten down to a torque of 30 lb-ft.

The correct type of replacement sparking plug is listed in Technical Data.

Modifications

The distributor, type DM2.P4, can be recognized by the single fixing screw for the fixed contact plate, and the notches for adjusting the gap between the contact points. These can be seen in **FIG 3:4**. The base plate components are assembled with a special lubricant and should need no further lubrication in the normal life of the distributor.

The new contact breaker base plates are not interchangeable with the previous type and many of the parts associated with the plates are also changed. It is therefore important to quote the number stamped on the side of the distributor when ordering spare parts.

Some engines will have a vacuum control pipe which incorporates a small tubular trap. This is fitted to prevent fuel from the carburetter entering the vacuum control unit. The modified pipe may be fitted to earlier engines.

Later DM2 distributors have the rolling weight centrifugal advance mechanism shown in **FIG 3:12**. The instructions given in this chapter for dismantling and assembling can be followed with this new type. The complete distributor is interchangeable with the previous model.

Fault diagnosis

(a) Engine will not fire

1 Battery discharged.
2 Contact breaker points dirty, pitted or out of adjustment.
3 Distributor cap dirty, cracked or 'tracking'.
4 Carbon brush inside distributor cap not contacting rotor.
5 Faulty wiring or loose connections in low-tension circuit.
6 Rotor arm cracked.
7 Faulty coil.
8 Broken contact breaker spring.
9 Contact points stuck open.

(b) Engine misfires

1 See 2, 3, 5 and 7 in (a).
2 Weak contact breaker spring.
3 Cracked or perished high-tension leads to sparking plugs and coil.
4 Sparking plug loose.
5 Sparking plug insulator cracked.
6 Sparking plug gap incorrect.
7 Ignition timing too far advanced.

CHAPTER FOUR

THE COOLING SYSTEM

Operation   Maintenance   Removing radiator   Water pump   Servicing early pump
Servicing later pump   Thermostat   Anti-freeze   Modifications   Fault diagnosis

This chapter deals with water cooling systems which have their normal thermo-syphon circulation augmented by a centrifugal impeller mounted at the rear of the fan spindle. The impeller receives water from the bottom tank of the radiator and passes it on to the cylinder block. From there, it moves up into the cylinder head until it reaches a thermostat at the front end. This is a temperature-operated valve which prevents cold water from rising through the top hose to the header tank of the radiator. The cold water re-circulates through the engine by means of a by-pass until it reaches a temperature which causes the thermostat valve to open. This re-circulation ensures that the engine reaches its working temperature as quickly as possible. When the thermostat has opened, the hot water can pass on to the radiator core, where, in falling to the lower tank again, it is cooled by the effect of the external air flow through the core fins. The volume of cooling air is increased by a belt-driven fan.

The system is sealed so that there is a pressure rise when the water is hot. This increase in pressure has the effect of raising the temperature at which the water will boil. A spring-loaded valve in the filler cap controls this pressure rise. It can be seen in **FIG 4:1**, which also shows the locking cam and safety catch. When the engine is hot, unscrew the cap slowly until the retaining tongues on the rim of the cap meet the safety catches. Wait until the pressure is released before finally removing the cap, protecting the hand against steam if the water has been boiling.

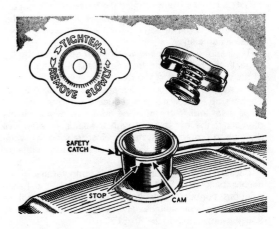

Fig 4:1   The radiator filler cap with relief valve. Pause at the safety catch when removing cap.

Maintenance

Overheating may be caused by a slack fan belt. When the tension is correct it should be possible to move the belt laterally about 1 in at the centre of its longest run. To adjust the belt, slacken the three nuts shown in **FIG 4:2.** This will allow the generator to be lifted by hand.

Fig 4:2 Loosen the three generator fixing nuts to adjust the fan belt.

Pull gently, and then tighten the link nut first. Tighten the generator pivot bolts and check the belt tension. It is most important not to run the belt too tight as this throws an undue strain on the generator and fan spindle bearings.

The bearings in the water pump rarely need replenishment as they are packed with grease on assembly. If it is thought necessary to introduce some extra lubricant it can be done by removing the large screw marked A in **FIG 4:3**. It will be found behind the fan pulley. Do not use a pressure gun or grease may find its way past the felt seals and on to the carbon face of the water seal. This will impair its efficiency.

To drain the radiator and water passages, open the tap beneath the radiator and the one on the right-hand side of the cylinder block at the rear. If there is anti-freeze in the system it can be collected, strained and used again. Topping up with water will reduce the protection, and some extra anti-freeze must be added to overcome the dilution. If the car is fitted with a heater, it is no use draining to protect the system against freezing, as water will remain in the heater. For this reason it is essential to use a good anti-freeze.

Because of pressurizing, the high temperatures in the header tank will lead to evaporation of anti-freeze solutions containing alcohol. Only ethylene glycol or glycerine types are suitable, and these should conform to Specification BS 3151 or BS 3152.

The water system should be flushed periodically to clear away any sludge and deposits which may tend to clog the passages, particularly those in the radiator core. Remove the filler cap, open the drain taps and flush the system with clean water from a hose held in the filler orifice. More serious clogging can often be cleared by removing the radiator, turning it upside down and flushing it through in the reverse direction. When re-filling, use soft water if possible. Close the drain taps, open the water tap to the heater, if one is fitted, and fill up slowly.

Removing the radiator

1 Drain the cooling system, release the hose clips and pull both top and bottom hoses off the radiator.
2 Remove the bolts securing the radiator core to the body flanges, noting that the spring washer is under the head of the bolt and the large flat washer fits against the radiator casing.
3 Store the radiator in an upright position so that sediment in the bottom tank cannot fall down into the cooling tubes.

The water pump

There are two types of water pump to be covered. The early model has separate ball bearings and seals, while the later type has the spindle, ball bearings and bearing seals as an assembly. In the Modifications section at the end of this chapter will be found the car numbers which indicate the changeover to the new bearing assembly.

Removing the pump (early type)

The following procedure will apply to all the cars with the exception of the Austins.
1 Remove the radiator as previously instructed.
2 Remove the battery negative terminal.
3 Remove the generator by releasing the hinge bolts and the link bolt.
4 Take out the four bolts holding the pump to the block.
To remove the pump on the 'A40', '50' and '55', do the following:
1 Remove the four bolts holding the pump body to the cylinder block. Remove the front hinge bolt from the generator.
2 Remove the bottom hose from the pump body.
3 If necessary, remove the fan blades.

Fig 4:3 Remove plug A from water pump body to introduce lubricant.

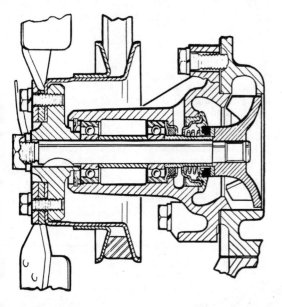

Fig 4:4 The first type of water pump showing the separate spindle and bearings.

Dismantling the pump

1 Remove the fan blades. Refer to **FIG 4:5** and remove the spindle nut 24 and washer 23.
2 Use an extractor to pull off the hub.
3 Prise out the woodruff key 22 from the spindle 11, and remove any burrs from the keyway.
4 Remove the circlip 15 and extract the dished grease retainer 16.
5 Hold the pump body and tap out the spindle towards the rear, using a soft-faced hammer. The impeller and spindle will be followed by the distance piece 13.
6 Lift out the rubber water seal assembly 12 from the recess in the body.
7 The front bearing of the pair 14 can be withdrawn by using an extractor. Then remove the distance tube 17. The rear bearing can be extracted too, but only through the front bearing housing in the body. It will be loose in the body bore, and the special tools needed to centralize it are generally found in a well-equipped garage dealing with BMC productions.
8 Behind the rear bearing is a grease-retaining assembly consisting of a felt washer 18 between dished washers 19 and 20. Replace the felt seal if there is evidence of grease leaking to the rear.

Reassembling

Replace all worn parts and reassemble the pump in the reverse order. Pay particular attention to the carbon face of the seal 12 and the mating face on the front of the impeller. Any wear or damage here will lead to water leakage. Pack the bearings with the correct grade of grease. Use a new paper joint washer 25 when refitting the completed pump to the cylinder block.

Removing the new-type pump

Follow the original instructions, but in the case of the 'A40', '50' and '55' it will now be necessary to remove the radiator and to slacken the top clip of the thermostat by-pass hose. After removing the generator the pump can be detached together with the by-pass hose.

Dismantling the latest pump

1 Remove the fan blades and fan pulley. Refer to the sectioned drawing in **FIG 4:6** for constructional details.
2 The fan hub is an interference fit on the spindle. Pull it off with a suitable extractor.
3 Pull out the bearing locating wire C which passes through a hole in the top of the pump body.
4 Gently tap the spindle rearwards. This will release the combined spindle and bearing assembly, together with the seal and impeller.
5 The impeller is also an interference fit on the spindle. Pulling it off by means of an extractor will release the seal assembly.

Check the spindle and bearing assembly for wear. The bearings cannot be serviced separately, so that the whole assembly must be renewed. Replace the seal if the carbon face is worn, or if there has been water leakage.

Reassembling

When following the reverse order, make certain that the hole in the bearing body is in line with the lubricating hole A before pressing the assembly into the pump housing. When fitting the impeller, note that the tips of the blades must clear the body by the dimension given in **FIG 4:6**.

If the interference fit of the fan hub was impaired when it was removed from the spindle, renew the hub. Take care that the face of the hub is flush with the end of the spindle as shown at B in **FIG 4:6**.

If the original spindle and bearing assembly has been retained, and it is thought advisable to introduce some extra lubricant, do so through the screw hole above point A. Do not exert undue pressure when doing this or lubricant may be forced past the spindle seals. Fit the pump assembly to the block using a new paper joint washer, and after replacing the generator and fan belt, adjust the belt to the correct tension.

Thermostat

This is located at the front end of the cylinder head, under the water outlet elbow 1 in **FIG 4:5**. Note that the thermostat 6 has a thin joint washer 7 beneath its flange. This fits into a recess in the head. If there is trouble with overheating and the thermostat is suspected, remove it for testing. Meanwhile the car can still be used by reconnecting the top hose. To remove and test the thermostat:

1 Drain the cooling system and remove the top hose from the outlet elbow.
2 Take off the three nuts and spring washers from the elbow and lift it off the studs. Remove the joint washer 2.
3 Lift out the thermostat. Should it be tight, there are two tapped holes in the top which can be utilized to ease it out.
4 Check the thermostat opening temperature given in Technical Data. Immerse the thermostat in water and raise the temperature of the water until it reaches the required figure. The dished valve in the top should now be fully open. If it fails to open, there is no way of

repairing the unit and it must be renewed.

Installation is the reverse of removal, but see that the joint washers are in good condition. The small hole in the head of the valve is a by-pass to cope with any change of pressure in the system while the valve is closed. When refilling the system with water, it is necessary to allow trapped air to escape through this hole before finally topping up. Run the engine until it is hot and then add sufficient water to raise it to the required level.

Anti-freeze

As mentioned earlier in this chapter, only ethylene glycol or glycerine type anti-freeze solutions are suitable. Before using anti-freeze it is advisable to open the drain taps and swill out the cooling system by inserting a hose in the filler neck. Examine the rubber hoses for defects and make sure that all clips and joints are leak-tight, as anti-freeze has a very searching effect on weak places.

The correct quantities of anti-freeze for different degrees of frost resistance are as follows:

Down to −14°C (7°F), a 15% solution.

Down to −18°C (0°F), a 20% solution.

Where temperatures below −18°C (0°F) are likely to be met, a solution of at least 25% of anti-freeze must be used to ensure immunity.

Top up with anti-freeze when the system is cold, and avoid loss through over-filling.

Anti-freeze can remain in the system for two years if the correct specific gravity is maintained. The manufacturers should be consulted on methods of checking this. After the second winter, drain and flush the system and start again with fresh water and anti-freeze.

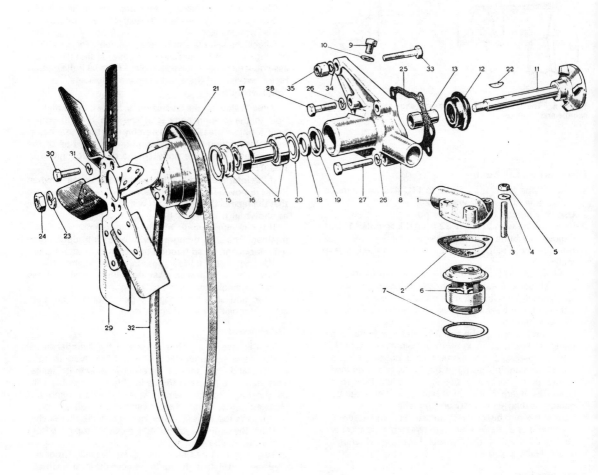

Fig 4:5   Components of first-type water pump. Some fans may have only two blades.

Key to Fig 4:5   1 Elbow—water outlet.   2 Joint—elbow.   3 Stud—elbow to cylinder.   4 Washer—stud.   5 Nut—stud.
6 Thermostat.   7 Joint—thermostat.   8 Body.   9 Plug.   10 Washer—plug.   11 Spindle with vane.   12 Seal.   13 Distance-piece—gland.
14 Bearing.   15 Spring ring—bearing.   16 Grease retainer—bearing.   17 Distance-piece—bearings.   18 Washer—felt.
19 Retainer—felt washer inner.   20 Retainer—felt washer outer.   21 Pulley and fan—water pump.   22 Key—pulley.
23 Spring washer.   24 Nut—pulley to spindle.   25 Joint—pump to block.   26 Spring washer.   27 Set screw—long—to block.
28 Set screw—short—to block.   29 Fan complete.   30 Set screw—fan to pulley.   31 Spring washer.   32 Belt—wedge type—fan.
33 Bolt—dynamo to water pump body.   34 Spring washer.   35 Nut—dynamo bolt.

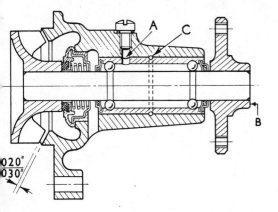

Fig 4:6 Latest type of water pump in section showing one-piece spindle and bearing assembly.

Modifications

The new water pump with the one-piece spindle and bearing assembly featured in **FIG 4:6** was introduced as follows:

On the transition from the Austin 'A50' to the 'A55'.

On the Oxfords 11 and 111 from the following engine numbers:

15M/MN/L27211 (Manumatic) onwards
15M/MN/H34816 (Manumatic) onwards
15M/N/L37661 to 15M/N/L37700 (normal gearbox)
15M/N/L37847 (normal gearbox) onwards
15M/N/H37963 to 15M/N/H38000 (normal gearbox)
15M/N/H38022 (normal gearbox) onwards.

On the Wolseley '1500' and Riley '1.5':
Commencing at engine numbers 15WA-U-L13749 and 15R-U-H715.

On the Wolseley '15/50':
From engines numbered 15W/U/H7070, 15W/U/L6632, 15W/MU/H5619 and 15W/MU/L4323.

On 'Magnettes ZA' and 'ZB':
From engines numbered 15GC/U/H11433 to 15GC/U/H11500, 15GC/U/H11538 onwards, and 15GC/MU/H11209 onwards.

In every case the pump is interchangeable with the original type, but only as a complete unit.

Wedge-type fan belt

This was introduced on the 'Oxford' at engine number BP15M17685. If the new belt is fitted to cars prior to this engine number it will be necessary to fit new pulleys to the water pump, crankshaft and generator.

Radiator side shields

These were introduced on later 'Oxford' models and can be fitted to earlier vehicles. They are fitted to prevent the ingress of water into the engine compartment. The shields are attached to the radiator block by the existing mounting bolts, and to the radiator grille by a No. $10-1\frac{3}{4}$ in pan-head screw and a distance piece.

Thermostat and radiator cap

On the Wolseley '15/50' this modification was incorporated from car number 41882. The thermostat was changed for one opening at 65°C (149°F), and the radiator cap embodied a 7 lb/sq in relief valve in place of the original 4 lb one. The new units must be fitted as a pair if interchanged with the earlier type.

Drain tap

All later models were fitted with a modified cylinder block drain tap with a plain BSP thread in place of the taper thread originally used. The new tap is interchangeable with the old, but a fibre washer is needed between the tap and the block.

Fault diagnosis

(a) Internal water leakage

1 Cracked cylinder wall.
2 Loose cylinder head nuts.
3 Cracked cylinder head.
4 Faulty head gasket.
5 Cracked tappet chest wall.

(b) Poor circulation

1 Radiator core blocked.
2 Engine water passages restricted.
3 Low water level.
4 Loose fan belt
5 Defective thermostat
6 Perished or collapsed radiator hoses.

(c) Corrosion

1 Impurities in the water.
2 Neglected draining and flushing.

(d) Overheating

1 Check 4, 5 and 6 in (b).
2 Sludge in crankcase.
3 Faulty ignition timing.
4 Low oil level in sump.
5 Tight engine.
6 Choked exhaust system.
7 Binding brakes.
8 Slipping clutch.
9 Incorrect valve timing.
10 Retarded ignition.
11 Mixture too weak.

CHAPTER FIVE

THE CLUTCH

The clutches fitted to all the cars covered by this manual are almost identical. An exploded view of the components is given in **FIG 5:1** and this can be used as a general guide. The section of the clutch shown in **FIG 5:2** will be found helpful when following the description of the working principles. Note, however, that the position of the slave cylinder and operating lever is not necessarily at the bottom as shown.

The clutch transmits power from the engine flywheel A to the splined gearbox first-motion shaft seen at the centre. On the splined part of the shaft is a driven plate C which has dry friction linings riveted to it. The plate is sandwiched between the rear face of the flywheel and the spring-loaded pressure plate P. This plate is carried round inside the cover D which is bolted to the flywheel face. The cover also carries the release mechanism shown as items H to O inclusive, the release plate H revolving with the cover. The non-rotating part of the release bearing, F and G, is pressed in and out by the operating lever and slave cylinder to be seen at the bottom. This cylinder is connected by pipe line to the master cylinder, which is directly operated by the clutch pedal. Part of the pipe line is flexible.

Movement of the clutch pedal causes a similar movement of the slave cylinder piston, and this in turn, operates the release mechanism. The release levers J pull back the pressure plate against the thrust of springs E. This frees the driven plate, thus disconnecting the gearbox from the output of the engine. When pressure is removed from the clutch pedal, the clutch springs force the pressure plate against the driven plate, which gradually and smoothly transmits the power of the engine to the gearbox. The smoothness of take-up is due in part to the cushioning effect of a ring of springs round the hub of the driven plate. This can be seen in item 11 of **FIG 5:1.**

Note: Before discussing work on the clutch it is important to realize that the clutch cover is normally serviced as an assembly, complete with pressure plate, thrust springs and release levers. This is done because it needs expensive gauging equipment to assemble the clutch accurately. This is work which should be entrusted to a competent agent, suitably equipped with the necessary tools. Inaccurate assembly can only lead to endless trouble with judder and worn release bearings.

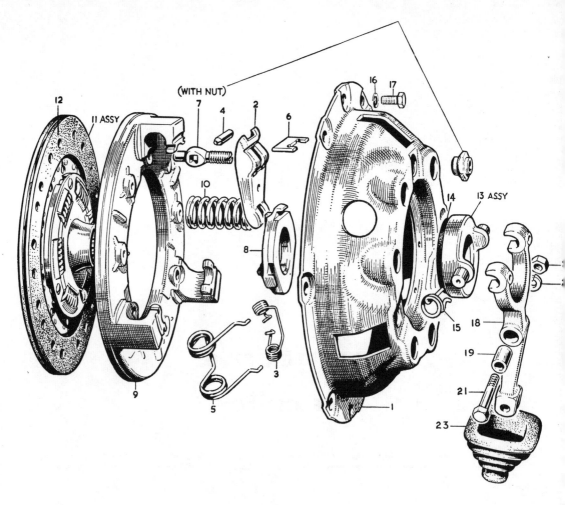

Fig 5:1 Clutch components exploded.

Key to Fig 5:1 1 Cover—clutch. 2 Lever—release. 3 Retainer—lever. 4 Pin—lever. 5 Spring—anti-rattle. 6 Stru
7 Eyebolt with nut. 8 Plate—bearing thrust. 9 Plate—pressure. 10 Spring—pressure plate. 11 Plate assembly—drive
12 Lining. 13 Ring assembly—thrust. 14 Ring—carbon. 15 Retainer. 16 Washer—spring—cover scre
17 Screw—cover to flywheel. 18 Lever assembly—withdrawal. 19 Bush. 20 Washer—spring—lever bolt. 21 Bolt—leve
22 Nut—bolt. 23 Cover—dust.

Removing the clutch

In the case of the Wolseleys, the Rileys and the 'Mag-nettes', it is necessary to remove the power unit complete, before detaching the gearbox. Instructions for the removal are given in the Engine Chapter.

On 'Oxfords' 11 and 111, and on all the Austins, the gearbox can be removed without disturbing the engine, by following the instructions given in the Gearbox Chapter.

In all cases, when the gearbox is removed by unscrewing the clutch housing bolts, be careful to support the gearbox until the first-motion shaft is clear of the driven plate and the release lever plate.

Detach the clutch from the flywheel by undoing the flange bolts a turn at a time, working diagonally until the spring pressure is relieved. Then remove the cover and pressure plate complete, leaving the driven plate free.

The driven plate

If the plate is going to be used again, do not touch th
linings with cleaning fluid of any kind. With the aid of th
following notes it will be possible to determine the co
ditions under which the plate has been working, ar
whether it is fit for further use.

First examine the hub and the cushion springs. Th
splines must not be worn nor the edges of the holes in th
central plate which engage the springs. The springs them
selves must not be broken, neither should they be so wea
that they are free to rattle.

Examine the linings for excessive wear, loose rivet
cracks or discolouration. A polished glaze is quite norm
and does not affect the ability of the linings to transm
power. They should be light in colour, with the grain
the material quite clearly visible through the glaze. Ev

ence of oil on the linings can be seen in a much darker
colour, and the obliteration of the grain by a glazed deposit
on the surface. This will cause two defects; the clutch will
slip under load, yet it will stick on engagement and be
difficult to free. These signs of oil on a clutch plate can be
attributed to leakage past the rear main crankshaft bearing, or from the gearbox.

It is not considered advisable to rivet new linings on to
an old plate, as the plate may be distorted and there may
be trouble with out-of-balance effects.

The pressure plate assembly

Use **FIG 5:1** for reference, and examine the friction
surface of the plate 9. If it is ridged or pitted, the assembly
must be renewed. This also applies to the machined surface of the release bearing thrust plate 8. The face must
be smooth and there must be no ridge round the outer
edge due to wear. If there has been trouble with slip,
judder or drag, and the pressure unit is suspected, it can
be checked by an agent with the necessary equipment.

Fig 5:3 Special tool 18G/39 for centralizing driven plate.

He will be able to look for weak or broken springs, and if
the cover is dismantled, he will be able to reset the release
fingers accurately. Excessive wear and faulty operation is
most readily cured by fitting an exchange unit complete.

The release bearing carbon ring 14 must have a smooth,
polished surface free from signs of cracks or pitting. It
must also stand proud of the housing cup by not less than
$\frac{1}{16}$ in. If it is worn more than this, both cup and carbon
ring must be renewed as an assembly. The two spring
retainers 15 hold the cup in the fork ends of the operating
lever 18. The bush 19 and bolt 21 can be renewed if there
is excessive play at this point. Do not, at any time, try to
cure troubles by adjusting the nuts which are part of the
assembly 7.

Refitting to flywheel

First check the flywheel with a dial gauge for 'run-out',
which should not exceed .003 in anywhere on the face.
If it is satisfactory, the clutch can be refitted. The important
part of this operation is that of centralizing the driven plate.
This is necessary because the gearbox first-motion shaft
must pass through the splined hub of the driven plate and
then enter the bush in the rear end of the crankshaft when
the gearbox is being refitted. This calls for perfect alignment of the hub and the bush.

To effect this alignment, use the special tool 18G/39
which is illustrated in **FIG 5:4**. The smallest diameter fits
in the crankshaft spigot bush and the next step in the
mandrel is a good fit in the bore of the driven plate hub.
As an alternative, it is possible to use a spare gearbox
first-motion shaft. Place the larger, chamfered spline, end
of the hub towards the rear.

Having centralized the driven plate, replace the clutch
cover assembly over the flywheel dowels and fit the
securing bolts, using spring washers. Tighten the bolts a
turn at a time by diagonal selection. When they are all
secure, the alignment bar can be removed. Refit the release
bearing and operating lever to the gearbox housing and
lift the gearbox into place. This must be done with great
care, supporting the whole weight of the gearbox in order
to avoid straining the shaft or distorting the driven plate
assembly. If new parts have been fitted it will be necessary to adjust the free travel of the clutch pedal. This
operation is covered in a later section on running adjustment.

Hydraulic clutch operation

The flexible mounting of modern engines makes it
difficult to use a rigid mechanical linkage between the
pedal and the clutch without having to face the problem
of judder. That is why hydraulic methods are used to
secure the necessary smooth 'take-up'. Most of the layout
of the system can be seen in **FIG 5:4** which is actually

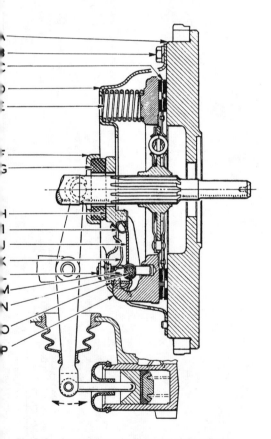

Fig 5:2 Section through clutch and slave cylinder.

Key to Fig 5:2 A Flywheel. B Securing bolts. C Driven
plate. D Clutch cover. E Thrust coil springs. F Release
bearing cup. G Graphite release bearing. H Release plate.
I Lever retainer springs. J Release levers. K Anti-rattle
springs. L Adjusting nuts. M Eyebolts. N Floating pins.
O Struts. P Pressure plate.

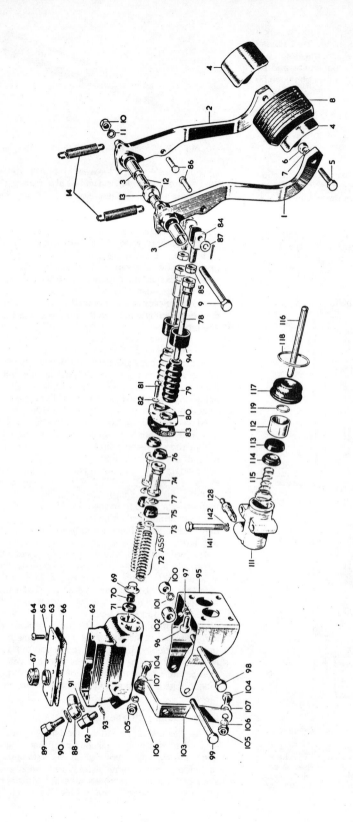

Fig 5:4 Lockheed twin master cylinder components, (Magnette)

Key to Fig 5:4 1 Pedal—clutch—R.H.D. 2 Pedal—brake—R.H.D. 3 Bush. 4 Pad—pedals. 5 Screw—pad to pedal. 6 Nut—screw. 7 Spring washer—nut.
8 Rubber—pedal pad. 9 Bolt—pedals to body. 10 Nut—bolt. 11 Spring washer—bolt. 12 Distance-piece—pedals. 13 Washer—distance—pedals.
14 Spring—pedal return. 62 Body—master cylinder. 63 Cover—body—master cylinder. 64 Screw—body to cover. 65 Shakeproof washer—screw. 66 Gasket—cover to body.
67 Cap—filler assembly. 69 Body—valve. 70 Cup. 71 Seat. 72 Spring—piston return. 73 Retainer. 74 Piston. 75 Cup—piston—primary. 76 Cup—piston—secondary.
77 Washer—primary cup to piston. 78 Push-rod. 79 Boot—push-rod to cylinder. 80 Plate—boot fixing. 81 Screw—plate. 82 Shakeproof washer—screw.
83 Gasket—fixing plate. 84 Yoke—push-rod to pedal. 85 Locknut—yoke. 86 Pin—clevis—yoke. 87 Washer—plain—clevis pin. 88 Banjo connection—R.H.D.
89 Bolt—banjo connection—R.H.D. 90 Gasket—banjo connection—large. 91 Gasket—banjo connection—small. 92 Adaptor—master cylinder—clutch.
93 Gasket—clutch master cylinder. 94 Seal—master cylinder to dash. 95 Bracket—cylinder to dash. 96 Screw—bracket to dash. 97 Spring washer—screw.
98 Bolt—long—master cylinder to bracket. 99 Bolt—short—master cylinder to bracket. 100 Nut—bolts. 101 Spring washer—bolts. 102 Spacer—bolt.
103 Stay—support—master cylinder. 104 Screw—stay to valance. 105 Nut—screw. 106 Spring washer. 107 Washer—plain. 111 Body—clutch cylinder.
112 Piston. 113 Cup—piston. 114 Filler—piston cup. 115 Spring—cup filler. 116 Push-rod. 117 Boot. 118 Clip—boot to cylinder. 119 Clip—boot to push-rod.

e one fitted to the 'Magnette'. Notice the twin master
ylinders in the body 62, the left-hand bore being for the
lutch piston, and the right-hand one for braking. The
ovement of the clutch piston 74 is through the agency
f the push-rod 78 which is connected to the clutch pedal.
his arrangement using a twin master cylinder is also
tted to the 'Oxfords' and to the Wolseley '15/50'. The
ther cars have the clutch and brake cylinders as separate
nits.

Pressure on the master cylinder piston forces fluid
rough a flexible hose to the clutch or slave cylinder 111
hich is mounted on the clutch housing. The slave piston
12 follows the movement of the master piston, pushing
n the rod 116 which in turn operates the lever connected
o the clutch release bearing. This principle is common to
ll the cars treated in this manual.

he master cylinder

It is proposed to deal with the 'Lockheed' systems first.
hese are fitted to the 'Oxfords', 'Magnettes'. Wolseley
5/50's' and the Wolseley '1500's' with the Riley '1.5's'.
he last two have separate cylinders for clutch and brake
peration, and a section of the clutch unit is shown in
IG 5:5. The internal working parts are practically
dentical throughout.

Removing

On 'Oxfords' 11 and 111.

Take out the screws and remove the floor and toeboard
cover. This is on the floor in front of the driver's seat.
The aperture in it gives access to the filler cap on the
master cylinder.

Remove the split pins and the clevis pins which connect
the push-rods to the brake and clutch pedals.

Disconnect the pipe lines by unscrewing the union nuts.
From below, remove the bolts securing the cross-
member and the master cylinder. Lift out the unit and
the push-rods.

On the 'Magnettes' and the Wolseley '15/50'
Remove the pedal mask and disconnect the clutch and
brake pedal return springs 14 in **FIG 5:4**.

2 Unscrew the nut 10 from the pivot bolt 9. Withdraw the
bolt and remove the distance pieces. Take away the
pedals complete with rubber boots and push-rods 78.
3 Disconnect the pipe line union nuts.
4 Remove the bolts 98 and 99, looking out for the distance
pieces 102 between the unit and the bracket 95. Withdraw the unit.
5 Do not unscrew the push-rods 78, but detach them
from the pedal levers by removing the clevis pins 86.

On the Wolseley '1500' and Riley '1.5'.
1 Remove the clevis pin connecting the master cylinder
push-rod to the clutch pedal lever.
2 Disconnect the pipe union from the cylinder, remove
the two bolts securing the cylinder flange to the bulkhead and withdraw the assembly.

Servicing 'Lockheed' master cylinder

Important: Extreme care is needed when dealing with
the internal parts of hydraulic mechanisms. The first
essential is absolute cleanliness. The second is to use
only the correct cleaning fluids. The hydraulic fluid used
in the system is the one for cleaning all the rubber components. If petrol, paraffin or trichlorethylene is used to
clean the metal parts, every trace of it must be removed
before the parts are reassembled. Use the fingers when
fitting rubber cups and seals so that there is no possibility
of damage which may lead to trouble with leakage.

Dismantling twin unit

1 Remove the filler cap and drain away the fluid.
2 Remove the end cover 80.
3 Withdraw the internal parts 72, 73, 74, 75, 76 and 77.
Note that these are nearest the viewer in **FIG 5:4** and
do not include the valve components 69, 70 and 71
which are found in the brake bore only.
4 The secondary cup 76 is removed from the piston by
stretching it over the end flange of the piston, using
the fingers.

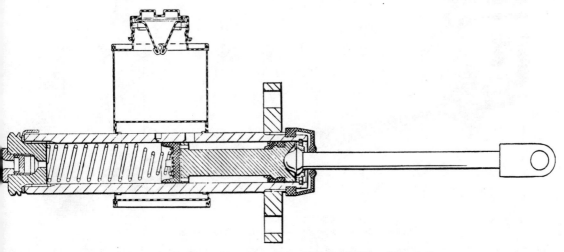

Fig 5:5   Lockheed single master cylinder, (Wolseley '1500' and Riley '1.5').

Dismantling single unit

1 Drain the fluid from the reservoir.
2 Remove the rubber dust cover from the right-hand end of the cylinder as seen in **FIG 5:5**. Inside the bore is a circlip which can be removed by using a pair of long-nosed pliers. This will release the push-rod and associated dished washer.
3 Withdraw the internal parts and remove the secondary cup from the piston. The parts are identical with those shown in perspective in **FIG 5:4**.

Assembling

After cleaning all the parts examine them for wear or damage, particularly the rubber components. It is generally advisable to fit new rubbers when rebuilding a cylinder. Dip all the internal parts in the correct fluid and assemble them wet.

1 Insert the spring with the retainer 73 in position to the rear. The retainer fits inside the primary cup 75.
2 Insert the primary cup lip first, taking care not to damage or curl back the lip, and press it down to the spring retainer.
3 Stretch the secondary cup 76 over the outer end of the piston 74. The lip of the cup faces into the bore in the same way as the primary cup. Work the cup into its groove with the fingers until it is properly seated.
4 Insert the piston using the same care with the lip of the cup. Push the piston down the bore and replace the cover plate 80 with a sound joint washer 83. In the case of the single cylinder unit fitted to the Wolseley '1500' and Riley '1.5' there is no cover plate and it is then a matter of following up the piston by inserting the push-rod and dished washer. These are held in place by the circlip mentioned in the dismantling instructions. Finally, fit the rubber dust cover.

Test the cylinder unit by filling the reservoir with fluid. Push the pistons down the bores, allowing them to return. After one or two strokes fluid should flow from the outlet. Even though the brake cylinder may not have been dis-turbed, it is as well to give it the same treatment. Refit the master cylinder unit by reversing the procedure for removing it. It will then be necessary to bleed both clutch and braking systems, as described in a later section.

The slave cylinder ('Lockheed')

The components are shown in **FIG 5:4**. The cylinder fitted to the 'Magnettes' and Wolseley '15/50's' is flanged and bolted to a bracket on top of the clutch housing, whereas the others are bolted directly to the housing lower down. Push-rods on some assemblies are attached to the clutch release lever by a clevis pin.

Removing and dismantling

If the slave cylinder is to be removed without touching the master cylinder unit then proceed as follows:

1 Attach a bleed tube to the nipple 128 on the body of the slave cylinder and open about a turn. Pump the clutch pedal until all the fluid has drained into a clean container. If the master cylinder has already been removed the slave cylinder can be unbolted without this operation.
2 Unscrew the pipe line and unbolt the cylinder, taking out the clevis pin from the push-rod fork if one is fitted.
3 Clean the exterior before removing the push-rod and rubber boot 117. Note the clip 119 holding the boot to the rod, and clip 118 which secures the boot to the body.
4 Withdraw the initial parts 112, 113, 114 and 115. Clean them in hydraulic fluid and renew any damaged parts. It is always advisable to fit a new cup 113.
5 Insert the return spring 115 with large coils entering first, and the cup filler 114 in place at the other end.
6 Replace the piston cup 113, lip first. Take care not to damage or turn back the lip. Press it down on to the cup filler.
7 Push the piston 112 down the bore plain end first.
8 Fit the retaining ring 119 inside the boot 117 and replace the boot on the cylinder body, holding it in place with ring 118. Replace the push-rod 116.

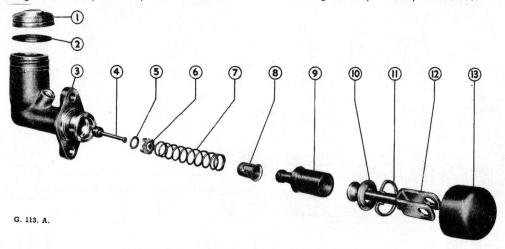

G. 113. A.

Fig 5:6 Girling master cylinder exploded, ('A40', '50' and '55').

Key to Fig 5:6 1 Filler cap. 2 Washer. 3 Master cylinder. 4 Valve stem. 5 Spring washer. 6 Valve spacer. 7 Return spring. 8 Thimble. 9 Plunger. 10 Dished washer. 11 Circlip. 12 Fork. 13 Dust cover.

To bleed the system

Disconnecting the pipe lines or dismantling either of the hydraulic units will mean the entry of air into the system. This must be bled off in the following way.

1 Fill the master cylinder reservoir with clean hydraulic fluid of the correct grade. The level should be about $\frac{1}{2}$ in from the bottom of the filler neck.

The correct fluid for the Wolseley '1500' and the Riley '1.5' is 'Lockheed' Super Heavy duty, or as a substitute SAE 70.R3. 'Oxfords' 11 and 111, the Wolseley '15/50' and the 'Magnettes' ZA and ZB should have the system filled with 'Lockheed' Genuine Brake Fluid or SAE 70.R1. No other will do.

2 During the process of bleeding, maintain the level in the reservoir so that it is never less than half full. An empty reservoir will allow air to enter the system, so that a fresh start has to be made.

3 Attach a rubber bleed tube to valve 128 on the slave cylinder. Immerse the open end in a small amount of hydraulic fluid in a clean container.

4 With an assistant to pump the clutch pedal, open the valve about a turn and give a stroke of the pedal. At the end of the down stroke on the pedal close the bleed screw before returning the pedal to the 'off' position. Continue this operation until clear fluid free from air bubbles is delivered into the container.

Clutch operation – 'A40', '50' and '55'

The Girling hydraulic system has a master cylinder which is shown in exploded form in **FIG 5 : 6.** The slave cylinder can be seen in **FIG 5 : 7,** being located in a clip on the lower part of the clutch housing.

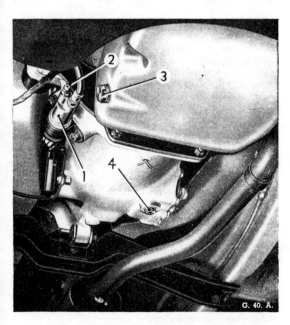

Fig 5 : 7   Location of slave cylinder ('A40', '50' and '55').

Key to Fig 5 : 7   1 Slave cylinder.   2 Clutch system bleed nipple.   3 Sump drain plug.   4 Gearbox drain plug.

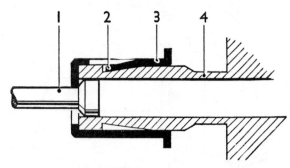

Fig 5 : 8   Fitting thimble and valve stem to Girling plunger.

Key to Fig 5 : 8   1 Valve stem.   2 Thimble leaf.   3 Thimble. 4 Plunger.

Removing master cylinder

1 Remove the battery and its tray.

2 From inside the car, remove the cover round the pedal levers just above the parcel shelf. This gives access to the master cylinder push-rod. Remove the circlip and clevis pin, which will release the push-rod from the pedal lever.

3 Disconnect the pipe union from the cylinder, remove the two flange bolts and withdraw the unit from the bulkhead. Note the packing pieces between the cylinder and the bulkhead so that they are correctly replaced.

Dismantling

1 Remove the filler cap and drain out the fluid.

2 Peel back the rubber dust cover 13 in **FIG 5 : 6.** Remove circlip 11 with a pair of long-nosed pliers. The push-rod and fork 12, with dished washer 10 can then be removed.

3 Extract the plunger 4 to 9 inclusive. Separate it by lifting the thimble leaf of item 8 over the shouldered end of the plunger. The parts can be identified in **FIG 5 : 8.**

4 Compress the return spring 7 and allow the valve stem 4 to slide out through the elongated hole in the thimble, thus releasing the spring. Remove the valve spacer 6, the spring washer 5 from under the valve head and remove the seal from the valve head. Examine everything, especially the seals, for wear or damage. Replace with new parts if necessary. Clean the internal parts with brake fluid or methylated spirits. Do not use petrol or paraffin.

Reassembly

1 Replace the seal on the valve so that the flat side is against the valve head. Then locate the spring washer 5 so that its domed face is against the underside of the valve as shown in **FIG 5 : 9.** It will be held in place by spacer 6 which has its legs facing towards the valve seal.

2 Place the plunger spring 7 centrally on the spacer, insert the thimble 8 into the spring and compress the spring until the valve stem enters the elongated hole in the thimble. Locate the stem centrally in the thimble, and check that the spring and spacer are also still central.

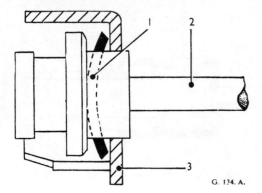

G. 134. A.

Fig 5:9 Correct location of domed washer under Girling valve.

Key to Fig 5:9   1 Washer.   2 Valve stem.   3 Valve spacer.

3 Fit a new seal on the plunger 9, with the flat face of the seal against the flat end of the plunger. Insert the forward end of the plunger into the thimble until the thimble leaf drops behind the shoulder on the plunger, as shown at 2 in **FIG 5:8**. Press home the leaf.

4 Smear the assembly with correct brake fluid and insert into the cylinder, valve end first. Ease the plunger seal lips carefully into the bore with the fingers. Replace the push-rod and washer, placing the dished side of the washer under the spherical head. Engage the circlip 11 in the groove at the mouth of the cylinder bore. Replace the dust cover.

5 Refit the unit into the hole in the bulkhead, fitting the $\frac{5}{16}$ in packing washer first. Refit the pipe union.

6 Working inside the car, line up the push-rod fork with the pedal lever and fit the clevis pin. Secure the pin with the circlip. Assemble the cover over the levers and parcel shelf. Then bleed the system as instructed after the next section.

The slave cylinder – 'A40', '50' and '55'

This consists of an alloy body, a piston with seal, a spring and a bleed screw with ball. The push-rod is attached to the clutch operating lever by a clevis pin. The cylinder is mounted through a steel clip and held in position by a pinch bolt, see **FIG 5:7**.

Dismantling

1 Remove the rubber dust cap from the bleed nipple 2 in **FIG 5:7**. Attach a bleed tube and open the valve nearly a turn. Pump the clutch pedal until all the fluid has been drained into a clean container.

2 Unscrew the pipe union and remove the pinch bolt. The cylinder can then be removed.

3 Take off the rubber dust cover and if an air line is available, blow out the piston and seal. Lift out the spring. Replace worn and damaged parts and always fit a new seal if possible. Clean in the manner described for the master cylinder parts.

Reassembly

1 Place the seal on the stem of the piston with the back of the seal against the piston, replace the spring with the small end on the stem and smear well with brake fluid. Insert into the cylinder.

2 Replace the dust cover and mount the assembly in the clip, ensuring that the push-rod enters the hole in the dust cover. Screw in the pipe union. Bleed the system in the following way.

Bleeding

The correct hydraulic fluid for the Austin Girling system is Girling Crimson Brake Fluid. It is not permissible to use any other fluid. Fill the master cylinder tank to the level indicated on the outside, and keep it topped up during the operation. Then follow the instructions given in an earlier section on bleeding the 'Lockheed' system. When finished, replace the dust cap on the bleed screw.

Adjustment

Normally the type of hydraulic clutch operation described in this chapter needs no adjustment. The clearance between the master cylinder push-rod and the piston governs the free movement of the clutch pedal and this is fixed when the car is assembled, on the Austins, the Wolseley '1500's' and Riley '1.5's' by packing washers between the cylinder and the bulkhead, and on the other cars by adjusting the length of the push-rods. The push-rod adjustment can be seen in parts 84, 85 and 78 in **FIG 5:4**.

If it is necessary to carry out the adjustment, check the free movement of the clutch pedal before the hydraulic master cylinder piston begins to move. This should be approximately $\frac{5}{32}$ in and can usually be felt by depressing the clutch pedal gently by hand. This is equivalent to a free movement of .030 in at the end of the push-rod 78 before it begins to move the piston 74. Adjust by releasing the locknut 85 and turning the push-rod.

Modifications

Withdrawal lever pivot bolt

This was modified on the following cars:
'Oxfords' from gearbox No. 2461, 'Magnettes' from Engine No. 9748. The bolt is increased in diameter and has a shoulder which makes an abutment for the self-locking nut and washer which supersede the nut and spring washer previously fitted. A larger bearing bush is required for the withdrawal lever, which means modifications to the lever and the bosses on the gearbox front cover. The modified parts may be fitted to earlier cars as a complete set. They are as follows:
Withdrawal lever pivot bolt
Pivot bolt washer
Self-locking nut
Withdrawal lever and bush
Gearbox front end cover

Modified clutch assembly

On the 'Oxford', commencing at car No. 231355, a modified clutch assembly was fitted which entailed a change in the slave cylinder and push-rod. The parts can be fitted as a pair to earlier cars. They are:
Clutch assembly, part No. 11G3217
Slave cylinder with push-rod, part No. 7H7974

Modified master cylinder

On the Wolseley '1500' and Riley '1.5' the method of securing the push-rod assembly in the master cylinder was changed. A Seeger circlip was fitted to replace the original plain circlip. The old and new circlip grooves are of different widths so that the push-rod assemblies are not interchangeable. Modified master cylinders can be identified by a groove cut around the barrel. Subsequently the push-rod length was increased to between 5.10 in and 5.12 in. The longer rod may be fitted in place of the shorter one if packing washers 21G5163 and 21G5164 are fitted as required between the master cylinder flange and the bulkhead. The changes do not affect the dismantling and assembling instructions.

Fault diagnosis

(a) Drag or spin

1 Oil or grease on the driven plate linings
2 Bent engine backplate.
3 Misalignment between the engine and the gearbox first-motion shaft.
4 Leaking master cylinder or pipe line.
5 Driven plate hub binding on first-motion shaft splines.
6 First-motion shaft spigot binding in crankshaft bush.
7 Distorted clutch plate.
8 Warped or damaged pressure plate or clutch cover.
9 Broken driven plate linings.
10 Dirt or foreign matter in the clutch.
11 Air in the clutch hydraulic system.

(b) Fierceness or snatch

1 Check 1, 2, 3 and 4 in (a).
2 Worn clutch linings

(c) Slip

1 Check 1 2 and 3 in (a).
2 Check 2 in (b).
3 Weak anti-rattle springs.
4 Seized piston in clutch slave cylinder.

(d) Judder

1 Check 1, 2 and 3 in (a).
2 Pressure plate not parallel with flywheel face.
3 Contact area of driven plate linings not evenly distributed.
4 Bent first-motion shaft.
5 Buckled driven plate
6 Faulty engine or gearbox rubber mountings.
7 Worn shackles.
8 Weak rear springs.
9 Loose propeller shaft bolts.
10 Loose rear spring clips

(e) Rattle

1 Check 4 in (d).
2 Broken springs in driven plate.
3 Worn release mechanism.
4 Excessive backlash in transmission.
5 Wear in transmission bearings.
6 Release bearing loose on fork.

(f) Tick or knock

1 Worn first-motion shaft spigot or bush.
2 Badly worn splines in driven plate hub.
3 Release plate out of line.
4 Faulty Bendix drive on starter.
5 Loose flywheel.

(g) Driven plate fracture

1 Check 2 and 3 in (a).
2 Drag and distortion due to hanging gearbox in plate hub.

CHAPTER SIX

THE GEARBOX

Operation   Removing   Dismantling   Examination for wear   Assembling   Replacing in car
Steering column change   Modifications   Fault diagnosis

All the gearboxes have four forward speeds and one reverse. Top gear is by direct drive, third and second by gears in constant mesh and first and reverse by sliding spur gears. Selecting top, second and third gears is made easier by the use of synchromesh cone clutches which enable the speeds of the revolving parts to be matched before the actual engagement. Servicing instructions for the internal mechanism of the gearboxes will hardly vary between the models, as most of the parts are identical. The only real differences are those concerned with methods of changing gear. The 'A40's' and '50's' and the early 'Oxfords' have a steering column gear lever, the other cars having a central gear lever on the floor. There are also small variations in methods of rubber mounting the gearbox casing in the car, but these will only affect the instructions for removing the unit.

The illustrations have been selected as being typical, and the owner should have no difficulty in working on his gearbox even though some parts may not be shown. The text will be found to cover all the essential details. **FIG 6:1** is an exploded view of the components of the early 'Oxford' gearbox with the steering column gear change. Gear ratios will differ in the various cars, but the arrangement of gears and shafts shown in this illustration will be identical in them all. The first-motion shaft 30 is 'ghosted' in the position it occupies in the gearbox casing. For clarity, the other shafts and gears have been drawn above the casing, but the actual position can be estimated by remembering that the spigot at the left-hand end of the third-motion shaft 50 runs freely in the roller bearing 36, located in the right-hand end of shaft 30. Shaft 50 also runs inside the extension 14. The layshaft gear unit 44 runs below the gears on the first- and third-motion shafts, the large gear at the left-hand end meshing constantly with the gear on shaft 30. The two inner gears on the layshaft unit mesh with gears 62 and 58 which run freely on shaft 50. The right-hand end of shaft 50 is connected to the rear axle by the propeller shaft.

Top gear is obtained by moving coupling 71 to the left. It slides on the outer splines of hub 67, and engages the dogs on the first-motion shaft 30. The drive is thus through the coupling to the hub, which being splined to shaft 50 transmits the drive to the rear axle.

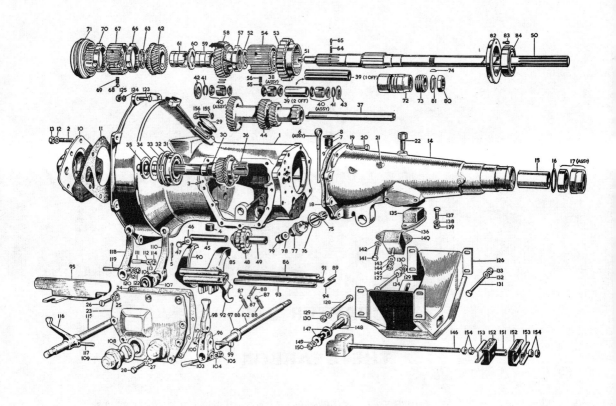

Fig 6:1 Gearbox components for Oxfords with steering column change. Internal parts similar for Austins 'A40' and 'A50'.

Key to Fig 6:1 1 Casing—gearbox. 2 Stud—front cover. 3 Dowel—side cover. 4 Plug—drain. 5 Split pin—clutch pit.
6 Indicator—oil level. 7 Felt—indicator. 8 Washer—top—felt retaining. 9 Washer—bottom—felt retaining. 10 Cover—front.
11 Joint. 12 Washer—spring—stud. 13 Nut—stud. 14 Extension—rear. 15 Bush. 16 Joint—oil seal cover. 17 Seal assembly—oil.
18 Joint—to casing. 19 Washer—spring—extension screws. 20 Screw—to casing. 21 Plug. 22 Breather. 23 Cover—side.
24 Joint—to casing. 25 Washer—shakeproof. 26 Screw—countersunk—to casing. 27 Washer—spring—screw.
28 Screw—to casing. 29 Cover—dust—casing. 30 Shaft—1st motion. 31 Bearing. 32 Spring ring—bearing. 33 Shim.
34 Washer—nut locking. 35 Nut—bearing. 36 Rollers—needle. 37 Layshaft. 38 Rollers—needle—centre.
39 Distance-piece—bearing. 40 Rollers—needle—front and rear. 41 Spring ring. 42 Washer—front thrust. 43 Washer—rear thrust.
44 Gear unit. 45 Shaft—reverse. 46 Washer—screw locking. 47 Screw—locking. 48 Gear assembly—reverse. 49 Bush.
50 Shaft assembly—3rd motion. 51 Restrictor—oil. 52 Washer—rear thrust. 53 Gear—1st speed. 54 Synchroniser—2nd speed.
55 Ball. 56 Spring. 57 Baulk ring—2nd speed gear. 58 Gear—2nd speed. 59 Bush. 60 Ring—interlocking 2nd and 3rd speed gear
bushes. 61 Bush. 62 Gear—3rd speed. 63 Washer—front thrust. 64 Spring—locking peg. 65 Peg—washer locking.
66 Baulk ring—3rd speed gear. 67 Synchroniser—3rd and 4th speed. 68 Ball. 69 Spring. 70 Baulk ring—4th speed gear.
71 Coupling—sliding 3rd and 4th speed. 72 Distance-piece—3rd motion shaft. 73 Gear—speedometer. 74 Key.
75 Pinion—speedometer. 76 Joint—pinion bush. 77 Bush. 78 Seal—oil. 79 Retainer—oil seal. 80 Nut—3rd motion shaft.
81 Washer—locking. 82 Housing—rear bearing. 83 Peg. 84 Bearing—3rd motion shaft—rear. 85 Fork—1st and 2nd change speed.
86 Rod. 87 Ball. 88 Spring. 89 Strip—rod locating. 90 Fork—3rd and 4th change speed. 91 Rod. 92 Fork—reverse change speed.
93 Rod. 94 Strip—3rd, 4th and reverse rod locating. 95 Gate assembly—change speed. 96 Fork—change speed operating.
97 Washer—packing. 98 Lever—change speed operating. 99 Pin—to fork. 100 Washer—pin. 101 Nut—pin.
102 Cross-shaft—change speed. 103 Cotter—fork to cross-shaft. 104 Washer—shakeproof—cotter. 105 Nut—cotter.
106 Seal—oil. 107 Ring—felt. 108 Joint—cap. 109 Cap. 110 Lever—outer. 111 Cotter—lever to shaft. 112 Washer—cotter.
113 Washer—spring—cotter. 114 Nut—cotter. 115 Cross-shaft—selector. 116 Lever—inner. 117 Pin—taper. 118 Lever—outer.
119 Cotter—lever to shaft. 120 Washer—cotter. 121 Washer—spring—cotter. 122 Nut—cotter. 123 Bolt—to mounting plate.
124 Washer—spring—bolt. 125 Nut—bolt. 126 Cross-member—gearbox mounting. 127 Bolt—long—to frame.
128 Bolt—short—to frame. 129 Washer—spring—bolt. 130 Nut—bolt. 131 Bolt—to frame. 132 Washer—spring—bolt.
133 Nut—bolt. 134 Spacer—frame side-member. 135 Rubber—centre—rebound. 136 Shim. 137 Screw—to cross-member.
138 Washer—spring—screw. 139 Nut—screw. 140 Rubber—gearbox mounting. 141 Screw—to gearbox.
142 Washer—spring—screw. 143 Washer—to cross-member. 144 Washer—spring—to cross-member. 145 Nut—to cross-member.
146 Rod—engine steady. 147 Bush—to gearbox. 148 Pin—to gearbox. 149 Washer—spring—pin. 150 Nut—pin.
151 Distance tube. 152 Buffer. 153 Plate—buffer. 154 Nut. 155 Washer—spring—screw. 156 Screw—to gearbox.

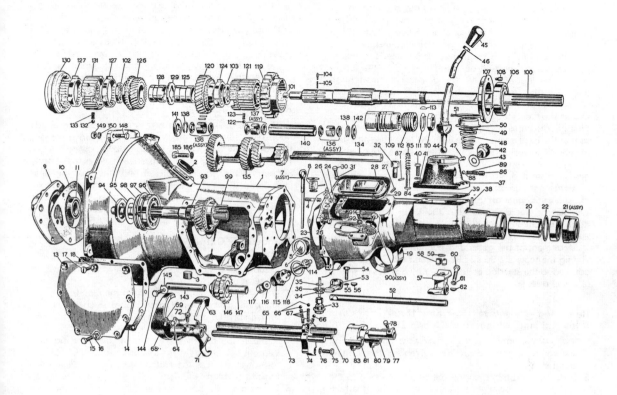

Fig 6:2 Gearbox components for Oxfords with central floor change.
Similar for Wolseleys '1500' and '15/50', the Riley '1.5', M.G. 'Magnette' and Austin 'A55'.

Key to Fig 6:2 1 Casing—gearbox. 2 Dust cover with insert. 3 Plug—drain. 4 Stud—gearbox extension. 5 Plug—blanking.
6 Washer. 7 Dipstick. 8 Felt. 9 Cover—front. 10 Joint—cover. 11 Oil seal—front cover. 13 Cover—side.
14 Joint—cover to casing. 15 Set screw—cover. 16 Spring washer. 17 Screw—countersunk—cover. 18 Shakeproof washer.
19 Extension—gearbox. 20 Bush—extension. 21 Oil seal assembly. 22 Joint—oil seal. 23 Joint—extension to gearbox.
24 Nut—stud—extension to gearbox. 25 Set screw—extension to gearbox. 26 Spring washer—studs and set screws.
27 Plug—taper—gearbox extension. 28 Cover—side—extension. 29 Joint—cover. 30 Set screw—cover. 31 Spring washer.
32 Breather assembly. 33 Body—oil level valve assembly. 34 Circlip—body. 35 Plate—valve. 36 Joint—valve body.
37 Tower—change speed lever. 38 Dowel—tower. 39 Joint—tower. 40 Set screw—tower. 41 Spring washer.
42 Switch—reverse light. 43 Joint—switch. 44 Lever—change speed. 45 Knob—lever. 46 Locknut—knob. 47 Snug—lever ball.
48 Spring—lever ball. 49 Washer—spring retaining. 50 Cover—spring. 51 Circlip—cover. 52 Shaft—remote control.
53 Lever—selector—front. 54 Set screw—lever—front. 55 Spring washer—screw. 56 Key—lever. 57 Lever—selector—rear.
58 Bush—lever. 59 Circlip—bush. 60 Set screw—lever—rear. 61 Spring washer—screw. 62 Key—lever.
63 Fork—first and second speed. 64 Screw—fork locating. 65 Shaft—first and second speed fork. 66 Ball—shaft. 67 Spring—ball.
68 Fork—third and fourth speed. 69 Screw—fork locating. 70 Shaft—third and fourth speed fork. 71 Fork—reverse.
72 Screw—fork locating. 73 Shaft—reverse fork. 74 Block—locating—shafts. 75 Set screw—block to casing.
76 Spring washer—screw. 77 Selector—first and second gear. 78 Screw—locating—selector. 79 Selector—third and fourth gear.
80 Screw—locating—selector. 81 Selector—reverse gear. 83 Screw—locating—selector. 84 Plunger—reverse selector.
85 Spring—plunger. 86 Plug—plunger. 87 Dowel—plunger. 88 Ball—plunger. 89 Spring—ball. 90 Arm—interlock (with plate).
91 Set screw—plate to casing. 92 Spring washer. 93 Shaft—first motion. 94 Nut—shaft. 95 Lock washer—nut.
96 Bearing—ball—shaft. 97 Spring ring—bearing. 98 Shim—bearing. 99 Rollers—needle—shaft. 100 Shaft—third motion.
101 Restrictor—oil. 102 Washer—thrust—front. 103 Washer—thrust—rear. 104 Peg—thrust washer—front. 105 Spring—peg.
106 Bearing—rear—third motion shaft. 107 Housing—bearing. 108 Peg—housing. 109 Distance piece—speedometer gear.
110 Nut—shaft and speedometer gear. 111 Lock washer—nut. 112 Gear—speedometer drive. 113 Key—shaft.
114 Pinion—speedometer drive. 115 Bush—pinion. 116 Oil seal—pinion. 117 Ring—oil seal retaining.
118 Joint—pinion bush to rear cover. 119 Gear—first speed. 120 Gear—second speed. 121 Synchronizer—second speed.
122 Ball—synchronizer. 123 Spring—ball. 124 Baulk ring—second speed gear. 125 Bush—second speed gear.
126 Gear—third speed. 127 Baulk ring—third and fourth gear. 128 Bush—third speed gear. 129 Ring—interlocking—second and
third gear bushes. 130 Coupling—sliding—third and fourth speed. 131 Synchronizer—third and fourth speed gear.
132 Ball—synchronizer. 133 Spring—ball. 134 Layshaft. 135 Gear unit—layshaft. 136 Bearing—needle-roller—layshaft—outer.
137 Bearing—needle-roller—layshaft—inner. 138 Spring ring—needle rollers. 140 Distance-piece—bearing.
141 Washer—thrust—front. 142 Washer—thrust—rear. 143 Shaft—reverse. 144 Screw—locking—shaft. 145 Lock washer—screw.
146 Gear—reverse. 147 Bush. 148 Bolt—gearbox to mounting plate. 149 Nut—bolt. 150 Spring washer—bolt.
185 Screw—starter to engine. 186 Spring washer—screw.

Third gear is obtained by moving the coupling to the right to engage the dogs on gear 62. This gear is driven constantly by the layshaft gear at a reduced speed, and so a similar reduced speed is transmitted to the shaft 50. In the same way an even lower speed is obtained for second gear by sliding the first-gear coupling 53 to the left to engage the dogs on gear 58. This gear is in constant mesh with the third gear along the layshaft and is turning slower than gear 62. The small spur gear at the right-hand end of the layshaft unit is used for first gear and reverse. First gear is obtained by sliding coupling 53 to the right so that the large gear engages with the small layshaft gear to give the lowest forward ratio of all. The pair of gears 48 are used to provide reverse. They are mounted on a separate shaft 45 and when the gear lever is moved into the reversing position, the large gear of the pair meshes with the small spur gear on the layshaft cluster, and its smaller associated gear engages with the large gear 53. This double reduction gives an even lower ratio for reversing and the necessary reversal in the direction of rotation.

Movement of the gears and couplings is arranged by sliding the forks 85, 90 and 92 fore and aft. The forks are coupled to the steering column lever by a series of shafts, levers and rods.

Removing –Wolseleys '1500' and '15/50', Riley '1.5' and 'Magnettes' ZA and ZB

1 Remove the engine and gearbox as a complete unit according to the instructions given in the Engine chapter.
2 Unscrew the bolts securing the clutch housing to the rear engine mounting plate. Withdraw the gearbox, taking the full weight of the gearbox off the first-motion shaft and keeping it in line with the engine until the shaft is clear of the clutch release bearing.

Note: When the slave cylinder is unbolted and tied to one side with the flexible hose intact, be careful not to operate the clutch pedal.

Removing – 'A40' and 'A50'

1 Drain the cooling system and disconnect the top hose from the engine. Disconnect the throttle linkage and release the exhaust pipe from the engine manifold. Jack up the front of the car and support it on stands.
2 Remove the gear control rods from the two levers on the side of the gearbox.
3 Remove the clevis pin from the slave cylinder operating rod and unbolt the cylinder from the clutch housing. Do not disconnect the pipe line.
4 Disconnect the speedometer cable. Remove the two bottom bolts through the clutch housing flange and the rear engine mounting plate. Then drain and remove the sump.
5 When all the non-flexible items have been freed from the engine, take the weight of the gearbox on a jack. Release the handbrake and remove the handbrake control rod bracket from the gearbox cross-member. Unhook the pull-off spring and push the rod to one side, clear of the gearbox support.
6 Mark the flanges of the rear universal joint to ensure correct reassembly. Uncouple the joint and withdraw the propeller shaft from the gearbox extension.
7 Remove the four setscrews securing the cross-member to the body and lower the jack under the gearbox

slowly. On cars fitted with a box-sectioned cross-member there are three setscrews at each end.
8 Continue to lower the jack until the engine rocker cover is just clear of the bulkhead, then block up the engine. At this point the gearbox can be removed backwards. Do not allow the weight of the box to hang on the first-motion shaft, keeping the gearbox in line with the engine until the shaft is clear of the clutch.

Removing – 'A55'

The gearbox on this car has the central gear lever on the floor. To remove the gearbox it is first necessary to remove the cover over the gearbox tower, working inside the car. The cover is secured by four crosshead screws to the body pressing. Take out the screws and unscrew the gear lever knob. Slide the cover up and over the gear lever. Remove the lever by extracting the spring ring at the top of the tower. The rest of the removal operation will follow the pattern suggested for the 'A40' and 'A50'.

Removing – 'Oxfords' with steering column change

1 Disconnect the battery, the starter lead and remove the starter motor.
2 Disconnect the exhaust pipe from the manifold.
3 Mark the rear universal joint flanges to ensure correct reassembly. Uncouple the joint and withdraw the propeller shaft from the gearbox.
4 Remove the clutch slave cylinder from the housing without detaching the flexible hose. After this, be careful not to depress the clutch pedal or the system will have to be bled.
5 Disconnect the speedometer cable. Release the gear control rods from the side levers on the gearbox.
6 Take out special bolt 148 in **FIG 6:1**. This will release the steady rod from the underside of the gearbox. Support the rear end of the engine.
7 Release the rear engine mountings from the cross-member and remove the bolts securing the cross-member. Two of the bolts on the driver's side are larger and also secure the master cylinder, passing through distance tubes. When replacing these bolts, remove the longitudinal member cover plates on the floor inside the car. These give access to the master cylinder and it will then be possible to ensure that the bolts pass through the distance tubes.
8 Lower the rear end of the engine, take out the clutch housing bolts and withdraw the gearbox, keeping the first-motion shaft in line with the engine and without any weight hanging on it.

Note when replacing the gearbox that the bolts securing the mounting rubbers to the cross-member have BSF threads. Those securing the cross-member are UNF.

Removing – Later 'Oxfords' with central gear change on the floor

1 Remove the power unit as instructed in the Engine chapter.
2 Part the gearbox from the engine in the manner described in the previous section.

Dismantling – Gearboxes with steering column gear change

1 Drain the oil, remove the dipstick 6 in **FIG 6:1**, and the speedometer drive, items 75 to 79.

2 Take out the eight setscrews and pull off the extension 14. Extract the two shifter rod locating strips 89 and 94 from the rear face of the gearbox casing.

3 Remove the side cover 23 by unscrewing the seven bolts and three countersunk screws. Take care of joint 24.

3 Remove cotters 111 and 119. The levers 110 and 118 can then be pulled off the shafts. The change speed gate 95 is prised out of its recesses in the casing and the shafts 102 and 115 can then be withdrawn. On the right-hand side of the casing it will be possible to remove the oil seals 106 and the felt washers 107. Note the packing washer 97 on the change-speed cross-shaft.

4 Knock out pin 117 to remove lever 116. On early models a pointed setscrew with locknut and washer was used instead of a pin. Change-speed fork 96 can be drawn off after removing cotter 103.

5 Inside the clutch housing, remove the locknut and washer from the clutch operating lever fulcrum pin. The pin screws into one of the brackets so do not attempt to drive it out. Remove the dust cover and withdraw the operating lever.

6 Remove the gearbox front cover 10 and joint 11. Note the shim (or shims) 33 and spring ring 32 between the front cover and the front bearing 31. This removal operation is made easier by tapping the selector rods 86, 91 and 93 forward slightly to push the cover away from the casing.

7 It is a good plan to use a 5 in length of bar $\frac{7}{16}$ in in diameter to push the selector rods through the forks 85, 90 and 92. As each rod is pulled clear, cover the fork with a cloth to prevent the loss of the balls and springs 87 and 88 as the bar is removed. Start with the reverse rod 93, pushing it forward and removing the fork 92. Push the third and top gear shaft 91 to the rear and remove the fork 90. Finally push the remaining shaft 86 to the rear, releasing fork 85.

8 Straighten the tab washer 46, remove the screw 47 and tap the reverse gear shaft 45 forward. Lift out the reverse gears 48.

9 Using a soft metal drift, drive out the layshaft 37 in a forward direction. Let the gear cluster 44 rest in the bottom of the box. Note the thrust washers 42 and 43. The cluster cannot be removed until the first- and third-motion shafts have been withdrawn.

10 Pull out the third-motion shaft 50 to the rear, complete with gear assemblies. At this stage, remove the eighteen needle rollers 36 to be found inside the rear end of the first-motion shaft 30.

11 Use a long drift inside the rear end of shaft 30 to drive it forward out of the casing, making sure that the laygear cluster is clear of the coupling dogs. The laygears may now be lifted out.

Dismantling third-motion shaft

1 Remove the following items in this order: baulk ring 70, synchromesh coupling 71 with hub 67 and baulk ring 66. If the coupling is pressed off the hub, cover with a piece of cloth to catch the three locating balls and springs, 68 and 69.

2 Press down the locking peg 65 so that the thrust washer 63 can be rotated until its splines are in line with those on the shaft. Remove the washer.

3 Remove the third speed gear 62 and its splined bush 61.

Withdraw the bush interlocking washer 60 thus releasing the second speed gear 58, its bush 59 and the baulk ring 57.

4 Remove thrust washer 52, and then hub 54 complete with first speed gear 53. Again be careful when parting these two items, as there are three sets of balls and springs 55 and 56 located in the hub.

5 Tap up the locking tab on washer 81, unscrew nut 80, withdraw the washer followed by the speedometer drive gear 73 with key 74, and distance piece 72. Press the rear bearing and housing 82, 83 and 84 from the shaft.

Dismantling first-motion shaft

1 Knock back the tab locking washer 34 and unscrew the shaft nut 35. Note that it has a left-hand thread.

2 Drive the shaft out of the bearing 31 by resting the circlip 32 on the jaws of an open vice and use a soft-faced hammer on the forward end of the shaft. This spigot runs in a bush in the crankshaft and every care must be taken not to damage it by hard blows with an ordinary hammer.

Rear oil seal

The assembly is number 17 in the illustration. It is almost impossible to remove it without damage. If it leaks, drive it off with a punch. The new seal is locked in position by pinching the housing, as can be seen from the old one.

Dismantling gearbox with centre floor gear change

FIG 6:2 shows the later 'Oxford' gearbox with the gear lever mounted in a tower on the rear extension. A similar gear box, with slight variations, is fitted to the Austin 'A55', the 'Magnettes' ZA and ZB, the Wolseleys '1500' and '15/50' and the Riley '1.5'. Dismantle the gearbox in the following way:

1 Drain the gearbox and remove the dipstick 7 and the speedometer drive 114 to 117 inclusive.

2 Remove the gear lever tower 37 and the joint 39. Remove the rear extension cover 28 and joint 29.

3 Unbolt the interlock assembly 90. On some models this assembly fits into recesses in the rear extension, and having no bolts, it is simply prised free.

4 Cut the locking wire and slacken the setscrew securing the selector lever 57 to the shaft 52 at the gear lever end. Remove the side cover 13 and joint washer 14. Note that there are three countersunk screws 17 along the top edge.

5 Remove the nut and seven setscrews securing the extension 19. Slide the selector lever 57 rearwards and pull off the extension, at the same time manoeuvring the front selector lever 53 out of the selectors 77, 79 and 81.

6 Cut the locking wire and unscrew the three change speed fork setscrews 64, 69 and 72. Unscrew the two setscrews 75 and remove the locating block 74 together with the shafts 65, 70 and 73. Note the two dowels in the block. If the shafts are withdrawn from the block, take care to catch the three sets of balls and springs 66 and 67.

7 Withdraw the forks in this order, reverse fork 71 first, top and third fork 68 next and first and second fork 63 last.

8 Unscrew the clutch operating lever pivot nut from

inside the clutch housing. The bolt is screwed in and cannot be driven out. Remove the bolt, the lever and the release bearing.

9 Remove the front cover 9, noting the shims 98 in front of the bearing.

10 Tap out the layshaft 134. Remove the setscrew 144 and tap out the reverse gear shaft 143 to release the gears 146. Withdraw the third-motion shaft 100 to the rear complete with gears. Extract the eighteen needle rollers 99.

11 Keeping the layshaft gear cluster 135 out of the way in the bottom of the box, drive out the first-motion shaft 93, using a long drift from the rear. Lift out the layshaft cluster and thrust washers 141 and 142.

12 Remove the setscrew 60 from the rear selector lever 57 and withdraw the lever and key 62. Unscrew the setscrew 54 from the front end and remove the lever 53 and key 56. Withdraw the remote control shaft 52.

Dismantle the first- and third-motion shafts by following the instructions given in the section on the steering column change gearbox.

Examination for wear

The item numbers are taken from **FIG 6:1**. Cross-reference will be needed to identify the same parts in **FIG 6:2** as the numbers are different. Bearings 31 and 84 may be worn. Renew them if there is slackness between the inner and outer races when rocked sideways.

The needle roller bearing may be worn. Renew the rollers 36 and possibly the shafts 30 or 50.

Bushes 61 and 59 must be a tight fit on shaft 50. Renew them if they are not. Gears 62 and 58 run on these bushes. Wear at this point indicates the need for renewing one or all of the parts.

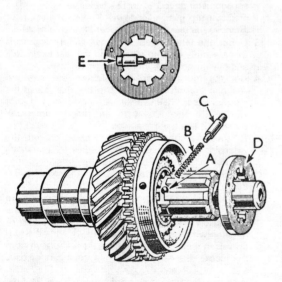

Fig 6:3 Locking peg and washer on third-motion shaft.

Key to Fig 6:3 A Hole for spring. B Spring. C Locking peg. D Locking washer. E. Peg located in washer.

Examine the layshaft 37 and the needle roller bearings 40, renewing them if worn. The thrust washers 42 and 43 are designed to allow end-float of the gear cluster 44 to a figure lying between .001 in and .003 in. If this float is excessive, the thrust washers must be renewed. The smaller washer 43 is made in various thicknesses so that the correct end-float can be obtained. Baulk rings 57, 66 and 70 have internal cones which are part of the synchro-mesh mechanism. They are made of phosphor bronze alloy and must be renewed if worn, or if the synchromesh action has been defective.

Assembling

Note that the first part of the instructions will deal with the shafts and gear assemblies. These are common to all the gearboxes whatever the type of gear change mechanism. Before going on to the actual assembly process it must be pointed out that the first speed gear 53 in **FIG 6:1** and the third and top gear coupling sleeve 71 are each paired with their respective synchronizer hubs 54 and 67 during manufacture. Only mated pairs of these parts should be replaced. Lubricate everything thoroughly.

1 Assemble the first-motion shaft 30 by drifting on the bearing 31 with its spring ring to the front. Screw nut 35 down on washer 34 and lock.

2 If the layshaft bearings have been in need of attention, remember that there are two types of assembly. Early models have three needle rollers races 40 and two distance tubes 39 equally spaced and retained by a circlip 41 at each end. Later models have a circlip at the rear end, a roller race and a single distance tube which is longer. Then follows another circlip, a roller race, a third circlip, another roller race and a final circlip at the front. Two races are fitted as a pair at the front and the single race is at the rear.

3 Drop the layshaft assembly into the bottom of the box, with the thrust washers in place, but without the shaft, which is fitted later.

4 Starting at the front end of the third-motion shaft 50, locate thrust washer 52 on the front end of the splines with the polished face forward.

5 Push the longer bush 59 on to the splines with the dogs to the front. This can be an easier operation if the bush is warmed to expand it slightly.

Note: There is an oil hole in the bush. This must line up with the one in the shaft, and the cut-away part of the front bush 61 must be over the locating peg hole when the bushes are engaged with the interlocking washer 60.

6 Fit the second speed gear 58 and baulk ring 57 on to the bush, oiling well. The plain side of the gear is to the front.

7 Slide on the interlocking washer 60 followed by the shorter bush 61, locating the locking dogs correctly. Fit the third speed gear 62 onto the front bush with the cone towards the front.

8 Insert the spring 64 and locking peg 65 into the hole in the shaft. Thread on the front thrust washer 63 with the machined face towards the gear. There is a hole in the cone of the gear 62. Using a piece of wire in this hole, press down the locking peg and push the washer over it. Turn the washer until the locking peg engages one of the splines, as shown by the insert in **FIG 6:3**.

9 Assemble the third and top speed synchronizer hub

67 and coupling 71 using the three sets of balls and springs 68 and 69. Locate the baulk rings 66 and 70 and slide the assembly on to the shaft with the plain face of the hub to the rear.

10 Assemble the following items from the rear end of the third-motion shaft. Fit the first speed gear 53 to the hub 54 using the balls and springs 55 and 56. Note that the gear is offset and the greatest width must lie to the rear as shown in **FIG 6:4**. It is also important to assemble the parts so that the internal splines are correctly placed to allow the baulk ring to pass through the machined grooves between the teeth.

11 Pass the assembly over the splines on the shaft, the synchromesh cone in the hub facing forward. Press the rear bearing 84 into the housing 82 and fit it to the shaft with the flange on the housing to the rear. Push on the distance piece 72, fit the speedometer drive gear 73 over the key 74 and follow with the lock washer 81 and nut 80. Tighten securely and lock.

Fig 6:4 First-speed gear and hub assembly with baulking ring.

Key to Fig 6:4 1 Gear. 2 Baulking ring. 3 Synchronizer.

With the shafts all assembled it will be possible to fit them into the gearbox casing. The instructions for all the gearboxes will not begin to diverge until we reach the point where the gear shift mechanism is involved.

1 The layshaft cluster is already in the box without its shaft. Turn the casing until the layshaft gears are well clear of the first-motion shaft housing and drift the first-motion shaft into place from the clutch housing end, using a soft drift. Ensure that the spring ring 32 is registering properly in the recess in the casing.

2 Smear grease in the bearing recess in the rear end of the shaft and fit the eighteen needle rollers 36. Pass the third-motion shaft into the casing from the rear, positioning the dowel 83 in the bearing housing so that it will line up with the extension 14 when the housing is pressed home. This is readily done by using the joint washer 18 as a guide. At the same time the spigot at the front end of the shaft will be entering the roller bearing in the first-motion shaft.

3 Lift the layshaft gears and thrust washers into position and fit the layshaft 37 with the cut-away at the front end lined up with the locating groove in the front cover 10.

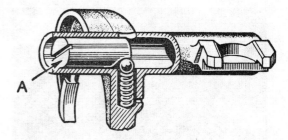

Fig 6:5 Pilot bar pre-loading ball and spring in selector fork.

At this stage the instructions will differ between the two types of gear change mechanism. We will deal with the steering column type first.

4 It is a tricky operation to fit the selector rods into the forks and keep the balls and springs in place. A suggested device is shown in **FIG 6:5**, consisting of a piece of bar suitably shaped to keep the ball pre-loaded while the selector rod is inserted. Insert the first and second speed fork 85 and then the third and top speed fork 90. Fit the third and top speed rod 91 so that its grooves are at the front end. Retrieve the pilot bar if one is used. Tap the rod into its final position. Insert the first and second speed rod 86. This has three grooves at the rear end.

5 Fit the reverse gear 48 and shaft 45, locking the securing screw 47 with washer 46. Replace the reverse selector fork 92 and then the rod 93, which has two grooves at the rear end.

6 If necessary, renew the cross-shaft oil seals 106 and refit the felt rings 107. Before fitting the change speed operating fork 96 to shaft 102, check the fit of lever 98. The fulcrum pin 99 should be tightened until the lever is just nipped, then slackened one flat before the castellated nut and split pin are fitted. The lever should then be free but without side movement. Fit lever 116 to the selector shaft 115. Insert both shafts into the casing through the side cover aperture, the change speed shaft 102 being to the rear. Set the levers well apart, and replace the change speed gate assembly 95. Feed lever 98 into the rear slot in the gate lever and lever 116 into the front slot and push the gate home until the ends drop into the recesses machined in the side cover opening.

7 Fit the outside operating levers 110 and 118. Note that later models in the Austin range have a curved rear lever which hangs down when fitted.

8 Replace the side cover 23 using a sound joint washer 24. Replace the front cover 10, not forgetting the shim(s) 33. On later models it will be found that there is an oil seal in the front cover to prevent leakage past the first-motion shaft into the clutch housing. Be very careful not to damage the lips of the seal when refitting the cover. Tighten nuts 13 a turn at a time by diagonal selection until they are all tight. Fit the clutch operating lever and dust cover. Tighten the fulcrum pin enough to take out side play.

9 Fit the rod locating strips 89 and 94 into the recesses in the rear face of the casing. Assemble the extension 14 over the third-motion shaft after the joint washer 18 has been fitted.

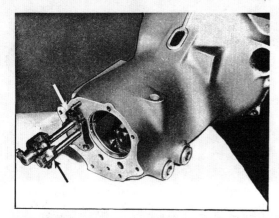

Fig 6:6 Shifter selectors and locating block for central floor change gearboxes.

The next section describes the final assembly of the gearbox with the central floor change lever, carrying on from the point where the layshaft is in position.

1 Refit the reverse gears 146, the shaft 143 and the lock-in screw 144 in **FIG 6:2**. Lock the screw with tab washer 145.

2 Refit the front cover 9, replacing any shims 98 in the bearing recess. Make sure that the front end of the layshaft is correctly located in the groove in the front cover. Refit the clutch operating lever and fork, tightening the fulcrum pin until it leaves the assembly free without side play.

3 Fit the selectors 77, 79 and 81 to the shafts 65, 70 and 73. Bolt the shaft locating block 74 to the rear face of the gearbox casing, replace the springs 67 and balls 66 and replace the shifter shafts.

4 Position the gear change forks in the box in the following sequence. First goes the reverse fork 71, then the first and second fork 63 and then the third and top fork 68. Push the shifter shafts into the box and through the forks. Insert and tighten the setscrews 64, 69 and 72, locking them with wire. Position the selectors on the rear ends of the shifter shafts, see **FIG 6:6**. Insert the setscrews 78, 80 and 83, tighten them and lock with wire.

5 Locate the remote control rod 52 in the rear extension 19. Fit the front lever 53 and the rear lever 57 over their respective keys 56 and 62 and lock with setscrews 54 and 60.

6 Fit the rear extension to the gearbox, locating the control shaft selector lever 53 in the selectors 77, 79 and 83.

7 Bolt the interlock arm 90 to the extension and refit the cover 28.

8 Bolt the gear lever tower 37 to the extension. Place the two halves of the brass gear lever snug 58 onto the lower end of the gear lever 44 and secure in place with the circlip 59. Fit the lever into the tower and secure it with the spring 48, washer 49, cover 50 and spring circlip 51.

9 Fit the side cover 13 with a new joint 14 if necessary. Screw in the speedometer drive assembly, the plugs and the breather. Fit the dipstick and fill the gearbox with the correct grade of oil.

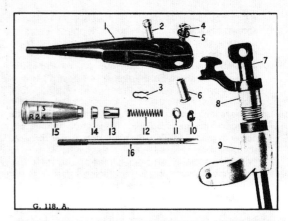

Fig 6:7 Column change components for Austins 'A40' and '50'.

Key to Fig 6:7   1 Lever.   2 Fulcrum pin.   3 Circlip.
4, 5, 6 Swivel and securing pin and shakeproof washer.   7 Gear change rod.   8 Pawl.   9 Column mounting bracket.
10 Circlip.   11 Washer.   12 Spring.   13 Nut.   14 Chrome cup.   15 Lever knob.   16 Knob spindle.

Replacing the gearbox

This is a reversal of the removing operation in every case. If the clutch has not been disturbed there should be no difficulty in lining up the first-motion shaft with the clutch driven plate hub and the spigot bearing in the end of the crankshaft. It is, however, of the utmost importance to ensure that the gearbox does not hang in the clutch. Take all the weight of the box and line up everything as accurately as possible.

If the clutch has been dismantled, refer to the Clutch chapter for instructions on the method of centralizing the driven plate before offering up the gearbox.

Steering column gear change – 'A40' and 'A50'

The components of the gear lever are shown in **FIG 6:7**. Lifting or depressing the change lever moves the selector rod 7. This movement is transmitted to the gearbox by rods and levers so that the selector gate 95 in **FIG 6:1** moves lever 98 into a position which selects the appropriate fork.

Moving the change lever to and fro operates the second set of rods and levers. These partially rotate shaft 102, causing lever 98 to slide the selected fork into the required position, engaging the gear.

Adjustment

The selector rod 7 in **FIG 6:7** is fitted with two adjusting nuts, one on each side of the selector operating lever at the end of the steering column. Slacken the nuts and push the front lever on the side of the gearbox rearwards to its fullest extent. Tighten the nuts, making sure that the gearbox lever does not move.

Wear in the gear change linkage is taken up at the adjuster fitted to the lower end of the rod which is connected to the gearbox lever at the rear. Disconnect the rod connector from the lever and slacken the locking nut. Turn the connector to make the necessary adjustment to the length of the rod. The correct position of the lever necessary to engage the gears can be ascertained by noticing that the lever clicks into position for each speed.

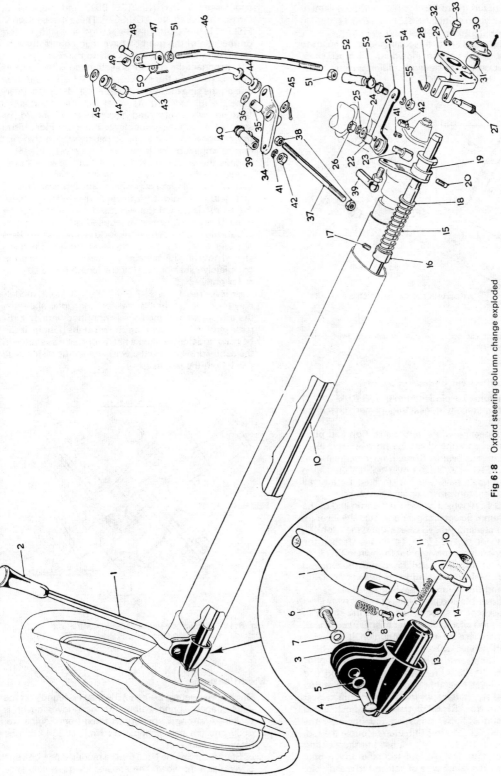

Fig 6:8 Oxford steering column change exploded

Key to Fig 6:8 1 Lever—gear change hand. 2 Knob—hand lever. 3 Bracket—pivot. 4 Pin—pivot. 5 Shim—pivot pin. 6 Screw—pivot pin. 7 Shim—screw. 8 Plunger—reverse stop. 9 Spring—lever return. 10 Rod assembly—control. 11 Spring—plunger. 12 Plunger. 13 Pin—pivot. 14 Washer—hand lever locating. 15 Spring—control rod steady. 16 Collar. 17 Screw—collar. 18 Washer—shifter. 19 Lever—shifter. 20 Screw—lever locking. 21 Lever—selector. 22 Bush. 23 Pin—operating. 24 Washer—pin. 25 Washer—spring—pin. 26 Nut—pin. 27 Pin—pivot. 28 Washer—pivot pin. 29 Support assembly. 30 Housing—spherical. 31 Bush—spherical. 32 Washer—spring—bolt. 33 Bolt—support to gearbox. 34 Lever—shifter relay. 35 Bush. 36 Washer. 37 Rod—shifter adjusting. 38 Nut—locking. 39 Joint—ball. 40 Clip—retaining. 41 Washer—spring—ball. 42 Nut—ball. 43 Rod—shifter—relay to gearbox. 44 Grommet. 45 Washer. 46 Rod—selector. 47 Fork end. 48 Pin—fork end. 49 Bush for pin. 50 Washer. 51 Nut—locking. 52 Joint—ball. 53 Clip—retaining. 54 Washer—spring—ball. 55 Nut—ball.

If wear occurs in the rod ball joints, slight adjustment can be made by removing the split pin and tightening the screw. Lock the screw with a new split pin.

At regular intervals apply a recommended lubricant to the ball joints of the linkage, including the cross-shaft, and to the bracket on the steering column which houses the gear lever shaft.

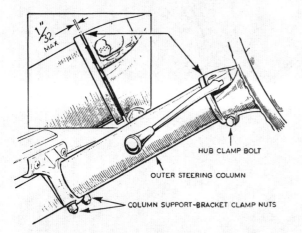

HUB CLAMP BOLT

OUTER STEERING COLUMN

COLUMN SUPPORT-BRACKET CLAMP NUTS

Fig 6:9 Correct clearance of steering wheel hub on 'Oxfords' with column change.

Steering column gear change – 'Oxford'

This is illustrated in exploded form in **FIG 6:8.**

If there is any difficulty in gear engagement check the following points.

1 Slacken the steering wheel hub clamp bolt and push the hub down until the clearance between the pivot bracket and the top bearing flange is no more than $\frac{1}{32}$ in as shown in **FIG 6:9.** Do not over-tighten the clamp bolt. Later models have the hub located by a small screw to prevent movement up and down.

2 Refer to **FIG 6:10** which shows the bottom end of the steering column. Select first gear and hold the lever up towards the steering wheel. Check the dimension 'X', which must not exceed $\frac{7}{16}$ in. To adjust, slacken the column support bracket clamp nuts shown in **FIG 6:9.** Move the outer column up and down until the required clearance is obtained, keeping the gear lever firmly up and tightening the clamp bolts when satisfied.

3 **FIG 6:11** shows old and new types of shifter relay lever and the latest type of selector rod. Note the shifter to gearbox relay rod which has rubber bushes at each end. Make sure that these are in good condition. If the holes for the bushes have sharp edges, countersink both sides. If in trouble with gear selection on cars prior to chassis No. 170534, remove the selector rod and shifter relay lever assembly, together with the shifter adjusting rod and shifter relay rod. Fit the modified lever assembly, Part No. ACH 5728. Using the adjustment at each end of the shifter adjusting rod, increase the length between centres to $5\frac{7}{8}$ in, then recouple the rod. On cars prior to 162203 only, substitute the existing selector rod, Part No. ACH 5463 and the rubber grommets, by the latest type of selector rod and yoke

end assembly, Part No. ACH 5673 and the bush at the rear end, Part No. ACH 5675. These can be seen in **FIG 6:11.** Make sure that the selector and shifter levers on the side of the gearbox have their cotters correctly fitted, with the nuts and washers to the rear.

Disconnect the selector adjusting rod with the gears in neutral. Move the selector lever, which is the front one on the side of the gearbox, back and forth to determine the full extent of its travel. The mid-point is the position when first and second gears should be selected. Keep the selector lever in that position. Move the rearmost, or shifter, lever backwards so that first gear is engaged. Rock the car if it proves difficult to engage the gears. The shifter lever will now be locked in mid-position with some free play. Place the lever mid-way in this free movement. Put the gear lever in first gear and hold it up towards the steering wheel. Adjust the length of the selector rod so that it can be fitted. If much adjustment is required, move the ends an equal amount, tightening the locknuts when the clevis pin will enter the yoke and lever freely. The gears should now engage perfectly. If a subsequent test is not completely satisfactory, alter the length of the selector rod slightly.

4 Gear lever rattle, see **FIG 6:12.** Early 'Oxford' models may need the slot in the lever lengthened as shown in the top drawing. If the lever is not fitted with an anti-rattle washer in the position shown at the bottom, it can be accomodated by filing a flat on one side as shown in the centre drawing. Fit the washer with the dished side away from the gear lever.

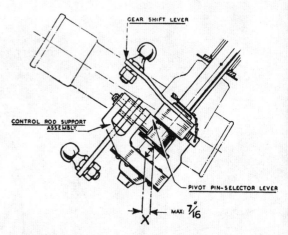

GEAR SHIFT LEVER

CONTROL ROD SUPPORT ASSEMBLY

PIVOT PIN-SELECTOR LEVER

MAX: $\frac{7}{16}$"

X

Fig 6:10 Correct clearance 'X' for control rod shifter on 'Oxfords' with column change.

Modifications

1 On the 'Magnettes' ZA and ZB it may be found that the cone-shaped spring below the gear lever cover is broken. A stronger spring was fitted from Engine No. 6555 and the new spring, Part No. 11G3144 can be fitted to earlier cars.

Starting at Engine No. 16986 a modified gearbox end cover was introduced. This ensures adequate clearance

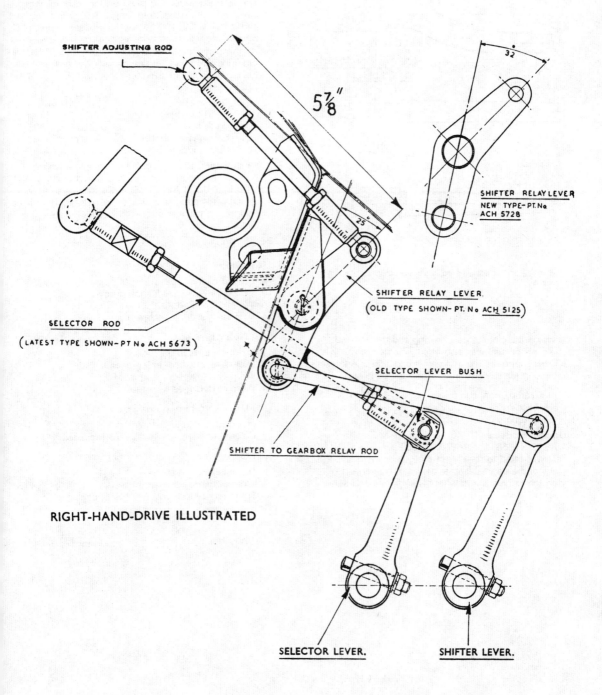

SHIFTER ADJUSTING ROD

$5\frac{7}{8}''$

32°

SHIFTER RELAY LEVER
NEW TYPE-PT.No
ACH 5728

25°

SHIFTER RELAY LEVER.
(OLD TYPE SHOWN- PT. No ACH 5125)

SELECTOR ROD

(LATEST TYPE SHOWN- PT No ACH 5673)

SELECTOR LEVER BUSH

SHIFTER TO GEARBOX RELAY ROD

RIGHT-HAND-DRIVE ILLUSTRATED

SELECTOR LEVER.

SHIFTER LEVER.

Fig 6:11   Modified linkage on Oxfords with steering column change.

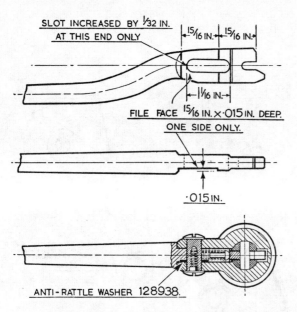

SLOT INCREASED BY 1/32 IN. AT THIS END ONLY

15/16 IN. + 15/16 IN.

1 1/16 IN.

FILE FACE 15/16 IN. x ·015 IN. DEEP. ONE SIDE ONLY.

·015 IN.

ANTI-RATTLE WASHER 128938.

Fig 6:12 Modifications to steering column gear lever on 'Oxfords'.

between the clutch thrust bearing and the first-motion shaft. An oil seal was also fitted. The new cover with oil seal cannot be fitted to earlier cars unless a thicker mounting plate is also fitted. The new parts are:

Gearbox front end cover 1H 3141
Oil seal 1H 3138
Mounting plate 1H 821

2 On the Wolseley '15/50', beginning at Engine Nos. 15W/U/H4866 and 15W/U/L2882 an improved oil seal was fitted to the rear of the gearbox extension in place of the original leather type. It is interchangeable with the early seal and will obviate failure and subsequent oil loss.

The same type of improved seal is fitted to 'Oxfords' starting at Engine Nos. 15M/N/H24889 and 15M/N/L24147. In each case the Part No. is 11G3270.

3 The gearbox mounting plate on the 'Oxford' was increased in thickness from Engine Nos. BP15M/H101 and BP15M/L201. The locking washers previously fitted to the setscrews were replaced by spring washers. At the same time the gearbox front end cover was modified and fitted with an oil seal. The new parts can be fitted to earlier cars but only as a complete set. The Part Nos. are:

Gearbox mounting plate 1H 821
Gearbox front end cover 1H 3137
Oil seal 1H 3138
Spring washers (4) .... LWZ 105
Spring washers (8) .... LWZ 106

A shortened and reset gear lever was fitted to the steering column change on 'Oxfords' from Car No. 191717. The Part No. is ACH5898. If it is desired to fit a hand lever with reduced travel, or to reduce rattle in cars before the number quoted, the modified lever may be fitted.

Fault diagnosis

(a) Jumping out of gear

1 Broken change speed fork shaft spring.
2 Excessively worn fork shaft groove.
3 Worn coupling dogs.
4 Fork shaft securing screw loose.

(b) Noisy gearbox

1 Insufficient oil in gearbox.
2 Excessive end-float in lay-gear.
3 Worn or damaged bearings.
4 Worn or damaged gear teeth.

(c) Difficulty in engaging gear

1 Incorrect clutch adjustment.
2 Column change interlinkage mal-adjusted.

(d) Oil leaks

1 Damaged joint washers.
2 Worn or damaged shaft oil seals.
3 Front, rear or side covers loose or damaged.

CHAPTER SEVEN

PROPELLER SHAFT,
REAR AXLE AND SUSPENSION

Propeller shaft   Removing   Servicing universal joints   Early rear axle   Servicing and removing
Later rear axle   Servicing   Removing and refitting   Rear suspension type   Servicing springs
Armstrong dampers   Telescopic dampers   Modifications   Fault diagnosis

The front and rear universal joints on the propeller shaft are of Hardy-Spicer manufacture. The four journals in each spider run in needle roller bearings, as shown in FIG 7:1. The half coupling of the front joint is splined (1) to the gearbox mainshaft and is free to slide. This sliding accomodates the fore and aft movement of the propeller shaft as the rear springs deflect under road conditions or loading.

Each spider journal 4 has an inner shoulder which locates a metal retainer holding a cork sealing ring. The inner open ends of the bearing cups seal against the cork rings to prevent loss of lubricant and the ingress of dirt. These two features are shown as item 6 in the illustration.

Lubrication

Use the correct grade of grease when lubricating through the nipple fitted to each spider. Oil from the gearbox lubricates the sliding splined joint between the propeller shaft and the gearbox. Whenever the propeller shaft is refitted to the gearbox, smear the splines with oil.

Removing

The joints can be tested for wear before removing the shaft. Try to lift each joint up and down. Slackness will indicate wear of the thrust faces on the spiders, and inside the bearing cups. If the joints can be partially rotated it is a sign that the bearings are worn. Two pointers to trouble can often be seen under the spring circlip 7. A bright ring on the outer face of the cup shows that it has been rotating, and rust powder indicates that the bearing has been running dry.

After scribing a line across the flanges of the rear joint to ensure correct reassembly, separate them. Place a tray under the rear end of the gearbox to catch any oil which drains out, take the weight of the shaft and draw the front splines out of the box.

Dismantling

Clean all dirt and enamel from the circlips 7 and remove them by squeezing the ends together with a pair of thin-nosed pliers. Tap the yoke with a lead or copper hammer as shown in FIG 7:2, and the top bearing cup should start to appear. If the cup sticks, it is permissible to tap on the inner lip if there is a gap between the cup and the inner seal. FIG 7:3 shows this operation being performed with a piece of flattened rod. Great care must be taken not to damage the cup. Pulling it out vertically downwards will keep the rollers intact.

After removing the opposite bearing, the spider 4 can be detached from the yoke. Repeat the dismantling process on the other two bearings. Examine all the parts for wear. The spider and the bearings are available in sets, and these can be replaced in the existing yokes providing the eyes in the yokes are not worn. If the bearing cups are not a light drive fit, the yokes will need renewal.

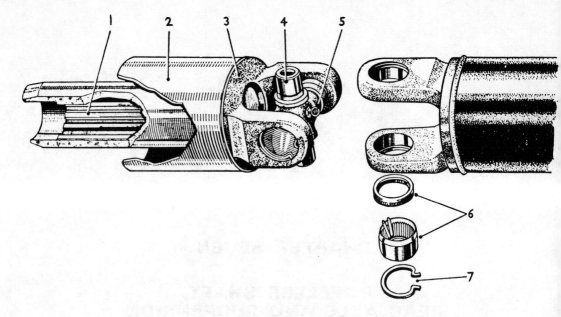

Fig 7:1   The front universal joint exploded.

Key to Fig 7:1   1 Internal splined end of propeller shaft.   2 Dust cover.   3 Front half coupling.   4 Spider.   5 Lubricating nipp
6 Needle bearing assembly.   7 Circlip.

Reassembling

It is always advisable to renew the cork washers and retainers. Coat the shoulders of the spider journals with shellac and press the steel retainers into position with a tubular drift. Fit the cork rings, fill the holes through the spider with grease and insert in the yoke. Stick the needles in a bearing cup with vaseline, add grease and tap the cup into position, using a soft drift slightly smaller in diameter than the eye in the yoke. Fit the circlip and repeat the assembly on the other side. If the spider seems to bind, tap the yoke lightly with a soft-faced mallet after the circlips have all been fitted.

To refit the completed propeller shaft, reverse the procedure for removal. Thoroughly clean the rear flange faces and the register, line up the marks on the flange edges and tighten the securing bolts diagonally and evenly.

The rear axle

With the exception of the early Wolseley '15/50's', all the cars dealt with in this manual have the same axle with only minor differences. Up to and including car No. 35857 the Wolseley '15/50' axle was a 'Morris' divided-type in which it was necessary to remove the axle from the car to dismantle the crown wheel and bevel pinion assembly. It is proposed to deal with this type of axle first.

The early Wolseley '15/50' rear axle

This is illustrated in component form in **FIG 7:4**, where the divided axle casing can be readily identified. The axle is of the semi-floating type where the hub bearings 31 are carried in the casing ends and the inner bearings 17 help to carry and locate the inner ends of the axle half-shafts

28, through the hubs of the differential carrier 8. The ax shafts can only be withdrawn after removing the whe brake drum and hub, brake back plate, and the beari housing 35. The wheel hubs are attached to the axle shaf by splines and a tapered split collar 34.

Only those repairs or adjustments connected with tl half-shafts, rear wheel bearings, brake drums and bra shoes can be carried out without removing the comple axle from the car.

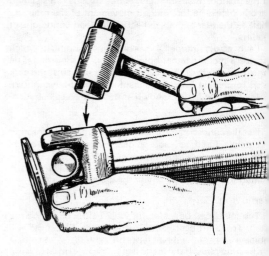

Fig 7:2   Remove circlip and apply light blows. The bearing c is emerging.

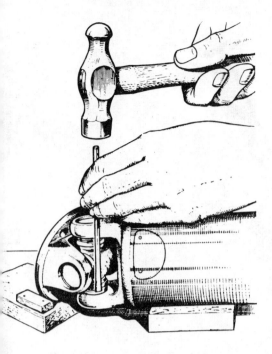

When reassembling make sure that the oil seal, if it is renewed, is fitted with the sharp lip of the rubber bore facing the bearing. Fit the brake backplate and then the split collar. This must be perfectly clean and free from burrs. Press the plain part into the seal and tap the collar home against the bearing with a hide hammer. Do not damage the taper in any way. The hub can then be re-fitted.

Removing axle – early Wolseley '15/50'

1 Lift the rear end of the car so that the axle and road springs can be drawn out. Chock the front wheels.
2 Remove the rear wheels and release the handbrake. Disconnect the flexible brake pipe from its bracket under the floor. Disconnect the brake cable anchorages from the spring brackets. Disconnect the brake cable forks from the levers projecting through the backplates.
3 Remove the nuts, flat washers and rubber bushes from the lower ends of the telescopic dampers. Support the axle on blocks.
4 Mark the rear propeller shaft flanges, part them and tie the shaft out of the way.
5 Remove the rear shackle nuts and bolts. The nut of each upper bolt is accessible through a hole, covered by a rubber plug, in the side of the boot. Remove the front anchorage bolts from the springs. The axle will then be free to be withdrawn rearwards. Replace in the reverse order but do not tighten the shackle and anchor bolts until the car is standing in the normally loaded position, so that the rubber bushes are flexed equally in both directions as the springs are deflected. Do not forget to bleed the brakes as instructed in the appropriate chapter.

The rear axle – Austin 'A40', '50' and '55', 'Oxfords' 11 and 111, Wolseley '1500', Riley '1.5' and later Wolseley '15/50' commencing car No. 35858

This is the BMC 'B' type axle illustrated in **FIG 7:5**. From this it can be seen that the bevel pinion, as part of item 22, is carried in a pair of tapered roller bearings 26 and 28. Oil seal 29 prevents oil leakage past the pinion shaft. The other half of item 22 is the crown wheel which is bolted to the differential cage 15. Both sides of the cage run in bearings 13 clamped under the caps of the bevel pinion carrier 8. The differential gear assembly, 16 to 21 inclusive, is mounted inside the differential cage, the pinion pin 20 being held in place by cross-pin 21. The internal splines in the gears 16 take the splines on the inner ends of the axle half-shafts 43. There is an integral flange at the outer end of the half-shaft which is bolted to the hub 86. Pressed into the hub are oil seal 39 and bearing 38, the inner race of the bearing being carried on the outer end of the casing 1. If the axle shafts are pulled out after removing screw 44, the carrier 8 can be removed complete with all the gears and differential assembly after unscrewing nuts 3.

Important: At this stage it is as well to point out that it is not permissible to fit a new crown wheel and pinion, pinion bearings or differential bearings, without working through a procedure which requires the use of many special tools and gauges. For example, the fitting of a new crown wheel and pinion involves the following operations: (1) Setting the position of the pinion. (2) Adjusting the

Important: The manufacturers do not advise the dis-antling of the axle or the renewal of parts unless it is bsolutely necessary. Dismantling for cleaning or exami-ation is permissible, providing care is taken to refit the stance-pieces and spacers in exactly the same locations they occupied originally. Fitting new parts and assem-ing the crown wheel and bevel pinion correctly is a ghly specialized job which requires expensive checking uges and a full range of distance pieces and spacers.

brication – early Wolseley '15/50'

Use only Hypoid oils of the approved grade. The filler ug is on the right-hand side of the pinion housing. Fill the bottom of the aperture. The hub bearings are auto-atically lubricated from the main supply in the axle casing.

emoving a half-shaft – early Wolseley '15/50'

Jack up the wheel and chock the others. Release the handbrake fully.

When the wheel has been removed, take out the split pin and unscrew the axle nut 29. Threads are right-hand on both sides.

The hub is locked to the shaft by a tapered split collar 34 in addition to the driving splines. An extractor is needed to free the hub from the taper.

Remove the brake backplate, preferably just far enough without detaching the brake fluid pipe line, as the system will need bleeding otherwise. Withdraw the split collar. The half-shaft can then be withdrawn complete with bearing 31, housing 35, and oil seal 33.

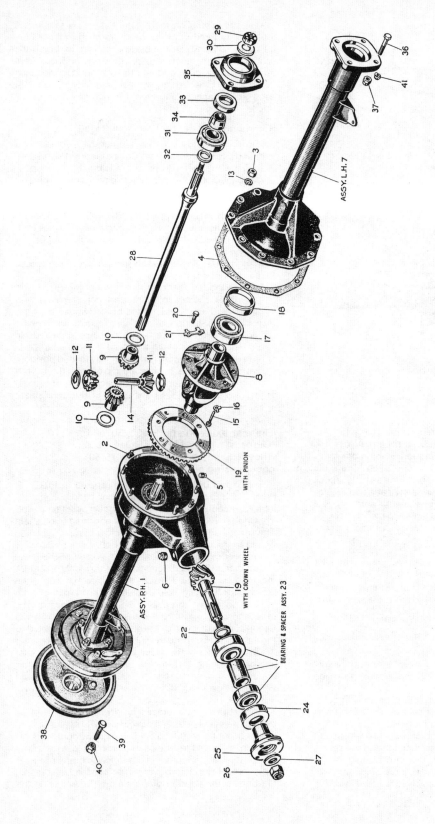

Fig 7:4 Components of rear axle on Wolseley 15/50's up to, and including, car No. 35857.

Key to Fig 7:4 1 Tube and casing assembly—R/H. 2 Stud—casing to cover. 3 Nut—casing to cover. 4 Joint—casing to cover stud. 4 Joint—casing to cover. 5 Plug—oil drain. 6 Plug—oil filler.
7 Tube and cover assembly—L/H. 8 Cage—differential. 9 Gear—differential. 10 Washer—differential gear. 11 Pinion—differential. 12 Washer—differential pinion.
13 Washer—spring—casing to cover stud. 14 Pin—differential pinion. 15 Bolt—pinion pin locking. 16 Washer—tab—pin locking bolt. 17 Bearing—differential.
18 Collar—bearing distance. 19 Wheel and pinion—crown. 20 Bolt—crown wheel to cage. 21 Tab—bolt locking. 22 Distance washer—pinion rear bearing.
23 Bearings and spacer assembly—pinion. 24 Seal—front—pinion oil. 25 Flange—universal joint. 26 Nut—flange to pinion. 27 Washer—flange nut. 28 Shaft—axle.

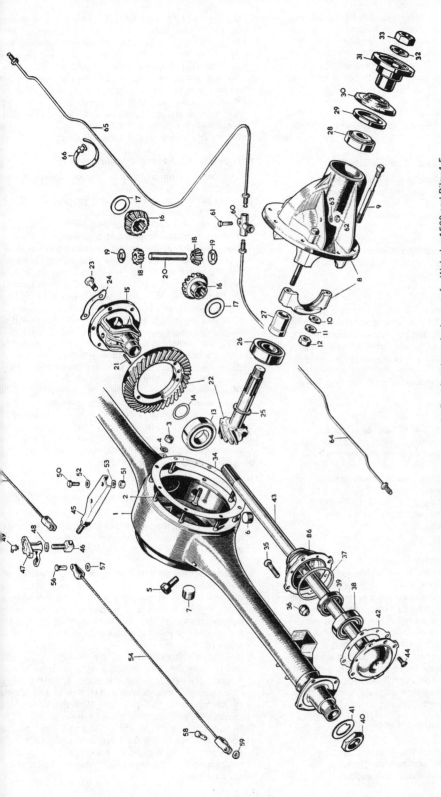

Fig 7:5 Components of the BMC 'B' type rear axle. Drawing shows brake parts for Wolseley 1500 and Riley 1.5

Key to Fig 7:5 1 Case. 2 Stud—differential carrier. 3 Nut for stud. 4 Spring washer for nut. 5 Breather. 6 Plug—oil drain. 7 Plug—oil filler. 8 Carrier (with caps). 9 Serrated bolt for cap. 10 Plain washer for bolt. 11 Spring washer for bolt. 12 Nut for bolt. 13 Bearing—differential. 14 Washer—bearing packing. 15 Cage—differential. 16 Gear. 17 Thrust washer—gear. 18 Pinion. 19 Thrust washer—pinion. 20 Pin for pinion. 21 Peg for pinion pin. 22 Crown wheel and pinion. 23 Bolt—crown wheel to cage. 24 Lock washer for bolt. 25 Thrust washer—pinion. 26 Bearing—pinion inner. 27 Distance piece—bearing. 28 Bearing—pinion outer. 29 Seal—oil. 30 Cover—dust. 31 Flange—universal joint. 32 Spring washer for nut. 33 Nut to pinion. 34 Joint—differential to axle case. 35 Stud—wheel. 36 Nut for wheel stud. 37 Ring—oil seal. 38 Bearing—hub. 39 Seal—oil. 40 Nut—bearing retainer. 41 Lock washer for nut. 42 Joint—hub to shaft. 43 Shaft—axle. 44 Screw—shaft to hub. 45 Support—balance lever. 46 Carrier—lever. 47 Lever. 48 Felt washer. 49 Lubricator. 50 Bolt—balance lever support to axle case. 51 Nut for bolt. 52 Plain washer for nut. 53 Spring washer for nut. 54 Cable—cross—R/H. 55 Cable—cross—L/H—short. 56 Pin—cable to balance lever. 57 Plain washer for pin. 58 Pin—cable to brake. 59 Plain washer for pin. 60 Connection—three-way. 61 Bolt—three-way connection to axle case. 62 Nut for bolt. 63 Pipe—three-way connection to R/H brake. 64 Pipe—three-way connection to L/H brake. 65 Pipe—three-way connection to L/H brake. 66 Strap for pipe.

bearing pre-load. (3) Adjusting the differential bearing pre-load. (4) Adjusting the backlash between the gears.

It is therefore necessary to entrust this work to a competent agent suitably equipped with the essential tools and gauges. Those operations which are within the powers of the average owner are described in the next sections.

Lubrication

The filler plug is in the rear cover of the axle casing. Using the correct grade of Hypoid oil, fill to the level of the filler opening.

Removing a brake drum and axle shaft

1 Jack up the car and place blocks under the spring as close as possible to the axle. Remove the wheel and release the handbrake.
2 Remove the two countersunk screws locating the drum and tap it off the hub.
3 Remove the screw 44 and withdraw the shaft by gripping the flange or prising it away with a screwdriver. Any damage to the paper washer 42 or to the flange faces must be made good.

Replacing

Reverse the previous instructions, noting that in some models the flange screw 44 is shorter than those locating the brake drum. There may also be a bearing spacer which is not shown in FIG 7:5. It was fitted to earlier axles between the axle flange and the outer race of the bearing. The sealing ring 37 may be absent on earlier axles and cannot be fitted to them unless the modified hub is also fitted, see FIG 7:8.

Removing a hub

1 Having removed the axle shaft and bearing spacer if fitted, knock back the locking washer tab and unscrew nut 40. Note that on later cars the left-hand nut has a left-hand thread.
2 Tilt the lock washer to disengage it and remove. Pull off the hub with an extractor, using a thrust pad on the end of the casing. Bearing 38 and oil seal 39 will come away with the hub. The bearing is not adjustable and must be renewed if worn.

Replacing

If a new bearing has been fitted, the outer race must protrude beyond the outer face of the hub and joint washer. In the case of those assemblies which include the spacer mentioned when replacing the axle shaft, it must protrude by the same amount. In both types of assembly, the paper joint washer 42 must be fitted before the check is made. Put a straight-edge across the bearing races and use a feeler gauge between it and the face of the joint washer. The amount projecting must lie between .001 in and .004 in. This ensures that the outer race of the bearing is nipped between the hub and the axle shaft flange. Pack the hubs with fresh grease even though they are lubricated from the axle casing during normal running.

Renewing the bevel pinion oil seal

This is item 29 in FIG 7:5.
1 Mark the rear universal joint flanges so that they may be replaced in the same position when reassembling. Disconnect the shaft and move to one side.

2 Unscrew nut 33. Two bolts in adjacent holes in flan 31 and a stout piece of square steel bar between the will enable the flange to be held while the nut is starte Withdraw the flange and end cover 30. Prise the oil se out of the housing. It will be wrecked in the process, that the operator must be certain that he has a replac ment to hand.
3 Press in a new seal, keeping it square. The edge of t rubber sealing ring faces inwards. Replace the flan carefully and tighten the pinion shaft nut to a torque 140 lb/ft. Reconnect the propeller shaft.

Removing the differential pinions

1 Drain the oil from the axle casing and remove the ax shafts as already instructed.
2 Uncouple the rear end of the propeller shaft aft marking the universal joint flanges.
3 Unscrew the nuts 3, and withdraw the carrier 8 co plete with gears and differential assembly.
4 Mark the bearing caps shown as part of assembly 8 they must be replaced in their original positions. No that the serrated bolt 9 is not fitted to early axles, whi have studs screwed in from the rear. With the remov of the caps the differential assembly will come awa
5 Tap out the dowel pin 21 from the crown wheel sid The hole on the other side is peened over, and it w help if this obstruction is cleaned out. Drive out th shaft 20, which will enable the pinions and thru washers to be removed. Examine them and renew a parts, taking care to peen over the entry hole for pin after it has been inserted through shaft 20.

Reassemble in the reverse order of dismantling, refillin the axle with fresh Hypoid oil when completed.

As mentioned earlier, this is as far as the owner can in replacing worn parts, and he is firmly advised to se expert help if he finds that his crown wheel and bev pinion show signs of the tooth surface breaking up, give indications of excessive wear.

Removing and refitting the axle

On 'Oxfords' 11 and 111, later Wolseley '15/50's and 'Magnettes' ZA and ZB

1 Raise the rear of the car and put blocks under the bump supports if a hoist is not available. Remove the re wheels, chock the front ones, and release the han brake.
2 Disconnect the flexible brake pipe at its junction wi the bracket on the underside of the floor. Disconne the brake cable anchorages from spring brackets. early 'Magnette' models the cable must also be di connected from the bracket on the axle. Disconnect t forked ends of the brake cables from the levers on t brake backplates.
3 Release the lower ends of the telescopic dampe taking away the nuts, washers and rubber bushes.
4 Support the axle on a suitable stand. Mark the flang of the rear universal joint so that they can be re-coupl in the same relative position. Part the flanges a support the propeller shaft out of the way.
5 Remove the rear shackle nuts and bolts, and t anchorage bolts from the front end of the spring. T axle can then be withdrawn backwards.

Replacement is the reverse of removal. Remember bleed the brakes.

n Wolseley '1500's' and Riley '1.5's'

Raise the rear of the car and put blocks under the frame in front of the springs. Remove the rear wheels, chock the front ones and release the handbrake.

Disconnect the flexible brake hose at the union on the right-hand chassis side member. Disconnect the brake cable from the relay lever on the back of the axle casing. Support the axle on a suitable stand.

Unscrew the nuts and locknuts from the 'U' bolts at the spring centres. Remove the damper bracket plates and locating plates with rubber pads.

Mark the rear universal joint flanges, uncouple them and support the shaft.

Remove the rear shackle nuts and plates. Lower the rear ends of the springs to the ground, and remove the axle.

Reverse the procedure to reassemble, bleeding the brakes to eliminate air from the hydraulic system, as described in the Braking chapter.

n Austins 'A40', '50' and '55'

Chock the front wheels, release the handbrake and disconnect the brake rod from the balance lever mounted on the right-hand side of the axle casing.

Uncouple the rear universal joint flanges after marking them for correct reassembly. Detach the damper links at the top ends. Remove the flexible brake pipe line from the floor bracket in front of the axle.

Jack up the car on both sides and remove the self-locking nuts under the spring retaining plates. These are at the bottom ends of the axle 'U' bolts. Knock up the 'U' bolts and remove the axle. On top of the springs are rubber pads held in metal casings. Remove these carefully.

To replace the axle unit fit the top rubber pads and casings over the heads of the centre bolts through the springs. Lift the axle into place and connect the brake cable to the balance lever before finally settling the axle into position. It might be difficult to connect the cable later on. Locate the axle mounting brackets so that the centre holes drop over the heads of the central spring bolts. Fit the 'U' bolts and the lower rubber pad with its casing. Position the securing plate and tighten the nuts. Connect the damper links and re-couple the propeller shaft flanges. Bleed the brakes after re-connecting the flexible hose.

Rear suspension

In every case the rear springs are semi-elliptic. The Austin spring eyes are fitted with silentbloc bushes, and the top shackle bearing at the rear has a phosphor-bronze bush which needs lubrication. All the other cars have rubber bushes in the spring eyes and top shackle bearing. There are zinc inter-leaves between the spring leaves on the Austins. Rubber pads are fitted to the ends of the spring leaves on the other cars.

Replacing bushes

On the Austin 'A40', 'A50' and 'A55'

Chock the front wheels and jack up the car on the side which is to receive attention. Put support blocks in place under the rear end of the body.

Put a jack under the axle so that it can be raised or lowered to relieve the load on the spring.

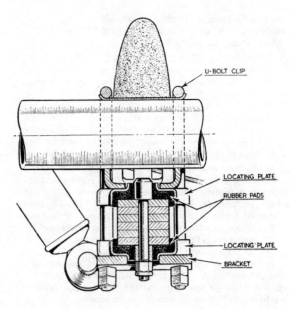

Fig 7:6 Typical spring mounting showing rubber pads and centre bolt.

3 Dismantle the rear shackle by removing the nut and spring washer from the lower pin, and the locknut, spring washer and nut from the upper pin. Pull off the inner shackle plate and tap each pin through a little at a time. Remove the nut and spring washer from the front pin and drift it out.

4 Unscrew the four self-locking nuts from the 'U' bolts holding the spring to the axle. Drop the spring complete with rubber pads and metal casings or locating plates.

5 The silentbloc bushes in the spring eyes are pushed out by applying pressure to the outer sleeve. When refitting a new bush, apply pressure to the outer sleeve only and ensure that the assembly is central in the spring eye.

6 At the rear end the upper shackle bushes are of phosphor bronze and they can be drifted out by tapping on the inner faces from opposite sides. Check that the lubricating hole is clear and then press the new bushes into place

7 Grease the upper shackle pin and assemble with the two plates. Tighten the nut and locknut enough to eliminate side play, but not so much that it prevents movement of the shackle.

8 Lift the spring and fit the front anchor pin, then fit the lower pin in the rear shackle. Do not tighten the nuts fully.

9 Assemble the rubber pads and locating plates on the centre bolt of the spring, as shown in **FIG 7:6**. Lower the axle into place, making sure that the head of the bolt goes up into the hole in the axle mounting bracket. Fit the 'U' bolts and self-locking nuts.

Lower the car and then tighten the two shackle pin nuts which were left loose. This will ensure that the rubber sleeves in the silentbloc bushes will be evenly deflected in both directions under road conditions.

**On the Wolseleys '1500' and '15/50',
the Riley '1.5', the 'Oxfords' 11 and 111 and the
'Magnettes' ZA and ZB**

1 Taking one spring at a time, raise the wheel concerned off the ground and put blocks under the body at the rear. Put a jack under the axle casing so that the loading on the spring can be relieved.

2 Remove the rear shackle nuts and plates. The flanged rubber bushes are in pairs and are easily removed and replaced by new ones if necessary. Do not tighten the the shackle pin nuts fully until the car is on the ground.

3 Remove the nut and spring washer from the anchor pin at the front end of the spring. There are holes in the head of the pin for a peg spanner which will prevent the pin from turning while the nut is unscrewed. Drive out the pin, lower the spring eye and extract the old bushes if worn. On some models it is better to remove the inner bush through the large hole in the anchor bracket before the spring eye is lowered. Do not tighten the nut on the anchor pin until the car is on the ground.

Note: Before tightening the nuts on the shackle pins and the anchor pin the normal working load must be applied to the springs. This ensures that the rubber bushes are flexed in both directions during service.

Removing rear springs

Follow the procedure for servicing the bushes, removing the shackle and anchor pins so that the springs can be lowered clear. Remove the nuts from the 'U' bolts securing the springs to the axle and drop the springs. The body and the axle must be securely blocked or jacked up during this operation.

Dismantling rear springs

Lay the spring on its side in a large vice and grip the top and bottom leaves adjacent to the centre bolt. Free the leaf clips, opening them slightly and retaining the rubber packing pieces. Remove the centre bolt and carefully open the vice so that the spring leaves will separate. Austin owners will find that there are zinc interleaves between the spring leaves. Clean all the leaves thoroughly and examine them for cracks. See that the centre bolt is sound and not bent.

Important: New leaves must be of the correct length and thickness, and have the same curvature as the remaining leaves. Where springs have lost their camber and have 'settled', a pair of new springs should be fitted.

Reassembling springs

Note: On Austin cars only, it is permissible to grease the spring leaves before they are fitted together. On no account lubricate the leaves on the other makes of car as there are rubber inserts at the spring tips. It is also unwise on all models to allow oil or grease to contact the rubber pads which are fitted to the centres of the springs.

Replace each spring in a vice, using a piece of rod to align the centre holes. Refit the centre bolt with the dowel head on top. Replace the rubber packing pieces and squeeze the clips together, or fit the bolts and distance tubes on some models. Fit the rubber pads and locating plates over each end of the centre bolt and lift each spring into position under the axle mounting brackets, as shown in section in **FIG 7:6**. Replace the 'U' bolts, raise or lower the axle until the spring eyes are lined up and fit the

shackle pins. Do not forget to delay tightening the shackle and anchor pin nuts until after the car is on the ground

**Hydraulic dampers – Austins 'A40' 50 and 55.
Wolseley '1500' and Riley '1.5'**

These are of the Armstrong double-acting type, the arms being connected to the axle by rubber bushed links. On the Austins, the arms are also connected to the ends of an anti-roll bar.

There is no provision for adjusting these dampers, and there is no point in trying to dismantle a faulty one. If the damper is still defective after checking the fluid level, then a replacement must be fitted.

Topping-up Armstrong dampers

Use only Armstrong Super (Thin) Shock Absorber Fluid No. 624 for preference. If it is not available, then use a good-quality mineral oil to Specification SA 20/20W, although the substitute is not suitable for low temperature operation.

Note: Clean all round the filler plug before removing it, so that dirt cannot fall in.

Add fluid to the level of the bottom of the filler hole, working the damper arm through full strokes to expel air. On early models of the Wolseley '1500' and Riley '1.5' it is necessary to remove the dampers to service them. Later models have rubber plugs in the rear seat pan for access to the filler plugs. The position of the Austin filler plug is shown in **FIG 7:7**.

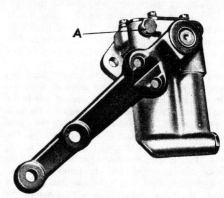

Fig 7:7   Filler plug 'A' on Armstrong dampers fitted to Austins

Testing Armstrong dampers

Note: Keep the dampers upright, as far as possible, when they are removed from the car. Otherwise air may enter the working chambers and cause erratic resistance.

To remove the dampers on the Austin models, it will be necessary to disconnect the anti-roll bar by removing a bolt and a 'U' bolt from each arm.

Grip each damper by the mounting lugs in a vice. Move the arm steadily up and down throughout complete strokes. Moderate and steady resistance should be felt all the way. If the resistance is erratic, with free movement of the arm noticeable, it may indicate lack of fluid. If there is no improvement after fluid has been added, a new or replacement unit must be fitted. This is also the only solution if the arm proves to be immoveable, as this indicates a seized piston or some internal breakage.

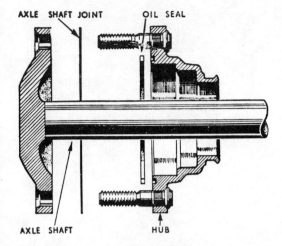

AXLE SHAFT JOINT   OIL SEAL

AXLE SHAFT   HUB

Fig 7:8   Modified hub with additional oil seal.

The rubber bushes integral with both ends of the damper-to-axle connecting links cannot be renewed, so the whole link must be replaced. Before fitting the link it is advisable to work the damper arm a few times to expel any air which may have found its way into the operating chamber.

Telescopic dampers – Wolseley '15/50', 'Magnettes' ZA and ZB, 'Oxfords' 11 and 111

These are of the double-acting type in which all the working parts are submerged in oil. They are set by the manufacturers and cannot be adjusted or refilled with liquid. Defective dampers must be renewed.

Note: It is important to keep the dampers in an upright position while they are removed from the car.

Removing

Unscrew the upper and lower mounting nuts, remove the washers and pull off the damper. With the damper held upright in a vice, check for smooth steady resistance in both directions. If unsatisfactory, replace with a new or reconditioned unit. Examine the rubber bushes in the damper eyes and renew them if necessary.

Replace by reversing the dismantling procedure.

Modifications
Wolseley '1500' and Riley '1.5'

Series WHS2 and RHS2 cars have the riding height reduced by $\frac{1}{2}$ in. Packing pieces of that thickness have been fitted between the rear spring locating plates and the axle mounting brackets. When the packing pieces are fitted it is necessary to use rubber buffers on top of the axle which are shortened by $\frac{1}{2}$ in too. The short buffers must only be used with the packing pieces, and not without.

'Magnettes' ZA and ZB and 'Oxfords' 11 and 111

On these cars modified hubs and bearing nuts were fitted to later models. The hub is shown in **FIG 7:8** where the additional oil seal can be seen. This was incorporated on the 'Magnettes' from Axle No. 18835. The new oil seal may only be fitted to earlier axles together with the later-type hub with the machined groove in its face.

The left-hand bearing nut on the rear axle now has a left-hand thread and is turned clockwise to unscrew. The right-hand nut has a right-hand thread. The change took place on 'Magnettes' from car No. 12639 and on 'Oxfords' from car No. 221619.

'Oxfords' 11 and 111

From car No. 168765 the axle shafts were increased in diameter at the hub end and the oil thread was deleted from the tube end of the axle casing. Later-type shafts cannot be fitted to earlier cases with oil threads. Earlier-type shafts can, however, be fitted to the new-type cases.

Fault diagnosis

(a) Noisy axle

1 Insufficient or incorrect lubricant.
2 Worn bearings.
3 Worn gears.
4 Too much or too little backlash between gears.

(b) Excessive backlash

1 Worn gears, bearings or bearing housings
2 Worn axle shaft splines.
3 Worn universal joints.
4 Loose or broken wheel studs.

(c) Oil leakage

1 Defective seals in hubs
2 Defective pinion shaft seal.
3 Defective seals on universal joint spiders.
4 Damaged gear carrier flange.

(d) Vibration

1 Propeller shaft out of balance.
2 Worn universal joint bearings.

(e) Rattles

1 Rubber bushes in damper links worn through.
2 Dampers loose.
3 Spring 'U' bolts loose.
4 Loose spring clips.
5 Worn bushes in spring eyes and shackles.
6 Broken spring leaves.

(f) 'Settling'

1 Weak or broken spring leaves.
2 Badly worn spring bushes and shackle pins.
3 Loose spring anchorages

CHAPTER EIGHT

THE FRONT SUSPENSION

The following table sets out the types of suspension systems covered in this chapter. From this, it will be seen that there are two basic springs, the coil and the torsion bar. Damping on some models is by Armstrong piston-type dampers which are mounted on the car body and have arms which act as upper suspension links. The other models have telescopic dampers which are connected between the lower wishbone arms and brackets on the car body.

Austin 'A40', 'A50' and 'A55': Coil springs. Armstrong dampers with double arms forming the upper wishbone links.
'Magnettes' ZA and ZB, Wolseley 15/50': Coil springs. Telescopic dampers inside coils.
'Oxfords' 11 and 111: Torsion bars. Telescopic dampers.
Wolseley '1500', Riley '1.5': Torsion bars. Armstrong dampers with single arms forming the upper links.

Description of Austin layout

The component parts of the Austin front suspension are shown in **FIG 8:1**. The assembly is illustrated in **FIG 8:3**, and the hub is seen in detail in **FIG 8:2**.

The cross-member is bolted to the car body and carries the dampers 3 and lower wishbones 6 at its outer ends, as shown in **FIG 8:3**. The damper arms and the lower wishbones are connected by a swivel pin, on which the swivel axle 9 partially rotates for steering purposes. The bottom end of the coil spring 5 is located on a plate 11 bolted to the lower wishbone. The upper end abuts against the cross-member. Some of the bearings are rubber bushed and some have metal bushes which require lubrication.

Lubrication

There are three nipples which must have regular attention with the specified grade of lubricant. These are numbered 33, 37 and 50 in **FIG 8:1**. They provide lubrication for the metal trunnion bushes 29 and 35, and for the swivel axle bushes 39 and 46.

Checking for wear

Jack up the car until the front wheels are clear of the ground. Grasp each tyre at the top and bottom and rock the wheel. Movement between the brake drum and backplate denotes worn hub bearings.

Grasp opposite points of the tyre in a horizontal position and rock the wheel. Free movement due to wear can then be detected between the top and bottom swivel pin trunnions 6 and 30 and the swivel axle assembly 42. The swivel pin or the bushes 39 and 46 may be worn and must be stripped for examination. Damper bearings are best checked when the suspension is dismantled. The top wishbone arms are clamped to the damper cross-shaft and excessive sideways movement at the outer end indicates wear in the shaft and bearings. The only cure is to renew the damper.

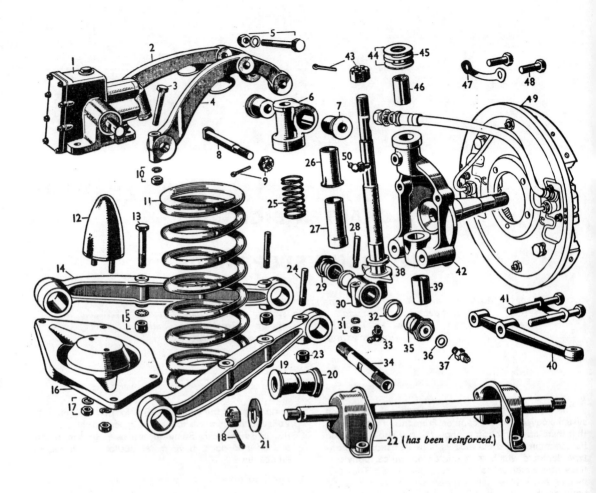

Fig 8:1   Components of a left-hand suspension unit for Austins 'A40', 'A50' and 'A55'.

Key to Fig 8:1   1 Shock absorber.   2 Rear top wishbone arm.   3 Clamping bolt for front wishbone arm.   4 Front top wishbone arm.
5 Joining bolt for top wishbone arms.   6 Upper trunnion link.   7 Trunnion rubber bearing.   8 Upper trunnion fulcrum pin.
9 Fulcrum locking nut and split pin.   10 Nut and washer for clamping bolt.   11 Coil spring.   12 Rebound rubber bumper.
13 Spring plate bolt.   14 Rear lower wishbone arm.   15 Simmonds nut and lockwasher.   16 Spring plate.   17 Rebound bumper nut and
washer.   18 Castellated nut.   19 An inner lower rubber bearing.   20 An outer lower rubber bearing.   21 Washer.
22 Lower link spindle and brackets.   23 Nut for bush cotter.   24 Bush cotter.   25 Swivel pin dust cover spring.
26 Upper dust cover.   27 Lower dust cover.   28 Cotter for fulcrum pin.   29 Rear screwed bush.   30 Swivel pin and lower trunnion.
31 Nut and washer.   32 Cork ring.   33 Trunnion oil nipple.   34 Screwed fulcrum pin.   35 Front screw bush.   36 Flat washer.
37 Oil nipple.   38 Cork ring.   39 Swivel axle lower bush.   40 Steering arm.   41 Steering arm setpin.   42 Swivel axle.
43 Swivel pin nut and split pin.   44 Staybrite washers.   45 Oilite washer.   46 Swivel axle upper bush.   47 Back plate setpin lockwasher.
48 Back plate setpin.   49 Back plate assembly.   50 Swivel pin oil nipple.

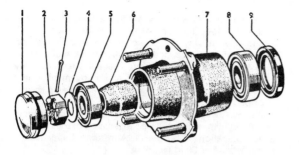

Fig 8:2   The standardised BMC hub exploded.

Key to Fig 8:2   1 Hub cap.   2 Castellated nut.   3 Split-pin.
4 Locating washer.   5 Outer bearing.   6 Distance piece.
7 Hub.   8 Inner bearing.   9 Oil seal.

Rubber bushes soften and deteriorate in time. Check those at the outer end of the upper wishbone, shown as item 7; and bushes 19 and 20 at the inner end of the lower wishbone. Excessive sideways movement in either of the bearings can be cured by renewing the bushes.

With the suspension dismantled, check the screwed bushes 29 and 35, and the pin 34 for too much free play. These parts can be renewed.

Removing a coil spring

1 Jack up the side of the car concerned and chock the body side member behind the suspension assembly.
2 Provide two $\frac{3}{8}$ in BSF bolts of high-tensile steel, five in long and screwed the whole way. Spring plate 16 is bolted to the lower wishbone arms by four bolts 13 with self-locking nuts. Remove two of the nuts situated diagonally, take out the bolts and replace them with the two long bolts. Screw two nuts right down the long bolts until the spring plate is secured and then remove the other two bolts 13.
3 Unscrew the nuts from the long bolts a little at a time, evenly until the spring is fully extended. Release the bolts and remove the spring plate and coil spring.

4 Check the spring length against the figure given in Technical Data and renew it if there is excessive variation from the correct dimension.

Replacing the spring is a matter of using the two long slave bolts again. The nuts are screwed down a little at a time until the spring plate can be secured by two of the bolts 13. The long bolts are then removed and the remaining two short bolts tightened down with the self-locking nuts.

Removing and dismantling the suspension

It is possible to remove the suspension unit complete, as in **FIG 8:3**.
1 Lift and support the front of the car. Take the weight of the engine so that it stays in its normal position when the front mountings are released from the cross-member. Raise the car to the point where the front wheels are just about to leave the ground.
2 Disconnect the pipe lines to the front brakes and the steering side-tubes from the steering and idler arms. The cross-member is now ready to be unbolted and wheeled away.

To dismantle the suspension in situ, proceed as follows:
1 Jack up the car and remove the wheel and coil spring as already explained.
2 Disconnect the steering side-tube from the steering arm 40. Disconnect the flexible brake pipe at the union on the chassis, plugging the main pipe to avoid loss of fluid. See the Braking chapter for the correct way of disconnecting the hose.
3 Remove bolt 5 from the upper arms 2 and 4. Remove split pin and nut 9. Withdraw the clamping bolt 3 from the front arm 4, working the arm along the damper spindle until pin 8 can be removed. The damper can now be taken off complete with arms and packing piece.
4 Withdraw the rubber bushes 7. Do not attempt to remove the swivel pin 30 without extracting the bushes first, as they fit in a groove in the pin.

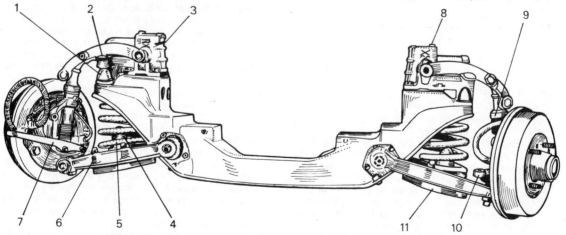

Fig 8:3   Complete suspension assembly for Austins 'A40', 'A50' and 'A55'. Front view.

Key to Fig 8:3   1 Rubber pad.   2 Rebound stop.   3 Damper.   4 Rubber pad.   5 Spring.   6 Lower wishbone.   7 Steering side lever.
8 Damper filler.   9 Swivel.   10 Steering side lever.   11 Bottom spring plate.

5 Pull out the split pin and unscrew nut 43, which will permit the removal of the upper trunnion 6 and the thrust washers 44 and 45. Lift off the swivel axle and hub assembly, of which 42 is a part. Slide off the cork washer 38.

6 Dismantle the outer bearing of the lower arms. Slacken nuts 23 and unscrew the two threaded bushes 29 and 35.

7 At each end of the inner lower arm spindle 22, remove the split pin and nut 18. Pull off the washers 21 and the arms 14 complete with bushes 19 and 20. The swivel pin and lower trunnion 30 with pin 34 will now be free. Unscrew nut 31 flush with the end of the thread, tap the cotter pin 28 free, remove the nut and drive the cotter right out. The fulcrum pin can now be withdrawn and the cork rings 32 removed.

8 The inner spindle for the lower arms is item 22. The bracket flanges are secured to the cross-member by bolts and nuts, and by setscrews, see **FIG 8:4**. One of the brackets is a fixture on the spindle, which can thus be withdrawn in one direction only.

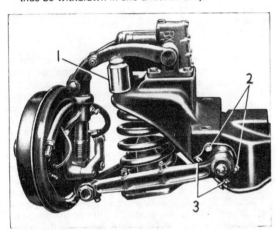

Fig 8:4 Using distance piece during final assembly. Note trunnion bracket fixings.

Key to Fig 8:4 1 Setting distance piece. 2 Trunnion setscrews. 3 Trunnion bolts.

Examination for wear

1 Check the swivel pin 30 with a micrometer. If not appreciably worn, slackness will be due to worn bushes 39 and 46. Drive out and replace with new ones, using a suitable drift. Before fitting the top bush, check that the oiling hole will finish opposite the hole in the swivel axle boss. The top face of this bush must be flush with the boss. The lower bush must be flush with the recess in the bottom of the swivel axle and protrude about $\frac{1}{8}$ in above the upper face. The bushes must be reamered with Service Tools 18G.64 and 18G.65. Remove dust covers 26 and 27 by telescoping together.

2 Renew screwed bushes 29 and 35 if they are slack on pin 34. If new bushes are still slack, renew the pin.

3 If there is wear and leakage from the damper cross-shaft, the whole damper must be renewed. Test the damper for resistance by nipping the mounting plate in a vice. Move the top wishbone arms through a full stroke each way. The resistance must be even and moderate. If erratic, check the fluid level. It should be just below the filler opening. Move the lever steadily through full strokes. If there is no improvement, a new damper is indicated. Solid resistance implies a seizure or breakage inside.

Note: Always keep dampers in their normal attitude, as turning them about will lead to aeration of the fluid and erratic operation. Top up with Armstrong Super (Thin) Shock Absorber Fluid No. 624.

Assembling

1 Replace the lower link spindle 22, feeding it in from the front. Secure the brackets to the cross-member. Fit the spindle bushes 19 and 20 to the front lower wishbone arm and assemble on the spindle, locating washer 21 on the spindle flats. Do not fully tighten the nut 18. Position the damper and packing piece, leaving the four setscrews loose.

2 On the bench, place cork washer 38 on the swivel pin and smear the pin with oil. Push the pin partly through the lower bearing of the swivel axle 42 and then thread the dust covers and spring, 25, 26 and 27 over it. Push the pin right home. Fit the thrust washers over the top of the pin. Oilite washer 45 lies between the two steel washers 44. Fit the upper trunnion 6 and the nut 43. Check the lift of the swivel axle on the pin. The maximum clearance is .002 and the washers 44 are made in various thicknesses to permit adjustment. When satisfied that the swivel axle is free to turn without excessive lift, slacken nut 43 for further assembly.

3 Moisten the rubber bushes 7 with water and fit in the trunnion 6. Centralize pin 34 in the lower trunnion of the pin 30 and lock it in place with cotter 28. Fit cork rings 32.

4 Offer up the assembly to the cross-member, entering the screwed fulcrum pin into the outer end of the lower arm. Place the upper trunnion between the damper arms and fit the fulcrum pin 8. Do not tighten the nut. Position the slackened damper arm on the cross-shaft, replace bolt 3 and tighten. The arms are then clamped together with bolt 5. Assemble the bushes in the rear lower arm 14 and replace it on the inner spindle. Leave the nut loose. Align the lower wishbone arms by fitting the spring plate 16 securely.

5 Screw the threaded bushes 29 and 35 home evenly and then slacken each one back one flat. Lock them in place with cotters 24. Do not overtighten or the bushes will be distorted. If correctly assembled, a .002 in feeler should fit between the shoulder of the bush and the outer face of each wishbone arm. The lower trunnion assembly should now work freely in the screwed bushes.

6 The next step can be seen in **FIG 8:4** which shows a distance piece inserted between the damper arm and the cross-member, opposite to the rubber rebound buffer. The piece must be $2\frac{1}{4}$ in long. Now carry out the final adjustments.

7 Tighten the lower link spindle nuts 18 and lock with split pins. Tighten the damper fixing bolts. Tighten nut 9 on upper fulcrum pin 8 and lock with a split pin. Tighten swivel pin nut 43 and lock with a split pin.

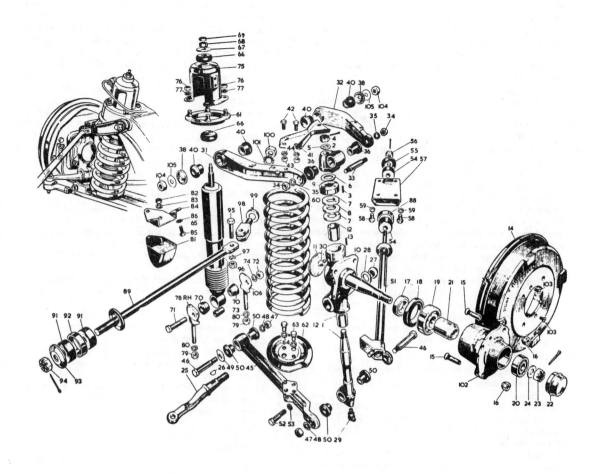

Fig 8:5 Components of suspension unit for Magnettes and later Wolseley '15/50's'.

Key to Fig 8:5 1 Pin—swivel. 2 Trunnion assembly. 3 Dowel pin—thrust washer. 4 Nut—swivel pin top.
5 Washer—plain—nut. 6 Shim—swivel pin. 7 Thrust washer—fixed—swivel pin. 8 Thrust washer—floating—swivel pin.
9 Housing—thrust washer. 10 Axle assembly—L/H. 11 Cover—axle. 12 Bush—axle. 13 Dowel pin. 14 Drum—brake.
15 Stud—wheel. 16 Nut—wheel stud. 17 Washer—distance—hub to axle. 18 Oil seal—front hub. 19 Bearing—inner—front hub.
20 Bearing—outer—front hub. 21 Distance piece—bearings. 22 Retainer—grease. 23 Nut—axle—L.H.T. 24 Washer—nut.
25 Lever—steering—L/H. 26 Key—lever. 27 Nut—steering lever. 28 Washer—plain—nut. 29 Nipple—lubricating—swivel pin.
30 Nipple—lubricating—axle. 31 Link—suspension—upper—front—L/H. 32 Link—suspension—upper—rear—L/H.
33 Pin—link to swivel pin. 34 Nut—link pin. 35 Spring washer—pin. 36 Bush—link pin to swivel pin. 38 Washer—cup—link bush.
40 Bush—link to cross-member pivot pin. 41 Plate—link bridge. 42 Screw—plate to link. 43 Nut—screw. 44 Spring washer—screw.
45 Arm—lower—suspension. 46 Pin—fulcrum—lower arm. 47 Nut—fulcrum pin. 48 Spring washer—nut.
49 Washer—spacing—pin to link bracket. 50 Bush—arm—tie-bar and frame. 51 Bar—tie—lower link to body bracket.
52 Bolt—tie-bar to lower arm. 53 Spring washer—bolt. 54 Bush—tie-bar to frame bracket. 55 Washer—cup—tie-bar to frame bracket.
56 Nut—slotted—tie-bar to frame bracket. 57 Bracket—tie-bar to frame. 58 Screw—bracket to frame. 59 Spring washer—screw.
60 Spring—front suspension. 61 Cap assembly—spring. 62 Seat assembly—spring. 63 Screw—seat to lower arm.
64 Spring washer—screw. 65 Damper assembly. 66 Bush—shock absorber upper. 67 Washer—bush. 68 Nut—damper to cover.
69 Locknut—damper to cover. 70 Bush—damper lower. 71 Bolt—damper to eyebolt. 72 Nut—bolt. 73 Tube—distance—bolt.
74 Spring washer—bolt. 75 Cover—damper. 76 Nut—cover and spring cap to cross-member. 77 Spring washer—nut.
78 Eyebolt—lower arm—R/H. 79 Nut—eyebolt. 80 Spring washer—nut. 81 Rubber—bump. 82 Nut—bump rubber to bracket.
83 Spring washer—nut. 84 Bracket—bump rubber. 85 Screw—bracket to frame. 86 Spring washer—screw. 88 Retainer—bush.
89 Rod—tie—upper link to frame. 91 Bush—tie-rod. 92 Retainer—bush. 93 Washer—cup—bush. 94 Nut—slotted—tie-rod.
95 Bolt—tie-rod to fork end. 96 Nut—bolt. 97 Spring washer—nut. 98 Fork—tie-rod end. 99 Distance piece—tie-rod.
100 Locknut—fork end to upper link. 101 Washer—shakeproof—locknut. 102 Hub—front. 103 Set screw—countersunk—
drum to hub. 104 Nut—pivot pin—cross-member. 105 Washer—top—pivot pin nut. 106 Eyebolt—lower arm—L/H.

8 Remove the lower spring plate and refit the coil spring as already described. Connect the brake fluid pipe after unplugging the main pipe line. Secure the side-tube to the steering arm, using a split pin to lock the nut. Refit the road wheel, lower to the ground and remove the temporary distance piece. Bleed the brakes as instructed in the Braking chapter.

The checking of castor, camber and swivel pin angles is covered by a section towards the end of this chapter.

Dismantling front hub—Austins 'A40', '50' and '55'

1 Jack up the side of the car concerned and put blocks under the spring plate. Lower the car on to the blocks.
2 Remove the wheel and the countersunk screw holding the brake drum to the hub flange. Pull off the drum, slackening the brake shoe adjusters if it binds on the shoes, see the Braking chapter.
3 Lever off cap 1 in **FIG 8:2**. Remove split pin 3 and nut 2, then ease off washer 4. Using an extractor bolted to the wheel studs, pull off the hub complete with inner and outer bearings 8 and 5, oil seal 9 and distance piece 6. If bearing 8 remains on the axle, look for two small holes behind the swivel axle, leading into the bearing housing. Use a piece of thin steel rod and tap each side of the bearing through each hole in turn, a little at a time.
4 Tap the outer bearing gently out of the hub, using a drift from the opposite end. Repeat for the inner bearing if it remains in the hub. The oil seal will precede it.

Reassembling the hub

Check the bearings for wear and roughness in operation and renew if necessary. Renew the oil seal if leakage has been apparent.
1 Fit the inner bearing 8 first with the side marked 'thrust' facing inwards. Pack the hub with the recommended grade of grease and insert the distance piece 6 with the domed end outwards.
2 Replace the outer bearing 5 with the side marked 'thrust' facing inwards. Use a soft metal drift on both bearings, tapping gently on diametrically opposite edges until they are fully home in the hub. Replace the oil seal 9 with the hollow side facing the bearing.

Refitting the hub

1 Drive the hub on to the swivel axle, using a hollow drift which will bear evenly on both races of the outer bearing. Gently tap the hub into place until the inner race feels solid against the shoulder on the axle.
2 Fit washer 4 and nut 2, screwing down finger tight. Spin the wheel and notice the amount of drag due to the oil seal. Tighten the nut, when a slight increase in the resistance should be felt. This is the effect of pre-loading the bearings by locking the inner races to the distance piece. Insert the split pin.
3 Pack the cap 1 with grease and tap into place. Replace the brake drum, securing it with the countersunk screw. Tap the inner flange of the drum here and there to ensure that it is fully home against the hub flange and check the screw for tightness. Refit the wheel.
4 Re-adjust the brake shoes, lower the wheel to the ground and finally tighten the wheel nuts.

Front suspension — 'Magnettes' ZA and ZB, Wolseley '15/50'

FIG 8:5 shows the component parts of the suspension unit fitted to the 'Magnettes. This is also the type fitted to the Wolseley '15/50' beginning at car No. 35858. Wolseley '15/50's' before that number had a similar unit but with a one-piece hub and drum. The inner wishbone bearing at the top had a setscrew instead of the nut 104, and the eyebolts 78 and 106 were slightly different in design. These minor differences will not prevent the operator from using the illustration to follow the servicing instructions.

FIG 8:6 shows the suspension assembly with the telescopic damper located inside the coil spring. The wishbone bearings are rubber bushed throughout. Note that the cross-member forming the upper abutment for the spring is an integral part of the chassis and is not detachable.

Removing and replacing a front damper

1 Jack up the car and remove the wheel. Place a second jack at the outer end of the lower suspension arm 45 in **FIG 8:5**. Raise the jack until the spring is compressed to about the normal standing position. Remove the parts 66 to 69 inclusive from the top of the damper cover 75.
2 On early models remove the brake hose bracket from the damper cover. Remove the cover nuts 76 and lift off the cover.
3 Unscrew the nuts 79 from the eyebolts and tap the eyebolts upwards with a soft-faced hammer until the damper can be lifted out.

   Note: Keep the damper in an upright position at all times to avoid aeration of the fluid and subsequent erratic operation.
4 To release the cover, hold the centre bolt by the flats and unscrew the nut 68 and locknut 69 if they were not removed in the early stages.
5 Hold the damper vertically in a vice and test it for smooth moderate resistance in both directions. There is no provision for adjustment, so that erratic performance cannot be cured and a new damper must be fitted.
6 When replacing a damper which has been detached from the bottom eyebolts, check the rubber bushes 70, renewing them if they are worn, and assemble the damper with the eyebolts set at approximately 12 deg to the axis of it. This angle can be seen in the section in **FIG 8:6**. Note also, that if the eyebolts are offset as shown, the cross-bolt 71 must be nearest to the wheel, with the bolt head to the front. Renew the rubber bushes 66 if worn or softened.

Dismantling the suspension unit

1 Raise the car and remove the wheel. Where the brake drum is separate from the hub, remove it by unscrewing the two countersunk screws 103. Prise off the cap 22.
2 Remove nut 23. The thread is left-handed on the left-hand side of the car. Using an extractor bolted to the wheel studs, pull off the hub, complete with brake drum on early models.

   Important: After removing the hub it is likely that inner bearing 19, oil seal 18, washer 17 and distance piece 21 will remain on the axle. These parts must be replaced in the hub before it is refitted. Distance washer 17 must be fitted on the axle with its chamfered face away from the inner bearing. The metal face of the oil seal 18 is also fitted away from the bearing.

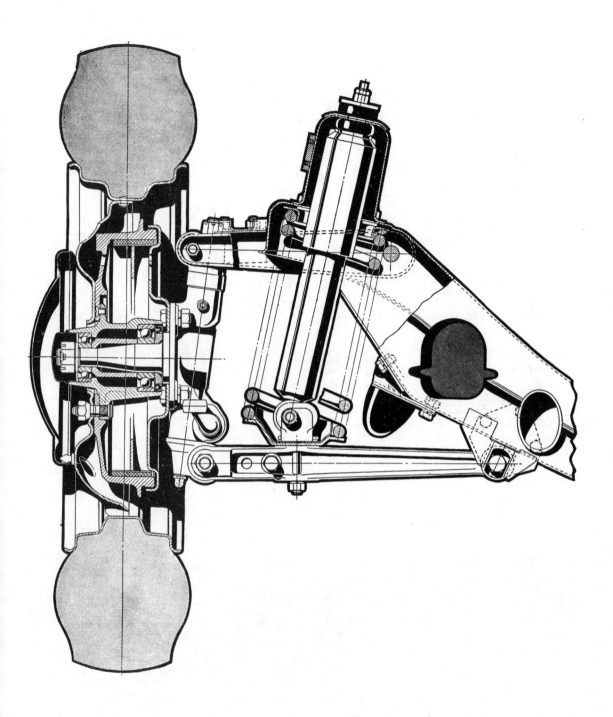

Fig 8 : 6   Section through Magnette suspension unit. Note offset of bottom damper mounting.

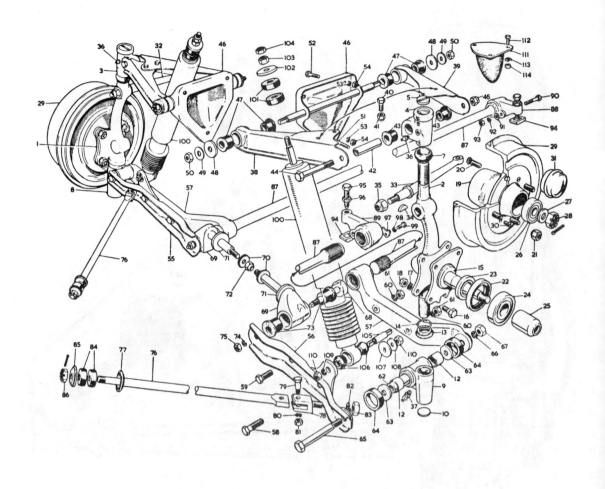

Fig 8:7 Components of the Oxford suspension as seen from the front.

Key to Fig 8:7 1 Swivel pin—R/H. 2 Swivel pin—L/H. 3 Link—R/H upper. 4 Link—L/H upper. 5 Plug. 7 Seal—rubber. 8 Link—R/H lower. 9 Link L/H lower. 10 Plug. 12 Bush—lower arm. 13 Seal—rubber. 14 Ring—seal retaining. 15 Stub shaft—L/H. 16 Bolt—stub shaft and brake plate to swivel pin. 17 Washer—spring—bolt. 18 Nut—bolt. 19 Hub assembly. 20 Stud—wheel. 21 Nut—wheel stud. 22 Seal—oil. 23 Washer—hub distance. 24 Bearing—inner. 25 Spacer—bearing. 26 Bearing—outer. 27 Washer. 28 Nut—L.H.T.—to stub shaft. 29 Brake-drum. 30 Screw. 31 Cap—grease-retaining. 32 Lever—R/H steering. 33 Lever—L/H steering. 34 Key—to swivel pin. 35 Nut—to swivel pin. 36 Lubricator—upper link. 37 Lubricator—lower link. 38 Arm—upper—joggled. 39 Arm—upper—straight. 40 Screw—arm to arm. 41 Nut—screw. 42 Spacer—upper link pivot. 43 Bush—rubber—upper link. 44 Bolt—arms to upper link. 45 Nut—bolt. 46 Bracket—upper arm pivot. 47 Bush—rubber—arm to bracket. 48 Washer—bush-retaining. 49 Washer—locking—pivot nut. 50 Nut—pivot. 51 Bolt—long—bracket to mounting box. 52 Bolt—short—bracket to mounting box. 53 Washer—spring—bolt. 54 Nut—bolt. 55 Arm—front lower—R/H. 56 Arm—front lower—L/H. 57 Arm—rear lower. 58 Bolt—long—arm to arm. 59 Bolt—short—arm to arm. 60 Washer—spring—bolt. 61 Nut—bolt. 62 Spacer—lower link pivot. 63 Washer—link—thrust. 64 Seal—dust. 65 Bolt—arms to lower link. 66 Washer—spring—bolt. 67 Nut. 68 Extension—lower arm. 69 Eyebolt—to frame. 70 Washer—inner—eyebolt. 71 Washer—outer—eyebolt. 72 Nut—eyebolt. 73 Bush—rubber—eyebolt to arms. 74 Washer—spring—extension to arm. 75 Nut—extension to arm. 76 Tie-bar. 77 Washer—cup. 78 Fork—to lower arm. 79 Bolt—to fork. 80 Washer—spring—bolt. 81 Nut—bolt. 82 Washer—spring—fork to lower arm. 83 Nut—fork to lower arm. 84 Bush—rubber—to frame. 85 Washer—cup. 86 Nut—to frame. 87 Torsion bar. 88 Bracket—R/H—vernier. 89 Bracket—L/H—vernier. 90 Bolt—bracket to frame. 91 Washer—bolt. 92 Washer—spring—bolt. 93 Nut—bolt. 94 Plate—abutment. 95 Bolt—vernier. 96 Nut—bolt locking. 97 Plate—retaining. 98 Washer—spring—retaining plate screw. 99 Screw—retaining plate. 100 Damper assembly. 101 Rubber—upper mounting. 102 Washer—mounting rubber. 103 Nut—to frame. 104 Locknut—to frame. 105 Pin—bottom pivot. 106 Bush—rubber—lower mounting. 107 Washer—pivot pin. 108 Washer—nut locking. 109 Washer—spring—pivot pin to bracket. 110 Nut—pivot pin. 111 Rubber—front suspension bump. 112 Screw—to bracket. 113 Washer—spring. 114 Nut—Screw.

3 It is necessary to compress the spring 60. On models with a one-piece hub and drum the Part No. of the tool to compress it is AJA 5011. On later models the Part No. is 18G.368. The tool consists of a cranked piece of thick rectangular bar tapped in the centre for a stout central bolt. The bolt head rests on a square of thick steel plate bolted in place of the damper cover. Fit the early type of bar between the second and third coils from the bottom. The cross-bar on later types goes between the third and fourth coils from the bottom.

4 Compress the spring and remove outer bolts 46 and 52. Tie-bar 51 can be taken away by releasing bracket 57 from the body. Remove bolt 46 from the inner end of arm 45, taking care not to damage the rubber seal on the steering rack housing. Remove the arm with bushes 50. Release the spring compressor and lift away the spring. Disconnect the flexible brake pipe by following the instructions in the Braking chapter.

5 At the top, take off bridge plate 41. Release tie-rod 89 by removing bolt 95. Unscrew nuts 34 from trunnion pin 33 and nuts 104 from the inner pivot pin. There will be bolts instead of nuts 104 on early models. The arms 31 and 32 can now be removed.

6 Dismantle the swivel pin 1 by unscrewing nut 4 to remove the trunnion 2 from its taper on the pin. Remove shims 6 and the thrust washers with housing 9. Axle 10 can then be lifted off.

Examination for wear

Renew all rubber bushes which are split, perished, oval or oil-soaked. Check the lower arm 45 for looseness as an assembly with the tie-bar 51, renewing the dowel if necessary. The end holes must not be elongated.

The faces of the thrust washers 7 and 8 must be smooth and flat within .0005 in. When new the washer 8 is .250 in and washers 7 between .178 and .180 in in thickness. Check swivel pin 1 for ovality.

If axle bushes 12 are worn, drive them outwards. Make sure that the oil holes line up and press the new bushes into place so that the outer face of the lower bush is $\frac{3}{16}$ in and the upper bush is $\frac{1}{16}$ in inside the axle housings. After fitting, the bushes must be reamered in line within the limits of .8755 to .8748 in.

Examine the coil spring for cracks and check the length against the dimension given in Technical Data.

The hub bearings must be cleaned to inspect them for wear. If they are washed in paraffin, this must be dried off and the bearings dipped in mineral oil as soon as possible after examination. It must be pointed out that repeated withdrawal of the bearings will reduce the interference fit of the races in their housings and on the axle shaft. If possible, clean and check them for wear without dismantling. Reject them if they are rough in action when unlubricated, or show signs of pitting of the tracks, broken balls or cracked cages.

Reassembling

1 Assemble the axle, thrust washers and trunnion without lubricant or shims. Measure the clearance between the lower face of the axle boss and the shoulder on the swivel pin, using a feeler gauge. Subtract .005 in from this clearance figure, and fit shims to the resultant thickness. The shims are available in thicknesses of .005, .010 and .020 in only. Therefore select the nearest

to the required figure, bearing in mind that the clearance must not exceed .005 in. Reassemble the swivel pin with lubricant.

2 Replace the upper arms 31 and 32, refitting the bridge piece and the pin 33. Leave the pivot nuts finger tight until the suspension is back to the normal static position, as will be explained later. Re-connect tie-rod 89. If the front end was dismantled, note that ring 92 is fitted over the inner rubber bush 91. This also applies to tie-bar 51.

3 Before replacing the lower arm 45 at the inner end, slacken the three setscrews which secure the rear bracket to the chassis cross-member. The bracket is shown dotted on the right-hand side of **FIG 8:6**. Locate the arm in the bracket complete with bushes, and replace bolt 46, leaving it loose. Tighten the three bracket setscrews, hold the arm horizontally and tighten the bolt.

4 Replace the coil spring with its flat end uppermost. Turn it about until it seats correctly on the assembly 62. Compress the spring.

5 Fit bushes 50 into the lower eye of the swivel pin and raise the arm 45 into alignment. Position the dowel in tie-bar 51 and insert bolt 46 from the rear. Fit bolt 52 and tighten both bolts evenly so that the dowel is not strained. Refit tie-bar bracket 57 to the body.

6 Remove the spring compressor, jack up the lower arm to compress the spring and replace the damper. Connect up the flexible brake hose, taking care to set it so that it cannot contact the suspension at any position of steering lock or springing.

7 Reassemble the hub. Press the outer bearing in first, after packing it with grease. Turn the hub over, fill it with grease and drop the distance piece 21 into place with the chamfered end touching the outer bearing. Press inner bearing 19 into its housing. Fit the oil seal with its plain side, and washer 17 with its recessed side, away from the bearing. Press the hub on the axle shaft, fit washer 24 and tighten nut 23, locking it with a split pin. Fill cap 22 with recommended grease and tap it gently into place. Refit the brake drum and bleed and adjust the brakes. Replace the road wheel and lower the car to the ground.

Note: The next step is important whenever the rubber bushes in the upper and lower arms have been dismantled or renewed. During the assembling instructions it will be remembered that the nuts on the pivot pins were left loose. Before these are tightened, the car must be standing in a normal static position on the ground. Go over the nuts 34, 47 and 104 until they are all tight. The rubber bushes will then be evenly stressed in both directions when the car is on the road.

Front suspension – 'Oxfords' 11 and 111

The right-hand side of **FIG 8:7** shows the unit in exploded form. In the top left-hand corner can be seen a right-hand assembly viewed from the front. The top wishbone is a pair of arms 38 and 39 bolted together and pivoted on the spindle of bracket 46 which is bolted to the car body. The outer end carries a rubber-bushed link 4 which is threaded internally to accept the top end of the swivel pin 2. The bottom end of the pin screws into link 9 which is rubber bushed and pivoted to the lower arms 56 and 57. The inner end of the rear arm 57 is splined to the front end of torsion bar 87. Both arms are bolted together and pivot on rubber bushes carried in eyebolt 69. The eyebolt is secured to the chassis side member. The rear end of the torsion bar is fitted with a bracket 89 which carries an adjusting screw 95 pressing on a fixed abutment plate 94. Turning the adjusting screw downwards has the effect of putting increased torsion on the bar. This will raise the car body relative to the road wheel. Turning the other way will lower the body. Lubrication is confined to the two nipples on the upper and lower swivel pin links, as shown in **FIG 8:8**.

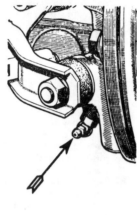

Fig 8:8   Swivel pin grease nipples on 'Oxfords' II and III.

Removing and replacing a front hub

Follow the instructions given for the 'Magnettes' and Wolseley '15/50's' when working on the hubs. The assemblies are, for all normal purposes, identical.

Removing and replacing torsion bars

1 Jack up the car and remove the wheel. Use a second jack to raise the outer end of the lower suspension arm.
2 At the lower end of the telescopic damper 100, remove the parts 107, 108 and 110, pull off the rear bush 106 and release the damper eye from the pivot pin 105. Release tie-rod 76 by removing bolt 79. Remove bolt 65 from the outer end of the arm. Take away the jack supporting the arm.
3 Mark the positions of the torsion bar relative to the lower arm and the rear bracket 89. Use a pencil line on chalk. Never scratch or centre-punch a torsion bar, as this may lead to eventual failure. Remove the retaining plate 97 from the rear bracket and the bolt 90 which secures the bracket to the chassis cross-member. Keep an eye on the abutment pad 94 as it is loose and could be mislaid. Withdraw the torsion bar to the rear.

Note: If both torsion bars are removed, make certain that each bar is returned to its original side. The bars are only interchangeable when new, and become 'handed' when used. Neither are they reversible end for end, as there are 48 splines on the front and 52 on the rear. This permits adjustment during assembly. When rotated one spline the lower suspension arm moves through $7\frac{1}{2}$ degs, whereas one spline of rotation in the same direc-

tion on the rear bracket moves it 7 deg. The effective rotation is thus only $\frac{1}{2}$ a deg which is equivalent to a vertical movement of the swivel pin of approximately 0.1 in.

4 To replace the torsion bar and set it correctly, the car must be standing on a horizontal surface which is flat and smooth. Use the second jack to raise the lower suspension arm to the position C in **FIG 8:9**. At this point the inner pivot should be $5\frac{1}{16}$ in higher than the outer pivot and there will be no load on the torsion bar when it is fitted. This does not apply to the fitting of new torsion bars as they will settle slightly after the car has been loaded. In this case increase the dimension to $5\frac{9}{16}$ in. Refit the bar and adjustment bracket but leave the locking bolt 90 slack, and turn the adjusting bolt 95 right back so that full adjustment is possible. Do not forget the pad 94. Turn the adjusting screw until the lower arm is accurately set to the height given, but do not lock it.
5 Raise the jack under the arm until it is possible to replace the outer swivel pin bolt 65, refit the tie-rod 76, the damper and the road wheel. Lower the car to the ground for a check under load. Unladen, the outer pivot should be at position B, which is $\frac{9}{16}$ in below the inner pivot. The outer pivot will be at position A when the car is fully equipped and carries three passengers. The lower arm is then horizontal. Set the position by turning the torsion bar adjusting bolt and then lock the bolt with nut 96. Do this with the torsion bar unloaded.

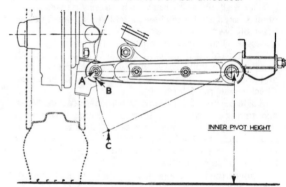

Fig 8:9   Torsion bar settings on 'Oxfords'.

Key to Fig 8:9   A Fully loaded.   B Standing unladen.
C With no load on bar.

Removing and replacing a swivel pin assembly

1 Jack up the car and remove the wheel. Disconnect the brake hose from its bracket by first detaching the pipe line and then unscrewing the large nut, holding the hose hexagon with another spanner to prevent it from twisting.
2 Release the steering tie-rod from the steering arm 33, following the instructions given in the Steering chapter.
3 Jack up the outer end of the lower arm to relieve the load on the pivot bolts 65 and 44. Remove both bolts. Separate the upper arms 38 and 39 by removing bolts 40 and part them enough to release the link 4 complete with bushes and spacer 42. Unscrew the link, recording the number of turns for correct replacement. Take away the swivel pin and lower link.

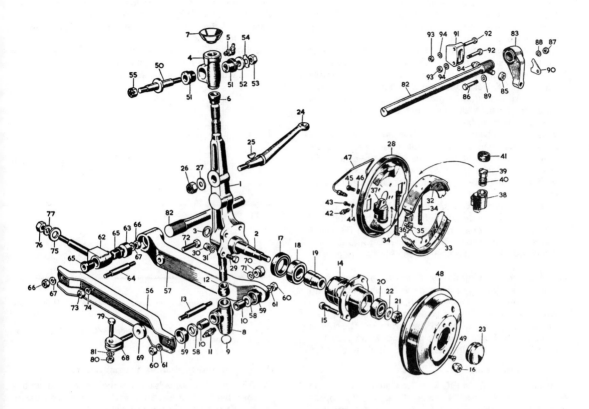

Fig 8:10 Components of a left-hand suspension unit for the Wolseley '1500' and Riley '1.5'.

Key to Fig 8:10 1 Pin—swivel—L/H. 2 Shaft—stub—L/H. 3 Circlip for shaft. 4 Link—upper—L/H. 5 Lubricator—link.
6 Seal—upper link to swivel pin. 7 Plug and stop plate assembly—upper link. 8 Link—lower—L/H. 9 Plug. 10 Bush.
11 Lubricator—lower link. 12 Seal—lower link to swivel pin. 13 Pivot—lower arm—outer. 14 Hub assembly. 15 Stud—wheel.
16 Nut for wheel stud. 17 Seal—hub oil. 18 Bearing—hub inner. 19 Spacer—bearing. 20 Bearing—hub outer.
21 Nut to stub shaft—L.H.T. 22 Washer—bearing-retaining. 23 Cap—oil-retaining. 24 Lever—steering—L/H.
25 Key—lever to swivel pin. 26 Nut for lever. 27 Plain washer for nut. 28 Plate—brake—L/H. 29 Bolt—brake-plate to swivel pin.
30 Nut for bolt. 31 Spring washer for nut. 32 Shoe assembly. 33 Liner. 34 Spring—shoe pull-off. 35 Adjuster. 36 Mask adjuster.
37 Cylinder—wheel—L/H. 38 Body—L/H. 39 Piston. 40 Seal—taper. 41 Boot. 42 Screw—bleeder.
43 Screw—wheel cylinder fixing (small). 44 Spring washer for screw. 45 Screw—wheel cylinder fixing (large).
46 Spring washer for screw. 47 Pipe—bridge. 48 Drum—brake. 49 Screw—drum to hub. 50 Pin—upper link (pivot).
51 Bush—pivot pin (rubber). 52 Washer for pivot pin (rear). 53 Nut—pivot pin to link. 54 Tab washer for nut.
55 Nut—pivot pin to shock absorber arm. 56 Arm—lower—front. 57 Arm—lower—rear. 58 Thrust washer for pivot. 59 Ring—sealing.
60 Nut for pivot. 61 Spring washer for nut. 62 Eyebolt—lower arm to body. 63 Spigot—pivot—rear.
64 Pin—fulcrum—eyebolt to lower arm. 65 Bush—rubber—fulcrum pin. 66 Nut for fulcrum pin. 67 Spring washer for nut.
68 Fork—bolt—tie-bar to lower arm. 69 Plain washer for fork—bolt. 70 Nut for fork—bolt. 71 Spring washer for nut.
72 Screw—front to rear arm. 73 Nut for screw. 74 Spring washer for nut. 75 Plain washer for eyebolt. 76 Nut for eyebolt.
77 Spring washer for nut. 79 Bolt—tie-bar to fork. 80 Nut for bolt. 81 Spring washer. 82 Torsion bar. 83 Vernier bracket.
84 Bolt—vernier bracket. 85 Locknut for bolt. 86 Bolt—vernier bracket to frame. 87 Nut for bolt. 88 Spring washer.
89 Plain washer. 90 Retainer—plate. 91 Abutment bracket. 92 Bolt. 93 Nut. 94 Plain washer.

4 Remove the brake drum and hub. Detach the brake backplate from the swivel pin by removing the four nuts and bolts. This will permit removal of the lower link.

5 Remove the dust seals 64 and thrust washers 63 from the lower link. The spacer 62 has a flat on it for half its length. Turn the flat to face the swivel pin thread, push out the spacer and unscrew the link.

6 Clean the parts and check for wear. Replace rubber bushes and seals which are soft, cracked or worn. The links should be free on the swivel pin without undue slackness. Regular lubrication will reduce wear on the threads so check that the grease nipples and lubricating holes are clear. A small amount of slackness in the threads is permissible.

7 When reassembling, screw on the lower link as far as possible and then turn it back just enough to bring the bolt hole in line with the holes in the lower arm. Fit seal 13 first. Insert spacer 62 and fit thrust washers 63 with seals 64. Check that the thrust washers have smooth parallel faces.

8 Place the lower link in the arm and fit bolt 65. Check the swivel pin for complete freedom on both locks. If satisfactory, the brake plate can be refitted. Fit seal 7 and replace the upper link. Fit the spacer and bushes. Insert bolt 44 leaving the nut loose. Bolt the upper arms together.

9 Connect the steering tie-rod. Connect the brake hose to its bracket, taking care not to twist it while tightening the securing nut. Replace the hub and drum, fit the wheel and lower the car to the ground. Now tighten the top pivot bolt nut which was left loose. The rubber bushes will then be evenly stressed when working. Bleed the brakes as instructed in the Braking chapter.

Telescopic dampers

These are item 100 in **FIG 8:7**. They are not adjustable and defective ones must be replaced. Refer to the appropriate section in the 'Magnette' instructions for details of the test procedure. Remove the damper by taking off the road wheel when it is clear of the ground. Remove the top nuts, washer and rubber bush, close the damper, unscrew nut 110 and pull off the bottom eye. Renew the bushes if necessary and replace the damper by reversing the procedure of dismantling.

Removing and replacing suspension arms

1 Remove bolts 40 and part the upper arms. Unlock tab washers 49 and remove the nuts, washers and rubber bushes. Remove bolt 44 and the arms will be free.

2 To remove the lower arm, pull out the torsion bar as instructed earlier. The arms are parted by removing nut 75 and bolts 58 and 59.

3 Replace the parts in the reverse order, leaving the nuts on the rubber-bushed pivot bolts slack until the car is standing on the ground. Remember to tighten them.

Front suspension – Wolseley '1500' and Riley '1.5'

The components of the system are shown in **FIG 8:10**. The upper pivot pin 50 is secured to an Armstrong damper which is bolted to the bulkhead. The swivel pin 1 is screwed at each end to carry the links 4 and 8. The lower link is bushed and pivoted to the outer ends of arms 56 and 57 which are bolted together. At the inner end the arms pivot on rubber bushes in the eyebolt 62 which is secured to the frame. The rear arm is splined to the front end of torsion bar 82, the rear end of the bar being held against twisting by bracket 83. The position of the bracket is adjustable through bolt 84 so that the suspension can be set accurately. The front hub follows BMC practice and is virtually identical with hubs covered earlier in this chapter. Rigidity of the system is helped by a tie-rod from the fork 68 to the frame.

Lubrication is confined to the threads at the top and bottom of the swivel pin, and oil must not come into contact with the rubber bushes used in the pivots.

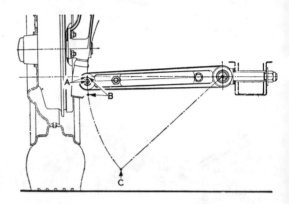

Fig 8:11 Torsion bar settings on Wolseley '1500's' and Riley '1.5's'.

Key to Fig 8:11 A Fully loaded.   B Standing unladen. C With no load on bar.

Removing and replacing a torsion bar

1 Raise the front wheels clear of the ground and remove the wheel concerned. Support the weight of the car on blocks beneath the door sills at the front end.

2 Jack up the outer end of the rear arm 57 until the upper damper arm is clear of the rebound rubber pad. Disengage the tie-rod from fork 68.

3 Remove front nuts 60 and 66, rear nut 70 and bolt 72, so that the front arm 56 can be pulled off. Disengage the swivel pin link 8 from the rear arm and lower the jack until the load is off the torsion bar.

4 Mark the ends of the torsion bar relative to the lower arm and the adjusting bracket 83. Use pencil on chalk and do not scratch or centre-punch the bar at any time as it may lead to failure at that point. At the rear, remove bolt 86 and retaining plate 90. Withdraw the bracket.

5 Pull on the rear end of the bar steadily while a second operator taps the back face of the suspension arm 57 with a soft-faced hammer. Tap more gently as the bar emerges, as it may come away with a rush. Mark each bar if they are both removed, so that they can be restored to their correct sides. This is most important, as the bars become 'handed' in use. They are only interchangeable when new.

6 There are 48 splines on each end of the bar and one spline of movement in the rear bracket moves the swivel pin up or down by $1\frac{1}{2}$ in.

7 Support the car on a smooth level floor and adjust the jack under the lower suspension arm until point C is reached as shown in **FIG 8:11**. The difference in

vertical height between C and the inner pivot bolt should be $7\frac{9}{16}$ in for a bar which has been in service. Increase the dimension to $7\frac{15}{16}$ in if a new bar is fitted, to allow for initial settling.

8 Having set the arm correctly, thread the torsion bar through the cross-member at the rear and bring it forward into engagement with the arm. Position the bracket on the rear splines, lining up the bolt hole with the slot in the cross-member. Enter bolt 86 and plain washer 89 from the front, fit retaining plate 90 and tighten the nut on a spring washer.

9 Raise the jack until the lower link 8 engages the suspension arm. Check that the thrust washers 58 and rubber seals 59 are in position and replace front arm 56. Replace the inner and outer pivot pin nuts but do not tighten the inner one as yet. Replace the tie-bar.

10 Lower the car on to level ground, tighten the pivot bolt nut which was left loose, and check the difference in vertical height between the inner and outer pivot bolt centres. With the car unladen, the outer pivot should be $1\frac{3}{4}$ in below the inner pivot, as shown at B. With a full load of driver, three passengers and full equipment, the outer pivot should be $\frac{3}{8}$ in below the inner one, as at A. Adjust by turning bolt 84 but only when the load has been taken off the bar by jacking up the car and bolt 86 is slack. Check that both right and left-hand suspension assemblies are set at the same height and finally lock the adjusting bolts with nuts 85. Tighten bolt 86.

Removing a swivel pin

1 Raise the front of the car and remove the wheel. Jack up the outer end of the lower suspension arm until the damper arm is clear of the rubber rebound pad.

2 The swivel pin can be removed complete with hub, brake drum and brake backplate, by disconnecting the flexible brake hose. Alternatively, the hub may be pulled off by following the instructions given in the section

devoted to the 'Magnette' and Wolseley '15/50'. The backplate 28 can then be detached from the swivel pin by removing the four bolts 29. The plate must be tied out of the way so that the flexible hose is not strained. This has the advantage that the brakes will not need to be bled during reassembly.

3 In either case the next step is to disconnect the steering tie-rod from the arm 24. Slacken the ball-joint nut till it is flush with the end of the thread, tap round the eye of the arm, using a block of steel behind it as a support and drive out the tapered bolt using a brass drift. Support the arm while doing this. When the tapers have parted, the nut can be removed and the parts separated.

4 Unlock and slacken nut 53 on the top pivot pin 50 and do the same to nut 55 at the front. Tap round the damper arm eye, place a support behind the arm and drive the bolt from its tapered seating with a brass drift. Remove nut 55, support the swivel pin assembly and withdraw pin 50 from the damper eye.

5 Release the tie-rod from fork 68. Remove bolt 72, front nuts 60 and 66, and rear nut 70. The front arm 56 is then detachable. Pull off the swivel pin with link 8 and lower the jack until there is no load on the torsion bar.

Dismantling a swivel pin

1 Remove pin 50 and rubber bushes 51 from the upper link 4. Remove thrust washers 58 and sealing rings 59 from the lower link. Unscrew the links from the swivel pin.

Note: The left-hand swivel pin has left-hand threads at each end. Check the rubber bushes for softening, cracking and wear. The swivel pin links must be free on the pin but without undue slackness. Some extra freedom is permissible in service, but the links must be renewed if wear is excessive. The rubber seals on the lower pivot pin must **not be** perished and the thrust washers must be smooth and flat, with parallel faces. Check that the grease nipples and holes are clear.

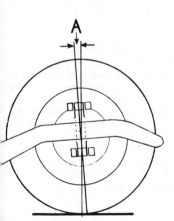 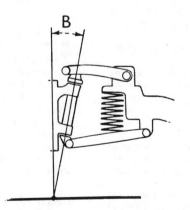 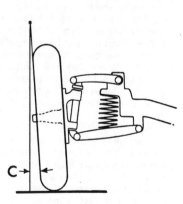

Fig 8:12   Angular settings of front suspension for all models.

Key to Fig 8:12   A Castor angle.   B Swivel pin inclination.   C Camber angle.

Reassembling

1 Notice the waist cut in the screw threads at each end of the swivel pin. This provides clearance for the pivot bolts as they pass through the links. Assemble by first screwing on a link until the pivot bolt hole lines up with the waisted part of the swivel pin. Fit the pivot bolt and screw the link farther on to the thread until it stops. There will be about three revolutions of total travel in the waist, so that the link must be backed off a turn and a half to find a central position where the pivot bolt has maximum clearance. Do this to both links, not forgetting the seals 6 and 12.

2 Remember to fit the swivel pin which has the left-hand threads to the left-hand side of the car. Fit the lower link to the rear arm and replace the front arm, leaving nut 66 loose. Re-connect the tie-rod to fork 68.

3 Lift the outer end of the lower arm after assembling the upper pivot pin 50, but leave nut 53 slack. Fit the pin to the damper arm, tightening and locking nut 55.

4 Replace the steering ball-joint and connect the flexible hose if it was removed. Alternatively, fit the brake back-plate to the swivel pin and replace the hub and drum.

5 Lower the car to the ground and tighten the nuts on those rubber-bushed pivot pins which were left loose. The bushes will then be evenly stressed under road conditions. Nut 53 is pulled up tight against the shoulder on the upper pivot bolt and locked with a tab on washer 54.

Removing and replacing the lower suspension arm

1 Remove the front arm 56, and the torsion bar as already instructed.

2 Remove the rear arm and inspect the rubber bushes. Do not separate the pivot bolt 64 from the rear arm unless it is absolutely necessary as it must always be a tight push fit.

3 Renew the rubber bushes if they are worn and then replace the parts in the reverse order of dismantling. Tighten outer nut 66 when the arm is almost horizontal or when the car is standing in a normal position.

Removing and replacing a hub

1 The hub is similar to the one fitted to the 'Magnette' and Wolseley '15/50' so that the instructions for dismantling and servicing it will be the same. Refer to the earlier section, noting that the axle nut on the left-hand side of the car has a left-hand thread.

2 The brake drum can be removed independently of the hub, by removing the screw 49.

Note: Do not slacken the axle nut 21 after tightening it, in an attempt to line up the slots and the hole for the split pin. Always tighten a little more until the next slot lines up and then fit the split pin.

Hydraulic dampers

These are Armstrong piston types which form part of the upper suspension arms. They are set by the manufacturer and cannot be adjusted. Do not try to dismantle them as it will serve no useful purpose.

Maintenance is confined to topping up with the correct grade of fluid. Before removing the filler plug, clean all round it very thoroughly, so that when it is unscrewed there is no chance of dirt dropping inside the damper. Fill to the bottom of the filler plug hole with Armstrong Super

(Thin) Shock Absorber Fluid No. 624. If this is not available it is possible to use a good-quality mineral oil to Specification SAE 20/20W, although it is not suitable for low-temperature operation.

Testing

Remove the dampers from the car and keep them vertical at all times to prevent aeration of the fluid and possible erratic action. Hold each damper in a vice by the mounting bosses and move the arm steadily through full strokes. There should be moderate resistance throughout. Erratic resistance with free movement may show a need for topping up. If there is no cure after working the arm several times, a new damper is required. Solid resistance indicates seizure or breakage, which also implies a replacement.

Removing

1 Raise the car and remove the wheel. Put blocks under the door sill at the front. Using another jack, lift the outer end of the lower suspension arm until the damper arm is clear of its rebound rubber.

2 Unlock nut 53 and slacken two or three turns. Remove the split pin from nut 55 and drive out the pivot pin from the damper arm after slackening the nut until it is flush with the end of the thread. Use a solid support behind the arm during this operation, and use a copper hammer on the end of the pivot bolt. When the tapers are free, remove the nut and ease away the pivot bolt.

3 Remove the nuts and bolts securing the damper to the bulkhead. Gain access to the nuts inside the car by removing the carpet-covered trim panel. Note the two locking plates under the heads of the bolts.

Replacing

1 Reverse the dismantling procedure. Ensure that the link at the top of the swivel pin is in the correct position by screwing it right down and then backing up approximately one turn so that the pivot bolt lug is facing inwards. Before fitting the pivot bolt into the damper arm, work the arm several times to dispel any air which may be in the fluid. Tighten and split-pin the nut 55, but leave the other nut until the car is lowered to the ground. When tight, lock the nut with the tab washer.

Castor angle, swivel pin inclination and camber angle – all models

FIG 8:12 identifies the above angles as A, B and C. The angles in degrees will be found in Technical Data under each model.

These three angles have an important effect on the steering and riding qualities of a car. As they are the result of machining and assembly during manufacture, they are not capable of alteration by adjustment. If it is suspected that wear or damage is affecting the steering or riding qualities of a car, the angles must be checked against the manufacturer's figures.

Castor angle

Shown at A, this is the tilt of the swivel pin when viewed from the side. The angle can be affected by damage to the upper and lower suspension arms.

Swivel pin inclination

Diagram B shows the tilt of the swivel pin when viewed from the front of the car. This again is most likely to be affected by damage to the suspension arms. The angle can be checked by using an alignment gauge.

Camber angle

This is the outward tilt of the wheel as seen at C. It is roughly checked in the following way. Put the unladen car on a piece of level ground, checking that the front tyres are evenly worn and have the same pressures. Hang a plumb line from the outside tyre wall, vertically above the hub. Measure the distance from the line to the outside wall of the tyre vertically below the hub. This distance must be the same for both wheels. General wear, and damage to the suspension arms, will affect the angle.

Modifications

Magnettes' ZA and ZB, Wolseley '15/50'

From car No. 11192 ('Magnette'), and car No. 21554 (Wolseley) the lower damper anchorage was modified as in **FIG 8:13**. The original loose bolt and distance tube were replaced by eye-bolt assembly ACH.4056. The opposite eye-bolt ACH.4053 had a hole which was chamfered round the inner edge.

Oxfords' 11 and 111

Lower arm extension 68 in **FIG 8:7** was increased in diameter from car No. 161001. The Part No. is ACH.4043. This strengthened part can be used on earlier cars by also fitting larger bushes 133684 to modified eye-bolts ACH.4042.

Later models were fitted with torsion bars of smaller diameter. The dimension is .850 and the bar can be identified by a $\frac{1}{16}$ in step machined in the rear end face. Modified front dampers were also introduced, both changes beginning at car No. 233497 (Saloon only).

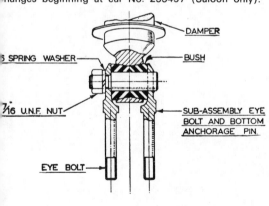

- DAMPER
- SPRING WASHER
- BUSH
- $\frac{7}{16}$ U.N.F. NUT
- SUB-ASSEMBLY EYE BOLT AND BOTTOM ANCHORAGE PIN
- EYE BOLT

Fig 8:13 Modified lower damper mounting — 'Magnettes' and Wolseley '15/50's'.

This affects the settings given for positions A, B and C in **FIG 8:9**. A is fully laden and at the same height as the inner pivot, B is $\frac{11}{16}$ in when unladen, C is the no-load position at 7 in below the inner pivot. When a new bar is fitted, add 1 in to the no-load setting at C to allow for initial settling under load.

The 'Oxford' Traveller up to car No. 274458 retains the larger diameter bars with settings of nil at position A and $5\frac{5}{8}$ in at C.

Wolseley '1500' and Riley '1.5'

The setting of the torsion bars on later models was altered to lower the front end. This improved the appearance and the road-holding capabilities. Refer to **FIG 8:11** and note that the new setting for the laden position at A is $\frac{1}{8}$ in vertically above the inner pivot. Unladen position B is $\frac{15}{16}$ in below the inner pivot, and position C is $7\frac{1}{16}$ in with no load. When fitting a new bar, add $\frac{3}{8}$ in to the dimension for position C to allow for the initial settling under load.

The introduction of Series WHS2 and RHS2 cars led to the riding height being reduced. The rear suspension was lowered by $\frac{1}{2}$ in and the front torsion bar settings altered to bring the front down by the same amount. This means adding $\frac{1}{2}$ in to, or subtracting it from, the figures for A, B and C in the previous paragraph. This will then put position A at $\frac{5}{8}$ in above the inner pivot, B will be $\frac{7}{16}$ in and C will be $6\frac{9}{16}$ in. However, when fitting a new bar, do not add the usual allowance for settling under load, but check the settings after the car has been on the road some time.

Fault diagnosis

(a) Wheel wobble

1 Unbalanced wheels and tyres.
2 Slack steering ball-joints.
3 Incorrect steering geometry.
4 Excessive play in steering gear.
5 Weak front springs.
6 Worn hub bearings.

(b) Wander

1 Check 2, 3 and 4 in (a).
2 Front suspension and rear axle mounting points out of alignment.
3 Uneven tyre pressures.
4 Uneven tyre wear.
5 Weak dampers or springs.

(c) Heavy steering

1 Check 3 in (a).
2 Excessively low tyre pressures.
3 Insufficient lubricant in the steering box.
4 Unlubricated steering connections.
5 Wheels out of track.
6 Incorrectly adjusted steering gear.
7 Misaligned steering column.

(d) Tyre squeal

1 Check 3 in (a) and 2 in (c).

CHAPTER NINE

STEERING

This chapter deals with two quite different types of steering gear. One uses a cam and lever gearbox, the motion being transmitted across the car by jointed tubes and an idler. This type is fitted to Austins 'A40', 'A50' and 'A55'. The other type is known as the rack-and-pinion gear, and this is fitted to all the other cars covered by this book. In this, a pinion which is coupled to the steering column meshes with a rack housed across the car body. Each end of the rack is connected by a side rod to the road wheel steering arm.

The 'A40', 'A50' and 'A55' system

FIG 9:1 is a skeleton view of the layout, and **FIG 9:2** shows the gearbox components. The steering wheel is splined to an inner column at 16, the lower end of the column carrying a cam 27. Rocker shaft and housing 8 moves freely in the gearbox. The housing normally faces left and carries a peg 11 which meshes with the cam. The bottom end is splined to lever 24. Thus, rotation of the cam moves the peg in an arc and the lever follows suit. In **FIG 9:1** the lever is seen connected to the road wheel steering arms by ball-jointed tubes 2, the one on the left being coupled to the right-hand axle. Cross-tube 11 transmits the motion of the gearbox lever to an idler lever which, in turn, is coupled to the left-hand axle by another side-tube.

Maintenance

Lubricate the following points regularly. Six nipples on the side- and cross-tubes, two nipples on the lower wishbone outer bearing, and the four which lubricate the swivel pin bushes. Fill the steering gearbox and the idler casing with the approved oil to the level of the filler apertures. Add a few drops of oil to the felt bush at the top of the steering column.

Side- and cross-tubes

There are two makes of ball-joint connections. Both types are self-adjusting and they are interchangeable when buying spares.

The side-tubes are of unit construction, so that wear in the ball-joints will entail the renewal of the complete assembly. The cross-tubes, however, have separate ball-joint connections with right- and left-hand threads. When locknuts 10 in **FIG 9:1** are slackened off, the tube can be rotated to adjust the wheel tracking. This operation will be described later.

Remove the ball-joint from a steering lever by slackening the castellated nut until it is flush with the end of the ball-pin thread. Tap round the eye of the steering lever smartly with a hammer to loosen the grip of the ball-pin taper. Hold a weight on the steering lever to ensure that it is not bent, and drive the pin free with a brass drift. The nut can now be removed and the connection released. This method will prevent damage to the ball-pin threads.

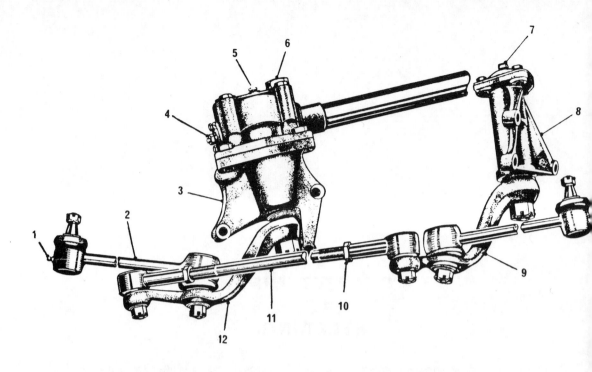

Fig 9:1   Layout of the steering gear on Austins 'A40', 'A50' and 'A55'.

Key to Fig 9:1   1 Lubricating nipple.   2 Side tube.   3 Steering box.   4 Stator tube nut.   5 Adjusting nut.   6 Filler plug
7 Idler filler plug.   8 Idler.   9 Idler lever.   10 Lock nut.   11 Cross tube.   12 Steering lever.

Adjusting the track – 'A40', 'A50' and 'A55'

The wheels must toe-in between 0 and $\frac{1}{8}$ in. Checking is done by using a proprietary alignment gauge or by making a suitable trammel which will provide two adjustable points at centre wheel heights. First set the car on level ground with the tyres correctly inflated. The wheels must be in the straight ahead position. Set the points of the trammel to wheel centre height, place to the front of the wheels and adjust the points so that they touch both wheel rims. Make a chalk mark where the points touch and then roll the car forward for half a turn of the wheels. Move the trammel to the rear of the wheels and try the points at the chalk marks on the rims. To be correct, the points should just touch the rims or be clear by no more than $\frac{1}{8}$ in on one side only. Adjust the steering cross-tube until the tracking is satisfactory. Carry out a check after every adjustment.

Removing steering gear

1 Drain the cooling system and remove the radiator as described in the Engine chapter. Disconnect and remove both battery and tray.

2 Remove the three grub screws from the steering wheel hub. They secure the horn button. Disconnect the horn cable at the bottom of the steering column by separating the nearest snap connection. Unscrew nut 31 in **FIG 9:2** and remove the olive 30. Pull on the horn housing in the steering wheel. This is joined to a small-diameter stator tube which runs down inside the inner column.

Pull steadily until the stator tube is clear of the column watching the cables at the bottom to see that they ar not damaged. Remove the steering wheel nut with felt bush and lockwasher. Withdraw the wheel with suitable extractor. Look out for a spring washe immediately behind the wheel.

3 Looking at **FIG 9:1,** disconnect the right-hand side tube and one end of the cross-tube from the steerin lever 12. From under the bonnet release the steerin gearbox bracket 3 from the car side frame by removin three bolts and a setscrew. Higher up the column on th 'A40' and '50' there is a bracket for the gear chang Take off the cap by removing the two setscrews. Ther is a peg in the cap which fits in a hole in the steerin column.

4 On the 'A55', work inside the car to remove the steerin column cover. Remove the two screws securing th top part of the cover, and the two which hold th lower part to the fascia.

5 On the 'A40' and '50' remove the lower half-cove first. Extract the screw from the top end and the nu from the stud which projects from the pedal casin above the parcel shelf. The upper half-cover is also hel by a bracket and stud at the lower end. The cover i held to the fascia by two setscrews which support th steering column 'U' bracket. In addition there is a singl setscrew and a nut and bolt which secure the handbrak bracket, and these also retain the cover. To extract them the column must be sprung slightly downwards awa

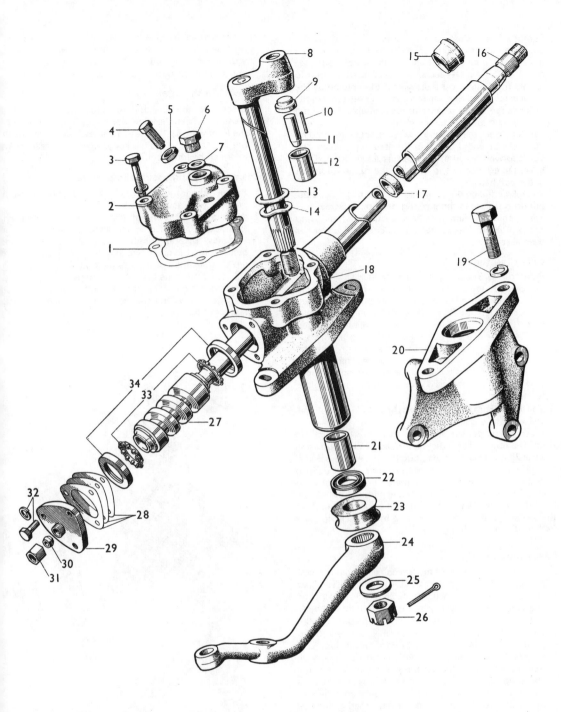

Fig 9:2 Components of the Austin steering gearbox.

Key to Fig 9:2 1 Joint washer. 2 Top cover. 3 Top cover setscrew. 4 Adjusting nut. 5 Lock nut. 6 Filler plug. 7 Washer. 8 Follower peg housing. 9 Thrust cap. 10 Needle roller. 11 Follower peg. 12 Needle roller housing. 13 Flat washer. 14 Spring washer. 15 Column top ball race. 16 Spline for steering wheel. 17 Felt bush. 18 Steering box. 19 Steering box to bracket setscrew and washer. 20 Steering box bracket. 21 Bush bearing. 22 Oil seal. 23 Dust excluder. 24 Steering lever. 25 Plain washer. 26 Castellated nut. 27 Cam and inner column. 28 Adjusting shims. 29 End cover. 30 Olive type washer. 31 Stator tube nut. 32 End cover setscrew and washer. 33 Upper and lower column ball races. 34 Upper and lower column ball race cups.

from the fascia. Before the cover can be removed, the direction indicator wiring must be disconnected at the three snap connectors beneath the fascia and the clamp of the switch mechanism slackened enough to enable the switch to be drawn off the column as the cover is removed. Slacken the clamping setscrew of the gear change upper bracket enough to enable the column to be drawn through the bracket.

6 On all models, the steering gear complete with column may now be withdrawn. Lift the steering gearbox and pull it forward through the aperture above the radiator grille, taking care not to damage the rubber grommet in the bulkhead.

7 To replace the column, reverse the removal procedure, but do not tighten the steering gearbox setscrew and bolts until the column has been secured in the driving position and the upper steering column half-cover has been assembled.

Dismantling the gearbox

Refer to **FIG 9:2** and proceed as follows:

1 Remove the top cover 2 and draw off lever 24 with an extractor. Turn the box over, support it on wood blocks and tap out the rocker shaft 8 using a soft metal drift. The peg 11 runs in a needle roller bearing 10 and 12. Take care of the needle rollers if the peg is removed.

2 Remove the end cover 29. Turn the column with the gearbox uppermost and bump the inner column on a block of wood. This will displace the cam and column 27 with the two bearings 33 and 34. Withdraw from the casing.

3 The top ball bearing 15 is a push fit in the outer column. Pull or prise it out.

Clean the parts and assemble them dry to check for wear. The rocker shaft must be a good fit in the box and the seal 22 must make good contact to prevent oil leakage. Peg 11 and housing 12 must not be worn so that the peg is appreciably slack. Renew if there are ridges or flats. Look also for break-up of the bearing surfaces of the cam 27 and races 34. Renew the parts if there is evidence that the splines on the rocker shaft and in the steering lever 24 have been 'working'.

Reassembling

1 Oil each part liberally. Fit the top ball bearing and insert the inner column with the two cam bearings assembled Fit the end cover 29, using shims 28 to adjust end play. The cam must spin freely without play. A tight assembly will lead to damage of the bearing races by pre-loading.

2 Fit the rocker shaft and peg assembly, slacken off adjuster 4 and refit the top cover with an oil-tight joint washer 1. Screw down the adjuster until there is no free movement of the steering lever in the straight ahead position. The lever is preceded by the dust excluder 23 and is being correctly replaced when its four broad splines mate with similar broad splines on the rocker shaft, in the straight ahead position.

3 Reassemble the steering gear in the car, tightening the bracket fixings last. A final adjustment can then be made. Set the steering in the straight ahead position whenever the adjuster is used to take out backlash. This is because wear in use is greater in the straight ahead position than on lock, and the cam is so made that there is slight end play towards each lock. When

satisfied that there is no backlash and no excessiv
tightness, lock the adjuster with nut 5. Fill the gearbo
with the recommended oil and make one more test t
ensure that the movement is free from lock to lock.

Removing the idler

1 Disconnect the left-hand side-tube and one end of th cross-tube from the idler lever 9 in **FIG 9:1**. Look und the front wing for two nuts and a setscrew which secur the idler body to the car body. Remove these and th idler can be lifted out.

Dismantling and assembling the idler

1 Remove the top cap 2 in **FIG 9:3**, after pulling off th lever 10 with an extractor.

2 Withdraw shaft 6 and after cleaning it, replace it an test for wear. If scored and slack, it may be necessar to renew it, and possibly the bushes 7, which ar pressed into the body. See that the oil holes in the sha are clear, as they pass oil to the bushes.

3 Oil seal 8 prevents loss of oil downwards and can b prised out if defective. It is difficult to do this withou damage, so be prepared to fit a new one by gentl tapping it into place.

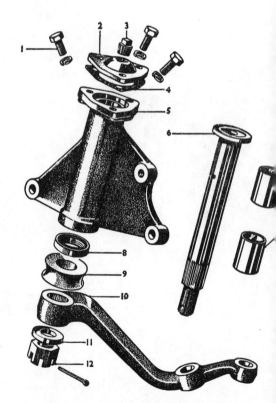

Fig 9:3 The Austin steering idler exploded.

Key to Fig 9:3 1 Cap setscrew. 2 Idler cap. 3 Fille plug. 4 Joint washer. 5 Idler body. 6 Idler shaf 7 Bush bearings. 8 Oil seal. 9 Dust excluder. 10 Idle lever. 11 Plain washer. 12 Castellated nut.

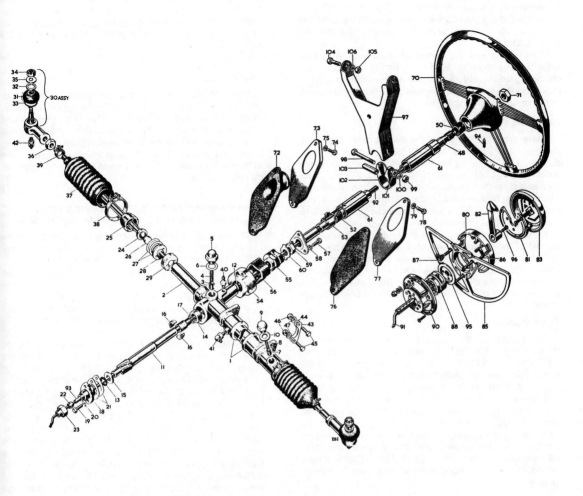

Fig 9:4 Components of the Magnette steering gear.

Key to Fig 9:4 1 Housing assembly—rack. 2 Rack. 3 Pad—rack primary damper. 4 Spring—damper pad.
5 Housing—damper pad. 6 Shim—pad housing. 7 Pad—rack secondary damper. 8 Spring—secondary damper.
9 Cap—damper pad. 10 Washer—pad cap. 11 Pinion—rack. 12 Seal—upper—pinion. 13 Seal—lower—pinion.
14 Washer—upper—pinion—thrust. 15 Washer—lower—pinion—thrust. 16 Collet—taper—pinion. 17 Circlip—pinion collet.
18 Bearing—pinion tail. 19 Screw—tail bearing to rack housing. 20 Washer—spring—tail bearing screw.
21 Shim—tail bearing adjusting. 22 Olive—stator tube. 23 Nut—olive. 24 Rod—tie. 25 Housing—female—ball. 26 Seat—ball.
27 Shim—seat adjusting. 28 Housing—male—ball. 29 Lock washer—male housing to rack. 30 Socket assembly—ball.
31 Boot—rubber. 32 Ring—boot to ball pin. 33 Clip—boot to body. 34 Nut—ball pin. 35 Washer—ball pin nut.
36 Locknut—socket to tie-rod. 37 Seal—rack housing to tie-rod. 38 Clip—seal to rack housing. 39 Clip—seal to tie-rod.
40 Greaser—straight—rack housing. 41 Greaser (67½ deg)—rack housing. 42 Greaser—ball socket. 43 Shim—thick—rack to frame.
44 Shim—thin—rack to frame. 45 Screw—rack to frame. 46 Nut—rack screw. 47 Washer—spring—rack screw.
48 Column assembly—inner. 50 Bearing—felt—upper—column. 52 Seal—felt—column lower.
53 Retainer—column lower seal. 54 Body—column to pinion coupling. 55 Dog—pinion driving. 56 Coupling—rubber—body to dog.
57 Screw—column to coupling body. 58 Washer—spring—column screw. 59 Nut—driving dog to pinion.
60 Lock washer—driving dog nut. 61 Tube—outer—column. 70 Wheel—steering. 71 Nut—steering wheel.
72 Seal—column to dash—rubber. 73 Plate—seal. 74 Screw—seal to dash. 75 Washer—spring—seal screw.
76 Seal—column aperture in dash. 77 Plate—seal—aperture. 78 Screw—aperture seal to dash. 79 Washer—spring—
aperture seal screw. 80 Guide—horn ring. 81 Plate—motif support. 82 Lever—switch. 83 Motif. 85 Ring—horn and contacts.
86 Cushion—horn ring. 87 Spring—horn ring return. 88 Switch—trafficator. 90 Sleeve and horn ring bracket assembly. 91 Cable.
92 Tube—stator—long. 93 Tube—stator—short. 94 Screw—grub—stator ring to steering wheel. 95 Contact—bottom—switch.
96 Screw—lever. 97 Bracket—column support. 98 Bolt—bracket to column. 99 Nut—bracket bolt. 100 Washer—spring—bracket bolt.
101 Washer—flat—bracket bolt. 102 Clamp—steering column. 103 Distance-piece—steering column clamp.
104 Bolt—bracket to body. 105 Nut—bracket to body bolt. 106 Washer—spring—bracket to body bolt.

4 Replace the shaft and fit the top cap, tighten the three setscrews and try the shaft for freedom to rotate without end-float. Adjustment is made by using the joint washers 4 as shims. Replace seal 9 and lever 10.

5 Refit the idler to the car using spring washers under the fixing nuts and the setscrew. Replace the steering connections.

Note: Both steering levers are machined with four broad splines to correspond with similar splines on the steering gearbox and idler shafts. When refitting a lever, make sure that the splines coincide, with the lever pointing in the straight ahead position.

Check on steering arms

These arms are bolted to the swivel axles and carry the outer ball-joints of the side-tubes. Check for mis-alignment by removing the ball-joint from an arm. Place a straight-edge behind and touching, the brake backplate so that it projects alongside the ball-joint end of the arm. The distance between the centre of the ball-pin hole, and the face of the straight-edge which touches the backplate, must be $\frac{3}{8}$ in plus or minus $\frac{1}{16}$ in.

Remove the arm and place a straight-edge through the centres of the securing bolt holes. The distance between the straight-edge and the face of the eye which takes the ball-pin nut, must be $\frac{7}{8}$ in plus or minus $\frac{1}{16}$ in. In the case of the 'A55', the distance between the brake backplate and the centre of the ball-pin hole should be $\frac{15}{16}$ plus or minus $\frac{1}{16}$ in.

Tight steering

The steering column may be pulled out of line. Remove the bottom cover and loosen the supporting bracket under the fascia, letting the column find its free position. If the steering remains stiff, withdraw the stator tube as already described. If the stiffness disappears the stator tube is probably bent and must be straightened or renewed. If there is no improvement, withdraw the steering wheel, check the tightness of the top bearing and renew if necessary. If the bearing is free but the steering remains tight, remove the bearing and see whether the inner column pulls heavily to one side. A slight offset will have little effect, but if the column is seriously bent, it must be renewed.

Loose steering

This is generally due to end play in the column which is adjusted by means of shims 28 in **FIG 9:2**. Check for end-float by disconnecting the side- and cross-tubes from the steering lever 24. Turn the steering partly to the right or left lock and hold the wheel to prevent it turning. Try to turn the steering lever. If the held steering wheel has a tendency to lift, it may be assumed that there is end-float.

The rack-and-pinion steering gear

This is fitted to all the 'Magnettes', the Wolseleys, the 'Oxfords' and the Riley '1.5'. The components of the 'Magnette' assembly are shown in **FIG 9:4**. Apart from minor differences in the shape of rack housing 1 and the position of damper housings 5 and 9, the following parts are similar in all the models-rack bar 2, pinion 11 and tie-rods 24 with associated ball-joints 30.

The principle of operation is that pinion 11 is coupled to an inner steering column 48 which carries the steering wheel. Rack 2 is toothed and is free to slide in housing 1. The pinion meshes with it, and rotation causes the rack to slide to and fro. The ends of the rack are connected to the steering arms on the swivel axles by ball-jointed tie-rods 24. The rubber mounted coupling, items 54 to 60 inclusive, is used on the 'Magnettes' and Wolseley '15/50' only.

Maintenance

The steering gearbox is replenished with the recommended oil through a nipple on the housing. On all models except the Wolseley '1500' and Riley '1.5', there is also a nipple on the pinion housing to lubricate the upper end of the pinion shaft. With the same exceptions, the steering column is carried in two felt bushes which are impregnated with oil and graphite. If they seem to be dry, a few drops of oil can be added.

Removing and replacing the steering wheel -- 'Magnettes' ZA and ZB, and Wolseley '15/50'

1 Disconnect the battery. Disconnect the steering column wiring from the snap connectors on the wing valance and unsolder the end caps from the wires.

2 Slacken the three grub screws 94 in the steering wheel hub. Withdraw the trafficator switch and horn ring taking care that the wires at the bottom end pass smoothly through nut 23. The stator tube 92 will also come away. Remove nut 71 and pull off the wheel with an extractor.

Reverse the process when reassembling, tightening the wheel nut to a torque wrench figure of 500 lb/in. Fit the stator tube 92 so that it engages with the short tube 93 at the pinion end. The short tube is held in place by olive 22 and nut 23. Thread the wires through the tubes until the keys on the switch tube of item 90 enter the slot in the top of the long stator tube. Set the trafficator switch by putting the steering wheel straight ahead and moving the switch lever to the left. Rotate the horn ring clockwise until the lever returns to the central position. Align the horn ring and steering wheels spokes. Tighten the three grub screws, replace the sheathing on the lower end of the wires, resolder the caps and connect to the snap fittings on the valance.

Steering column bushes

These are items 50 and 52. The top one is removable when the steering wheel is off. Coat a new bush with graphite grease and press it down to the circlip in the tube. Renew a bottom bush by removing the steering column as instructed in a later section. Bend up the ears of retainer 53 and remove it. Pull out the bush 52. Fit a new bush after soaking it in graphite grease, replace the retainer and bend down the ears.

Removing and replacing the steering wheel - 'Oxfords' 11 and 111

Follow the 'Magnette' instructions but do not unsolder the end caps from the wires. The stator tube is in one piece, as shown as item 83 in **FIG 9:5** and it will remain in place when the wires are pulled through.

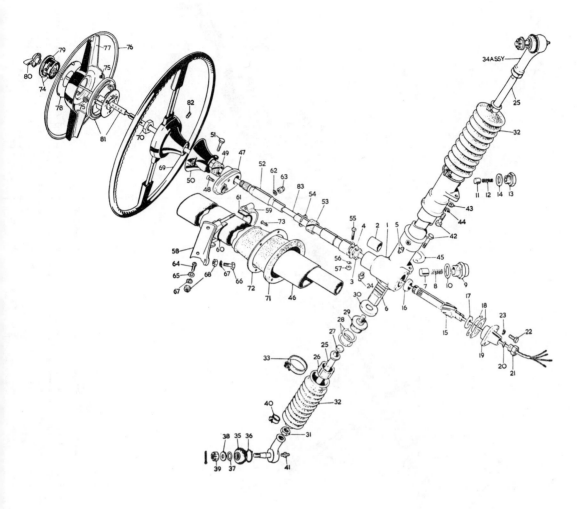

Fig 9:5 Components of the Oxford steering gear.

Key to Fig 9:5   1 Housing—rack.   2 Bush—pinion.   3 Washer—cork.   4 Retainer—cork washer.   5 Greaser—rack.   6 Rack.
7 Pad—damper.   8 Spring—pad.   9 Housing—pad.   10 Shim—housing.   11 Pad—secondary damper.   12 Spring—secondary pad.
13 Housing—secondary pad.   14 Washer—housing.   15 Pinion.   16 Washer—top thrust.   17 Washer—bottom thrust.   18 Shim.
19 Bearing—tail.   20 Olive.   21 Bolt—hollow.   22 Bolt—bearing to gearbox.   23 Washer—spring—bolt.   24 Greaser—steering-box.
25 Rod.   26 Ball housing—female.   27 Seat—ball.   28 Shim—ball seat.   29 Ball housing—male.   30 Washer—male housing locking.
31 Locknut—ball socket.   32 Seal—to rack housing.   33 Clip—seal to housing.   34 Socket assembly.   35 Boot—rubber.
36 Clip—boot to body.   37 Ring—boot to ball pin.   38 Washer—ball pin.   39 Nut—ball pin.   40 Clip—seal to tie-rod.   41 Greaser.
42 Bolt—to member.   43 Washer—bolt.   44 Washer—spring—bolt.   45 Lock plate—bolt—pinion end.   46 Column—outer.
47 Flange—top bearing.   48 Screw—flange to column.   49 Bearing—felt—top.   50 Hub.   51 Bolt—hub clamping.
52 Tube—steering-column.   53 Bearing—felt—bottom.   54 Retainer—bearing.   55 Bolt—column tube to pinion clamping.
56 Washer—spring—bolt.   57 Nut—bolt.   58 Bracket—column support upper.   59 Bracket—column support lower.
60 Packing—upper.   61 Packing—lower.   62 Washer—spring—stud.   63 Nut—stud.   64 Screw—to rail—C/P.   65 Washer—screw.
66 Bolt—to rail.   67 Washer—spring—screw and bolt.   68 Nut—screw and bolt.   69 Wheel—steering.   70 Nut.
71 Cover—rubber—bottom.   72 Retainer—cover.   73 Screw—cover.   74 Switch—trafficator.   75 Spring—horn-push return.
76 Ring—horn-push (Oxford only).   77 Plate—horn bar cover and top contact.   78 Plate—cover—C/P.   79 Contact—horn bottom.
80 Lever—trafficator switch.   81 Plate and sleeve—stator.   82 Screw—to steering-wheel.   83 Tube—stator.

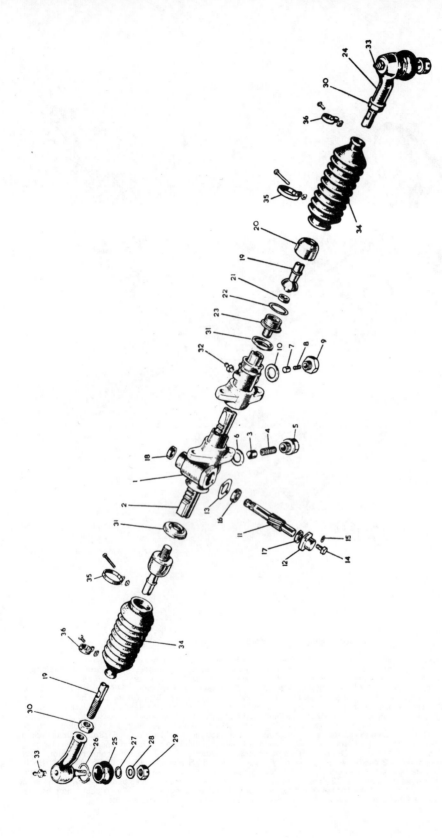

Fig 9:6 Components of the steering gearbox on Wolseley 1500's and Riley 1.5's.

Key to Fig 9:6 1 Housing. 2 Rack. 3 Pad—damper. 4 Spring—damper. 5 Housing—pad. 6 Shim for housing —.003 in and .010 in. 7 Pad—secondary damper. 8 Spring—secondary damper. 9 Housing—secondary damper. 10 Washer for housing. 11 Pinion. 12 Bearing—pinion tail. 13 Shim—tail bearing—.003 in, .005 in, and .010 in. 14 Screw—bearing to rack housing. 15 Spring washer for screw. 16 Thrust washer—pinion (top). 17 Thrust washer—pinion (bottom). 18 Seal—pinion. 19 Tie-rod. 20 Ball housing—female. 21 Seat—ball. 22 Shim—.003 in, .005 in, and .010 in. 23 Ball housing—male. 24 Socket assembly—outer ball. 25 Boot. 26 Clip—boot to body. 27 Ring—boot to ball pin. 28 Washer for ball pin. 29 Nut for ball pin. 30 Locknut for ball socket. 31 Lock washer for ball housing. 32 Lubricator—rack housing. 33 Lubricator—ball socket. 34 Seal—rack housing. 35 Seal for seal (inner). 36 Clip for seal (outer).

116

Removing and replacing the steering wheel – Wolseley '1500' and Riley '1.5'

FIG 9:6 shows that there is no stator tube passing through the pinion shaft as on the previous models. Disconnect the horn wire from the snap connector at the base of the steering column. Remove the two screws from the side of the steering wheel hub and withdraw the horn push. Remove the wheel retaining nut and pull off the wheel with an extractor. When reassembling, tighten the nut to a torque figure of 41 lb/ft.

Removing and replacing the steering column – 'Magnettes' ZA and ZB, Wolseley '15/50'

1 Remove the steering wheel as instructed. Take out the two screws 74 from sealing plate 73 in **FIG 9:4**. Remove the pedal mask. Disconnect and lift out the windshield washer container.

2 Separate the coupling under the bonnet from the inner column 48 by removing the three screws 57. Release the upper clamp 102 on the 'Magnette' and detach the bracket from the fascia on the Wolseley. Remove the column upwards into the body.

When replacing, make sure that the coupling and column are bolted together with the front wheels in the straight ahead position and the steering wheel and trafficator switch correctly positioned.

Removing and replacing the steering column – Oxfords' 11 and 111

When dealing with 'Oxfords' with a central floor gear change lever, ignore any references to the column change control rod assembly and gear shifter lever.

1 Remove the right-hand front wheel. Cut the wire and remove the square-headed screw locking the gear shifter lever 19 in **FIG 6:8** in the Gearbox chapter. Now return to **FIG 9:5**.

2 Disconnect the battery. Detach the wiring snap connectors at the base of the column. Remove screws 73 from the retaining plate 72. Release the cap 59 of the support bracket 58. Remove the bottom clamping bolt 55 from the column.

3 Withdraw the assembly carefully, leaving the stator tube 83 in position. If the tube is removed, oil will drain out. To do this, slacken nut 21 to release the olive 20, withdraw the tube and catch the oil.

When reassembling, turn the road wheels to the straight head position and refit the steering wheel with the spokes horizontal. Align the horn switch bar with the wheel spokes and tighten the three grub screws 82. If the stator tube was removed, leave the olive nut 21 loose, place the indicator switch in the central position, turn the assembly until the lever is vertical and tighten the olive nut.

Removing and replacing the steering column – Wolseley '1500' and Riley '1.5'

Disconnect the battery, and the horn and trafficator wires from the base of the steering column. Remove the clamping bolt from the lower end of the column and release the column support bracket from the fascia.

2 Disengage the splines connecting the column to the pinion shaft and lift the assembly away.

When replacing the column the splines must be mated correctly. Set the road wheels straight ahead and look on the end of the pinion shaft for a mark. This should be at bottom dead centre. Fit the column clamp so that its slot coincides with the pinion mark.

Dismantling the steering column assembly – 'Oxfords' 11 and 111

1 Remove the steering column assembly as instructed earlier, having first withdrawn the steering wheel. Withdraw the inner column 52 with felt bearing 53. The top felt bearing 49 will remain in the flange 47.

2 Slacken clamp bolt 51 and remove the lower hub 50. On later models there is a self-tapping screw into the bearing flange 47. Withdraw the gear lever, control rod, pivot bracket and locating washer as an assembly from the flange. **FIG 6:8** gives details of the assembly in the Gearbox chapter. Remove the flange. References to the gear lever apply only to the column change.

3 Dismantle the gear lever by removing the countersunk screw, pivot pin and shims. Note the plungers and springs shown in the inset to **FIG 6:8**.

Reassemble the steering column as follows:

1 Fit the gear lever with the longest tongue to the bottom. It must enter the slot in the control rod from the side opposite to the recess at the bottom end which locates screw 20 in **FIG 6:8**.

2 Refit the upper bearing flange. Slip the locating washer up the control rod and fit the rod in the flange, followed by the inner column and upper felt bush. Secure the lower hub in position. Check for the permissible clearance of $\frac{1}{32}$ in which is shown in **FIG 6:9**.

3 Thread the cover 71 over the column, with retaining plate 72. Replace the collar, spring and flat washer on the lower end of the control rod. Set the road wheels straight ahead and look for the groove on the end of the pinion shaft 15. Position the column assembly and engage the splines of the inner column with those on the pinion shaft so that the slot in the column clamp is in line with the pinion shaft groove. Push the column down and replace the bolt 55. Secure the column in the upper support bracket.

4 Fit the shifter lever 19 in **FIG 6:8**, locate the register in the control rod and tighten the square-headed screw into it, locking afterwards with wire. Slide the spring collar 16 down the rod until it is about 3 in from the toeboard and tighten the setscrew. Secure the retaining plate over the rubber cover. Check dimension 'X' in **FIG 6:10** in the Gearbox chapter.

The replacement of the steering wheel assembly and wiring has been covered in a previous section.

Removing and replacing the steering gearbox – 'Magnettes' ZA and ZB, Wolseley '15/50'

1 Withdraw the horn and trafficator wiring as detailed earlier. In the case of the Wolseley, disconnect the handbrake cable from the lower end of the relay lever. Remove the three screws 57 in **FIG 9:4**. These connect the inner column to the coupling. Release the sealing plate 73 and the clamp 102. On the Wolseley, detach the upper support bracket from the fascia instead. Raise the column to give access to coupling nut 59.

2 Set the front wheels in the straight-ahead position and mark the coupling body 54 in line with the mark on the

end of the pinion shaft as shown in **FIG 9:7**. This will ensure correct reassembly. Unlock and unscrew the nut 59 and pull off the coupling.

3 Detach the outer tie-rod ball-joints from the steering arms. Take out the split pins and unscrew the nuts until they are flush with the ends of the ball-pin threads. Tap the circumference of each steering arm eye sharply, place a support above the arm and drive each taper pin from its seating. Remove the securing nuts and lift off the tie-rods. Never try to drive out the ball-pins by removing the nut completely and hammering on the threaded end.

4 Remove the four bolts securing the rack housing to the suspension cross-member and lower it away.

Replacement is a reversal of the preceding instructions, but note that the lugs on the rack housing are fitted on the left-hand side of the lugs on the cross-member. This applies to a RHD car. If necessary, fit shims between the lugs where they do not touch, to prevent distortion when the bolts are tightened.

Removing and replacing the steering gearbox – 'Oxfords' 11 and 111

1 Remove the steering column assembly as instructed under that heading.
2 Jack up the car and remove the front wheels. Detach the outer tie-rod ball-joints using the method described in the preceding section.
3 On cars with a column gear change, release the shifter lever and rod assembly from the shifter relay lever and detach the forward end of the selector rod at the ball-joint on the selector lever. To identify these parts, refer to **FIG 6:8** in the Gearbox chapter. Remove the two bolts securing the gear control rod support to the steering rack and remove the assembly complete with the selector lever.
4 Slacken nut 21 in **FIG 9:5** and withdraw the stator tube, plugging the hole in the nut to prevent oil from draining out. Unlock and remove the four bolts holding

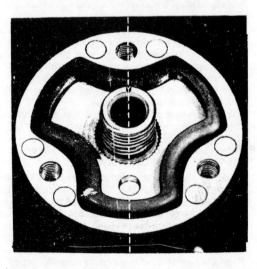

Fig 9:7 Pinion shaft and coupling alignment on 'Magnettes' and Wolseley '15/50's'.

the rack assembly to the underside of the engine bulkhead. Take away the rack assembly. Replace in the reverse order.

Removing and replacing the steering gearbox – Wolseley '1500' and Riley '1.5'

1 Remove the steering column as described under that heading. Remove the outer tie-rod ball-joints according to the 'Magnette' instructions.
2 The rear of the engine must be lowered two or three inches. Disconnect the propeller shaft at the rear axle flange and support it. Jack up the rear end of the gearbox and remove the rear engine cross-member. Lower the rear of the engine a few inches only, do not overdo it.
3 Remove the four bolts, spring and plain washers from the lugs holding the steering rack housing to the body. Withdraw the housing from the front wheel aperture on the right-hand side.

Replacement is the reverse of the removal instructions but do not tighten the bolts securing the rack housing to the body brackets until after the steering column assembly has been fitted and secured to the column support bracket. This ensures that the rack pinion is in line with the column.

Dismantling the steering gearbox – all models with rack-and-pinion steering

There are only minor differences between the assemblies and they do not affect the instructions for dismantling the gearbox. The 'Magnette' exploded drawing in **FIG 9:4** will be used to refer to the parts, and some cross-reference will be needed to identify the same parts on other models, but there should be no difficulty about this.

It will be noticed that it is only on the 'Magnettes' and Wolseley '15/50's' that a coupling is used between the inner steering column and the pinion shaft. On the other cars the column is clamped direct to the shaft. Note also, that the Wolseley '1500's' and Riley '1.5's' have a solid pinion shaft and no stator tube up the column, so that the bottom tail bearing has a closed end.

1 Measure and record the distance from the spanner flats on tie-rods 24, to each of the ball-joint locknuts 36. This will enable them to be reassembled in the same relative positions and save a lot of trouble in re-tracking. Slacken the locknuts and unscrew the ball-joints.
2 Place the rack housing over a container to catch the oil and then remove the rubber gaiters 37 by releasing clips 38 and 39.
3 Unscrew the primary pad housing 5, extracting the spring 4 and pad 3. The pad housing is located underneath on some models. Take special care of any shims 6 which may be fitted. Remove the secondary damper 7 to 10 inclusive. Washer 10 is not a shim except on late Wolseley '1500's' and Riley '1.5's'.
4 From the 'Magnettes' and Wolseley '15/50's', remove the circlip 17 and the split collets 16. The coupling body 54 is located against these collets.
5 Remove the tail bearing 18, preserving the shims 21 carefully. Withdraw the pinion shaft 11 upwards by turning the rack housing upside down. The bottom thrust washer 15 can be lifted off, but the top thrust washer 14 will remain behind as it is trapped by the rack teeth.
6 Hold the rack housing in a vice, using suitable clamps. Tap back the lock-washers 29 to release the ball-joint housing caps 25. These are unscrewed with a 'C

spanner, followed by shims 27. Use a pin spanner to unscrew housing 28. It is possible that the attempt to unscrew cap 25 will result in the whole ball-joint assembly becoming unscrewed from the rack. In this case the joint must be separated by using both 'C' and pin spanners. Inside the joint is the ball seat 26.

7 The steering rack 2 can now be withdrawn and the top thrust washer 14 extracted.

Examination for wear

Clean the parts and examine the teeth of the rack and the pinion for fractures, hollows or roughness of the surface. It is most important that the rubber gaiters are sound as they prevent loss of oil and keep out road grit from the working parts. Check that the grease nipples are not blocked. If oil has been leaking, check the felt seal 12 at the top of the pinion shaft bearing and the rubber seal 13 at the bottom.

The outer ball-joints 30 are not adjustable. Renew them if they are worn. The rubber boot 31 must be sound.

Examine the inner end of the tie-rod 24 and its seating 26. It also seats inside cap 25 and all the spherical surfaces must be smooth and unworn.

Reassembling

There are two ways of meshing the pinion and rack and we will deal with the 'Magnette' and Wolseley '15/50' method first.

1 Replace the thick upper thrust washer 14 into the rack housing with its oil grooves away from the pinion teeth. Replace the smaller thrust washer 15 on the lower end of the pinion shaft with the chamfered edge towards the pinion teeth.

2 The pinion can only be replaced with the rack at the end of its outward movement, as the rack teeth are relieved at this point to give clearance to the pinion. Place the rack in the housing so that its last groove at the inner end is central with the pinion opening. Insert the pinion with the mark on the threaded end at 9 o'clock. Push the pinion home so that the mark finishes up at approximately 8 o'clock. Turn the pinion anti-clockwise by one and two-third turns, which will bring the mark to twelve o'clock and the rack in the straight ahead position. This ensures that the pinion is meshing in the middle of the hardened teeth in the centre of the rack.

3 Replace the tail bearing 18 and adjust the end play of the pinion shaft by means of the shims 21. The play must be between .002 in and .005 in.

4 Fit a new lock-washer 29 to one end of the rack and re-place the ball seat housing 28, tightening it well. Fit the ball seat 26. Slip housing 25 over the tie-rod and screw it tightly home. The joint must be a reasonably tight sliding fit without play. Use shims 27 to adjust for this condition. They are available in thicknesses of .003 in and .005 in. When adjusted, lock the housing cap by tapping the flange of the lockwasher into the 'C' spanner slots. Fit the ball seat at the other end in the same way.

5 Refit the rubber gaiters and clips. Replace ball-joints 30 and locknuts 36, screwing them on until they arrive at their original positions.

6 Adjust the primary rack damper by fitting the housing 5 with plunger 3, but without the spring or the shims. Tighten the housing until it is just possible to rotate the

pinion shaft by pushing the rack through its housing. Then use a feeler gauge to measure the clearance be-tween the flange of the damper housing and the machined seating on the rack housing. Add between .002 in and .005 in to the clearance figure and fit .003 in thick shims to suit, after replacing the damper pad 3 and spring 4. Replace the secondary damper 7 to 10 inclusive. There is no provision for adjusting this one.

7 Pump approximately half-a-pint of approved Hypoid oil into the rack housing through the nipple 41.

Reassembling procedure for 'Oxfords' 11 and 111, Wolseley '1500' and Riley '1.5'

1 Using a new lock-washer, fit and tighten the ball-seat housing 29 in FIG 9:5, into one end of the rack. Re-place shims 28 and ball-seat 27, thread the ball housing 26 over the tie-rod 25 and tighten securely on the male housing. The joint must be a reasonably tight fit, sliding without play. Adjust by means of the shims which are available in thicknesses of .005 in, .008 in and .010 in. When satisfied, lock the female housing in three places by tapping the flange of the lock-washer into the spanner slots.

2 Insert the thicker thrust washer 16 into the rack housing with its chamfered edge towards the rack, and slide the rack into place. Refit the second ball-joint at the other end, adjusting the fit as before.

3 Draw the rack through the housing until the centre tooth is central in the pinion housing. This will be tooth number 14 from either end of the 'Oxford's', and tooth number 12 from either end on the Wolseley's and Riley's. Insert the pinion so that the centre tooth of the rack is in line with the mark on the splined end of the shaft.

4 Fit the small thrust washer 17 to the bottom of the pinion shaft with its chamfered edge towards the pinion teeth. Replace the tail bearing 19 with shims 18, bolting the gear control rod support bracket in place at the same time when dealing with the 'Oxford' assembly which has a column gear change. Check the end-play of the pinion shaft. It should be between .002 in and .005 in, and adjustment is made by means of the shims. They are available in thicknesses of .003 in, .005 in and .010 in.

5 Refit the rubber gaiters and their clips, and replace the outer ball-joints and lock nuts 31. Set the joints in their original positions according to the measurements made when dismantling.

6 Replace the primary damper pad assembly 7 to 10 inclusive, using the method described in paragraph 6 of the 'Magnette' assembly instructions, to arrive at the required thickness of shims 10. Replace the secondary damper 11 to 14 inclusive.

7 Fit a new pinion shaft seal 3 and, in the case of the 'Oxfords', pump about half-a-pint of the approved Hypoid oil into the rack housing through the nipple 5. Alternatively, release one of the outer gaiter clips 40 and pour the oil in through a funnel. Pump in 10 fluid ounces of oil into the Wolseley or Riley housing. Move the rack to and fro to distribute the oil.

Adjusting the track – all models except 'A40', 'A50' and 'A55'

The method is fully described in the section devoted to the Austin range, but the amount of toe-in varies, and the method of adjustment differs.

The wheels must run parallel and have no toe-in on the 'Magnettes' ZA and ZB, the Wolseleys '1500' and '15/50' and the Riley '1.5'.

On the 'Oxfords' 11 and 111, the wheels must toe-in by $\frac{3}{32}$ in. This means that the measurement across the front must be $\frac{3}{32}$ in less than that across the back.

To adjust the tracking, slacken the locknut for each tie-rod ball-joint. The location is shown in **FIG 9:8**. Also slacken the clips round the rubber gaiters and the tie-rods, at the outer ends. Rotate each tie-rod equally in the required direction. As the tie-rods have right-hand threads the effect of screwing them into the ball-joints will be to make the wheels toe-out on the 'Oxfords', the Wolseley '1500' and the Riley '1.5', and to make them toe-in on the 'Magnettes' and the Wolseley '15/50'. There are spanner flats on the tie-rods for easy rotation. Do not forget to tighten the locknuts and gaiter clips.

Important: To ensure that the steering rack is in the central position and that the steering geometry is correct, it is important to adjust the tie-rods to equal lengths. Check this by measuring from the spanner flats to the tightened locknuts on each side.

The trafficator switch can be centralized in the steering wheel by slackening the three grub screws in the hub, and the nut clamping the stator tube at the foot of the steering column. Set the switch and tighten the nut first, followed by the grub screws.

Modifications

'Magnettes'

Later 'Magnettes' from car No. 15545 have a steering rack assembly which is rubber bushed at the mounting points to eliminate noise due to vibration. The rack housing has been modified and the assembly is interchangeable only as a set. Also on later cars, a modified steering rack assembly, Part No. ACH.6144, was introduced to eliminate rattle. The rack, Part No. ACH.6146, had a flat for the damper pad, which needed a modified pad housing, Part No. ACH.8425. The new rack can only be fitted to the original steering rack assembly together with the new pad housing. The change began at car No. ZB.20167.

'Oxfords'

On later 'Oxfords' a modified steering column bearing retainer was fitted. It is item 54 in **FIG 9:5** and was intended to prevent steering column rattle. The new retainer has Part No. ACH.6112, is round in section and is reduced in diameter. When assembling the retainer, which may be fitted to earlier models, make sure that the inside of the steering column tube is free from irregularities. It is also advisable to renew the felt bearing, soaking it in engine oil before fitting.

A modified steering rack assembly was fitted to later 'Oxfords' after car No. 249243, with the object of eliminating rattle. The Part No. is ACH.6141. The rack, Part No. ACH.8424, had a flat for the damper pad which called for a modified pad housing, Part No. ACH.8425. The new rack can only be fitted to the original steering rack assembly together with the new pad housing.

Wolseley '1500's' and Riley '1.5's'

Later cars were fitted with a larger-diameter primary steering rack damper pad and a new damper pad housing to eliminate rattle. These are items 3 and 5 in **FIG 9:6**. If rattle is suspected check the following for tightness: the steering column clamp bolts, the shock absorber mountings, the suspension tie-rod fixings, the steering arm to swivel pin nuts, the steering rack to mounting bracket bolts, and the steering wheel nut. Also check the end-float on the pinion shaft 11. Renew the steering column felt bush if worn.

If the rattle persists, remove the original damper pad housing 5, the spring 4, the pad 3 and the shim(s) 6. Fit the modified pad and housing using the original spring, and screw the housing home until the steering wheel begins to feel stiff in the straight-ahead position. Do not fit the shims. Measure the clearance between the housing flange and the housing face and fit shims to a thickness equal to the clearance plus .002 in. Check the steering wheel stiffness again and adjust if necessary.

A modified secondary damper pad 7 was fitted from Wolseley car No. 67908 and Riley car No. 27569, to eliminate steering rack knock. The pad has a radiused tip of increased diameter and is interchangeable with the superseded part, but if it is decided to fit the new pad it is necessary to use steel shims under the pad housing instead of the fibre sealing washer used originally. This entails following the same routine described when fitting the primary damper, but the thickness of the shims must equal the clearance plus .001 in instead. It is important that the damper is adjusted to the minimum clearance consistent with free rack travel.

Fig 9:8 Tie-rod locknut is arrowed. Slacken both sides to adjust wheel tracking.

Latest cars are fitted with Nylon-seated ball-joints at the outer ends of the steering tie-rods. These are sealed during manufacture and require no further lubrication. It is most essential that no dirt or road grit should get into the joint through a damaged rubber boot, see item 25 in **FIG 9:6.** If such damage has taken place while the car has been used, it is necessary to replace both the ball-joint and the rubber boot. If, however, the boot is torn during an overhaul, only a new boot need be fitted. Make sure that the ball-joint is clean, and smear the adjacent areas with Dextagrease Super G.P. before fitting the boot.

Fault diagnosis

(a) Wheel wobble

1 Unbalanced wheels and tyres.
2 Slack steering connections.
3 Incorrect steering geometry.
4 Excessive play in steering gear.
5 Weak front springs.
6 Loose idler mounting or worn idler shaft.
7 Worn hub bearings.

(b) Wander

1 Check 2, 3 and 4 in (a).
2 Front suspension and rear axle mounting points out of alignment.
3 Uneven tyre pressures.
4 Uneven tyre wear.
5 Weak dampers or springs.

(c) Heavy steering

1 Check 3 in (a).
2 Very low tyre pressures.
3 Neglected lubrication.
4 Front wheels out of track.
5 Steering gear badly adjusted.
6 Steering columns bent or mis-aligned.
7 Steering column bushes tight.

(d) Lost motion

1 End play in steering column.
2 Loose steering wheel, worn splines.
3 Worn steering gearbox and idler.
4 Worn ball-joints and swivel axle.

CHAPTER TEN

THE BRAKING SYSTEM

Operation   Maintenance   Adjusting shoes   Bleeding   Notes on dismantling   Linings
Girling master cylinder   Servicing   Lockheed master cylinder   Servicing   Brake shoes
Flexible hoses   Wheel cylinders   Pipe lines   Handbrake adjustment   Pedal clearance
Unbalanced brakes   Modifications   Fault diagnosis

The instructions given in this chapter will deal with two different makes of hydraulic braking equipment. Austins 'A40', 'A50' and 'A55', and Riley '1.5's' have the Girling system which uses a separate brake master cylinder. The Lockheed system is fitted to the 'Magnettes' and Wolseley '15/50's', using a twin brake and clutch master cylinder with pendant pedals. The Wolseley '1500' has a separate Lockheed master cylinder. 'Oxfords' 11 and 111 have a twin Lockheed master cylinder under the floor.

Description

The principles of operation are the same for both braking systems. The foot brakes on all four wheels are hydraulic-ally operated, being connected by pipe lines to a master cylinder which provides the hydraulic pressure. A reservoir attached to the master cylinder keeps the system full of fluid at all times. Pressure on the brake pedal is transmitted to a piston in the master cylinder, forcing fluid along the pipe lines to the wheel cylinders. Here, other pistons are thrust outwards by the fluid pressure to push the brake shoes into contact with the drums. When the pedal is released, strong springs across the brake shoes push the pistons back into their bores, thus forcing the fluid back into the master cylinder. The handbrake is connected by a mechanical linkage to levers which expand the rear brake shoes only.

Maintenance

Routine maintenance is normally confined to topping up the master cylinder reservoir, lubricating the handbrake linkage and adjusting the brake shoes.

Topping up

In both systems it is important not to let the fluid level in the master cylinder reservoir fall too low. If air instead of fluid enters the pipe lines and cylinders, the brakes will have a 'spongy' feeling. It will then be necessary to bleed the system to get rid of the air. It is also most important to use only the manufacturer's recommended fluid and to be scrupulously clean when carrying out the filling operation. Wipe the filler cap and the adjacent areas so that when the cap is unscrewed, it is impossible for dirt to fall into the reservoir.

On Austins 'A40', 'A50' and 'A55'

Keep the reservoir about three-quarters full, using Girling Crimson Brake Fluid.

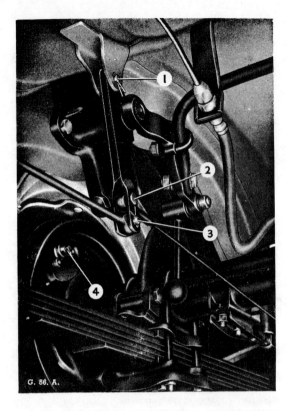

Fig 10:1 Austins 'A40', 'A50' and 'A55'. Oil pivots 1, 2 and 3 regularly. Rear brake adjuster is No. 4.

On Wolseley '1500's'

Use Lockheed Super Heavy Duty Brake Fluid or a fluid to Specification SAE 70.R.3.

On 'Magnettes' ZA and ZB, Wolseley '15/50's' and 'Oxfords' 11 and 111

The reservoir should never be less than half full, or the fluid nearer than $\frac{1}{2}$ in to the bottom of the filler neck. Use only Lockheed Genuine Brake Fluid, or if this is not available, a fluid to the specification SAE 70.R.1.

On Riley '1.5's'

Use Castrol Girling Brake and Clutch Fluid Crimson, and maintain the fluid level so that the reservoir is about three-quarters full. An alternative fluid conforms to specification SAE 70.R.3.

Lubricating

On Austins 'A40', 'A50' and 'A55'

Refer to FIG 10:1 and use the oil can on points 1, 2 and 3. Use the grease gun on nipple 4 in FIG 10:2 and the oil can on the other numbered points.

On 'Magnettes' ZA and ZB, Wolseley '1500' and '15/50', and 'Oxfords' 11 and 111

Lubricate all clevis pins connecting the cable ends to the handbrake lever, balance link and brake levers. In the case of the 'Oxford', the balance lever is mounted on the rear of the axle casing. Oil the top pivot only.

Fig 10:2 Austins 'A40', 'A50' and 'A55'. Use oil can on points 1, 2, 3 and 5. No. 4 is pivot grease nipple.

On Riley '1.5's'

Similar points needing lubrication will be found on these cars in much the same locations as those on the Austins.

Adjusting the brakes

On Austins 'A40', 'A50' and 'A55'

A separate adjuster is provided for each front brake shoe. The locations are shown in FIG 10:3.

1 Jack up the wheel of the brake to be adjusted until it is clear of the ground. Turn both adjusters anti-clockwise until they are fully released.
2 Turn one adjuster clockwise until the brake shoe touches the drum and then back it off until the drum is just free. Repeat with the other adjuster.
3 Spin the wheel to check that the shoes are clear of the drum, and repeat the operation on the other front wheel. It is not advisable to adjust one brake only.

The rear brake adjuster can be seen as number 4 in FIG 10:1. This will adjust both shoes.

1 Release the handbrake after chocking the front wheels and jack up the car.
2 Turn the squared head of the adjuster in a clockwise direction until resistance is felt. Slacken back two clicks and check that the drum rotates freely.
3 Slacken one extra click after fitting shoes with new linings. This allows for possible lining expansion initially. When the linings have settled down, revert to the normal adjustment.

On 'Magnettes' ZA and ZB, Wolseleys '1500' and '15/50', 'Oxfords' 11 and 111

1 Jack up a front wheel and remove the hub cap. In the case of the Wolseley '1500', also remove the wheel and a metal plug in the brake drum.
2 Turn the wheel until one of the adjustment screws can be seen through the hole in the wheel and drum. On the Wolseley '1500' just turn the drum.

3 Using a screwdriver, turn the screw clockwise until the drum is locked solid, then turn it back one notch only. Rotate the wheel through half a turn and adjust the second screw in the same way. Spin the wheel to check that the shoes do not rub and repeat the operation on the other front wheel.

Use the same method to adjust the rear brakes but note that there is only one adjuster to each brake. When this is correctly set, it will also bring the handbrake into adjustment.

Note: Even and efficient braking is best achieved by adjusting all four brakes in one complete operation.

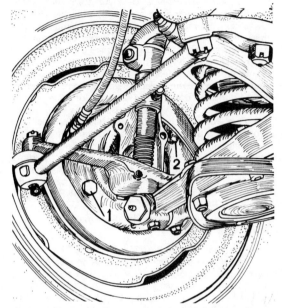

Fig 10:3 Austins 'A40', 'A50' and 'A55'. Front brake adjusters 1 and 2.

On Riley '1.5's'

1 Refer to **FIG 10:4** to identify the two square-headed adjusters on one of the front brakes. Jack up the wheel and turn one of the adjusters clockwise until the drum is locked. Slacken it off two 'clicks', which should then free the drum.
2 Repeat the adjustment on the other shoe and spin the wheel to check that the shoes do not rub anywhere.
3 Do the other front wheel. It is never advisable to do just one wheel alone.

On the rear brakes there is only one adjuster to each brake. Set this in the same way.

Note: If the car is fitted with wheels which have a hole for brake adjustment, line up this hole with the one in the drum whenever the wheel is removed and replaced.

On some models with holes in both wheel and drum, a seal was fitted between the two to prevent the ingress of dust and water into the brake. These seals are a loose fit when the wheel is removed and may drop out, but they are secure when the wheel is on. They may be fitted to existing vehicles which are without them.

Fig 10:4 Riley '1.5'. Front brake adjusters 1 and 2, shoe steady post 3.

Bleeding the brakes

The method described is suitable for all systems.
1 Fill the master cylinder with the approved fluid as specified in the section on topping up. Keep it at least half-full during the operation, otherwise air will be drawn into the system, necessitating a fresh start.
2 Slacken off the front and rear brake adjusters to allow the shoe springs to push the pistons into the cylinder bores, leaving a minimum space for air or fluid. Also release the handbrake.

Note: On Girling rear brakes fitted to the Austins and the Riley '1.5', turn the adjuster fully clockwise which will lock the drum and push the piston into the bore.
3 Behind each brake backplate will be found bleed screws which look rather like grease nipples. Clean them thoroughly. They screw into the wheel cylinder housings, and there will be one for each front brake and one for each rear brake.
4 Attach a length of rubber tubing to the bleed screw farthest from the master cylinder and submerge the free end in a small quantity of brake fluid in a clean glass jar. Open the bleed screw a little less than a turn.
5 A second operator will be needed to depress the brake pedal through a fast full stroke, allowing it to return freely. Let him repeat the process while the other operator watches the flow of fluid into the jar. When air bubbles cease to appear from the tube, close the bleeder screw during a last slow pedal application. It is important not to over-tighten the bleed screws.
6 If the bleeding of any one cylinder continues without success for some time, it is possible that air is being drawn in past the bleeder screw threads. In such a case, tighten the bleeder screw at the end of each down stroke of the pedal and allow the pedal to return fully before reopening it. Close it finally during the last pedal operation.
7 Repeat the operation on each wheel, finishing at the wheel nearest to the master cylinder. When satisfied, adjust all the brakes and top up the master cylinder to the correct level.

Important: Dirty fluid must be discarded. Clean fluid bled from the system will be aerated and it must stand for at least 24 hours before it can be used again.

If a braking system needs frequent bleeding, look for fluid leakage at pipe unions, and suspect failure of the seals in the master cylinder or wheel cylinders. All evidence of fluid leakage must be given immediate attention.

Notes on dismantling – all systems

The following points are made here to avoid unnecessary repetition when dealing with individual systems.

1 Always exercise extreme cleanliness when dealing with any part of the hydraulic system. Do **not** clean the rubber parts with anything but the approved brake fluid, used in a clean container. Do not use a receptacle which has been washed with trichlorethylene.

2 Do not handle any rubber or internal parts with greasy hands or greasy rags. Keep the hands clean at all times.

3 Take care not to scratch the highly polished surfaces of cylinder bores or pistons. Leakage past the pistons in hydraulic cylinders is prevented by rubber seals or cups. These have a raised lip which presses firmly against the polished cylinder bore. The lip faces fluid pressure, and the greater the pressure, the firmer the seal. Damaged bores and dirt in the fluid will prevent this perfect seal. Therefore wash off all outside dirt before dismantling.

4 Examine all rubber seals, hoses and other parts for damage, and renew all unserviceable parts. It is always advisable to renew every seal when the system is being overhauled. The necessary parts can be bought in complete sets.

5 To avoid damage, remove and replace all seals with the fingers. Start reassembly by wetting all internal parts with the approved brake fluid. Replace the rubber piston seals by first entering the raised lip into the cylinder bore, making sure that it is not trapped or turned back on itself.

6 On Girling brakes, use Girling Rubber Grease No. 3 (Red) for packing rubber boots and dust covers, or for lubricating any parts which may contact rubber components. Never use Girling White Brake Grease for these purposes.

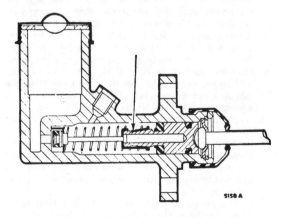

SISB A

Fig 10:5 Section of Girling master cylinder. Thimble leaf is arrowed.

7 **Important:** If the brake shoes are removed from the backplate at any time, be very careful not to depress the brake pedal or the wheel cylinder pistons will be forced out of their bores. It is a good plan to prevent this by wiring the pistons or by fitting a clamp over them. A warning notice can also be placed on the pedal, especially if the car is to be left without brake shoes for some time.

Brake linings

Always use the correct grade of brake lining material as specified by the manufacturer. The right material for each model is listed in Technical Data. As replacement shoes with linings properly fitted are readily available, it is not advisable to attempt the re-lining process. When expertly fitted, the linings are firmly bedded down, and ground so that they are concentric with the brake drums. They will then quickly settle down into full contact. Linings which are not perfectly bedded down on the shoes will give a 'spongy' feeling to the brakes. Always fit complete sets of shoes, with the correct grade of lining, or there may be trouble with out-of-balance effects. Shoes with linings which are worn thin, or which have been in contact with oil or grease, must be renewed. It is useless to try to clean oily linings as nothing permanent can be done. Before fitting shoes which have new linings, slacken the brake adjusters right off and release the handbrake. After fitting the shoes and adjusting the brakes, run the car until the brakes have had several hard prolonged applications, and then adjust the brakes again.

The Girling master cylinder – Austins 'A40' 'A50', 'A55' and Riley '1.5'

This is shown in section in **FIG 10:5**. The reservoir is to the left and the push-rod which is connected to the brake pedal lever is on the right. The push-rod acts on a piston which is provided with two rubber seals to prevent fluid leaking past. The piston is pressed to the right by a spring. A valve with a long stem can be seen inside the spring, the right-hand end of the stem being free to slide in the piston. The valve head on the left is fitted with a rubber seal, and in the position shown the valve is slightly open so that fluid in the reservoir can flow into the cylinder bore. When the brake pedal is depressed the push-rod moves the piston to the left and a domed spring washer under the valve head presses the valve seal to the left also. This closes the port into the reservoir and further movement of the piston forces fluid up the angled outlet seen above the bore, and so to the brake pipe lines and wheel cylinders. Fluid is not normally used up unless there is leakage somewhere, the object of the port from the reservoir opening at the end of the return stroke is to ensure that the system is full of fluid at all times.

Removing and dismantling the master cylinder – Austins 'A40', 'A50' and 'A55'

1 Inside the car, remove the cover over the pedal levers just above the parcel shelf. This will expose the clevis pin and circlip linking the push-rod and fork 12 to the brake pedal lever, see **FIG 10:6**. Later models have a split pin instead of a circlip. Remove the clevis pin.

2 It makes things easier to remove the battery and tray. Working under the bonnet, disconnect the pipe union from the master cylinder 3. Remove the two securing bolts from the cylinder flange and withdraw the unit. Carefully preserve the packing pieces which will be

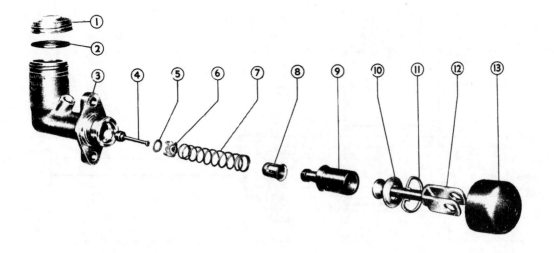

Fig 10:6   Girling master cylinder components.

Key to Fig 10:6   1 Filler cap.   2 Washer.   3 Master cylinder.   4 Valve stem.   5 Spring washer.   6 Valve spacer
7 Return spring.   8 Thimble.   9 Plunger.   10 Dished washer.   11 Circlip.   12 Fork.   13 Dust cover.

found under the flange as these must be replaced in order to set the pedal clearance correctly.

3 Drain the fluid from the reservoir. Pull back dust cover 13 and remove the circlip 11 with long-nosed pliers. Remove the push-rod. Pull out the plunger with its rubber seals, and parts 4 to 8 will come with it.

4 Thimble 8 has a leaf on it which is shown as item 2 in **FIG 10:7.** Lift this leaf and slide the thimble off the plunger stem. Depress the plunger return spring 7 to allow the valve stem 4 to slide out through the elongated hole in the thimble. The tension on the spring will then be released.

5 Remove the spring, the valve spacer 6 and domed spring washer 5. Remove the rubber seal from the valve head, using the fingers.

Clean the parts according to the instructions given under the heading 'Notes on dismantling'.

Reassembling

1 Wet all the internal parts with approved brake fluid. Replace the valve seal on the head of the valve stem 4, being careful to seat the flat side on the valve head.

Locate spring washer 5 with the domed side against the underside of the valve head, as shown in **FIG 10:8.**

2 Fit the valve spacer 6 with its legs facing towards the valve seal. Replace the return spring centrally on the spacer, insert the thimble in the other end and depress the spring until the valve stem can be entered into the elongated hole in the thimble. Check that the stem is central in the thimble, and that the spring is still centrally disposed on the spacer.

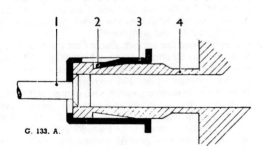

Fig 10:7   Thimble fixing on Girling master cylinder plunger.

Key to Fig 10:7   1 Valve stem.   2 Thimble leaf.   3 Thimble.
4 Plunger.

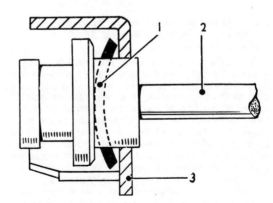

Fig 10:8   Location of domed washer under valve head in Girling master cylinder.

Key to Fig 10:8   1 Washer.   2 Valve stem.   3 Valve spacer.

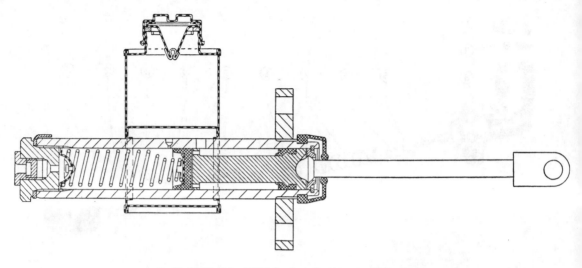

Fig 10:9   Wolseley '1500'. Section of Lockheed master cylinder.

3 Fit the seal to plunger 9 with its flat face against the inner face of the plunger. Some models may have two seals on the plunger. The lips of the seals always face into the bore.

4 Insert the small end of the plunger into the thimble, pushing it home until the leaf can be pressed down behind the shoulder on the end. Refit the push-rod and dust cover.

5 Fill the reservoir with fluid and press the push-rod inwards for one or two complete strokes until fluid flows from the outlet. Replace the completed cylinder on the bulkhead, putting the packing pieces back under the mounting flange. Connect up the pipe line and the push-rod and bleed the system according to the instructions under that heading.

Removing and dismantling the master cylinder – Riley '1.5'

As this is also a Girling system and almost identical with that fitted to the Austins covered in the preceding section, those instructions should be followed.

The Lockheed master cylinder – 'Magnettes' ZA and ZB, Wolseleys '1500' and '15/50', 'Oxfords' 11 and 111

The master cylinder section in **FIG 10:9** is a single-unit type as fitted to the Wolseley '1500', but the internal arrangement of the parts is similar in the twin-bore units fitted to the other models. Note also that the type of reservoir shown fitted to the cylinder is the one for a single-bore installation, the reservoir being part of the body casting in the twin-bore type. The cylinder bore contains a bobbin-like piston provided with rubber seals to prevent fluid leakage. This appears at the right-hand end of the bore in the illustration. The push-rod transmits movement of the brake pedal lever to the piston. When the pedal is released, a spring returns the piston to the position shown. Just in front of the left-hand seal of the piston is a small hole leading into the reservoir. This allows fluid to enter the cylinder bore. A larger hole to the right lets fluid into the annular space round the piston and between the seals.

Pressure on the brake pedal moves the piston to the left, closing the small port. Further application of the pedal will force fluid past the check valve on the left, through the pipe lines and so to the wheel cylinders. Spring action returns the piston when the pedal is released. Pressure from the brake shoe return springs on the wheel cylinder pistons will then force the fluid back into the master cylinder past the check valve. Note that on some models this valve may differ in design and will have a rubber seat. It can be seen as items 69, 70 and 71 in **FIG 10:10**. However, a rapid return of the piston may create a vacuum in the master cylinder. This is filled by fluid from the annulus round the piston. The vacuum causes the main piston seal to collapse and allow fluid to pass through small holes drilled in the piston head. This additional fluid will eventually return into the reservoir when the small port is uncovered by the fully-returned piston. The purpose of the check valve is to prevent fluid from re-entering the master cylinder bore during the operation of bleeding the brakes. This ensures a fresh charge of fluid at each stroke of the brake pedal.

Removing and dismantling the master cylinder – 'Magnettes' ZA and ZB, Wolseley '15/50'

1 Working inside the car, remove the pedal mask. Disconnect the clutch and brake pedal return springs 14 in **FIG 10:10**. Remove the pedal pivot bolt 9 and the distance pieces. Withdraw the pedals complete with rubber boots 79 and push-rods 78.

2 Working under the bonnet, disconnect the pipe lines from adaptors 89 and 92. Remove bolts 98 and 99 from bracket 95, releasing the master cylinder unit. The rear bolt has a distance piece 102 on each side of the unit.

3 Drain the fluid reservoir and remove end plate 80. The right-hand, or brake bore can be serviced alone, if the clutch system does not require overhaul. The brake bore is fitted with check valve parts 69, 70 and 71. The other numbered internal parts are for the clutch bore as illustrated, but they will be found to be identical in the brake bore.

4 With the fingers, peel off secondary cup 76 from piston 74. Note washer 77.

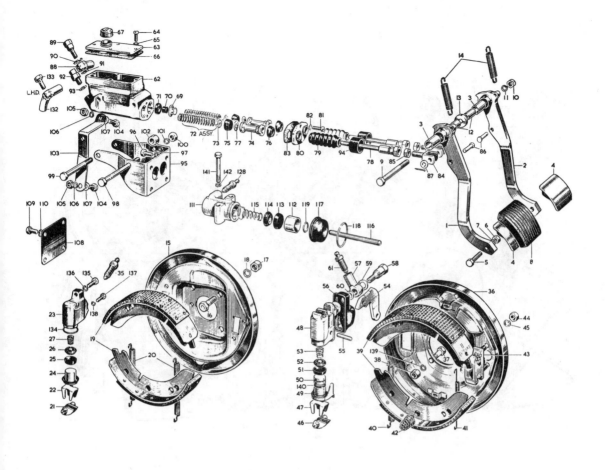

Fig 10:10 Brake components and twin Lockheed master cylinders on 'Magnettes'.

Key to Fig 10:10 1 Pedal—clutch—R.H.D. 2 Pedal—brake—R.H.D. 3 Bush. 4 Pad—pedals. 5 Screw—pad to pedal.
6 Nut—screw. 7 Spring washer—nut. 8 Rubber—pedal pad. 9 Bolt—pedals to body. 10 Nut—bolt. 11 Spring washer—bolt.
12 Distance-piece—pedals. 13 Washer—distance—pedals. 14 Spring—pedal return. 15 Plate—L/H—front brake.
16 Bolt—plate to stub axle. 17 Nut—bolt. 18 Spring washer—bolt. 19 Shoe—lined—brake. 20 Spring—shoe pull-off. 21 Adjuster.
22 Mask—adjuster. 23 Body—L/H. 24 Piston and dust cover. 25 Cup—piston. 26 Filler—piston cup. 27 Spring—filler.
35 Screw—bleeder. 36 Plate—L/H—rear brake. 37 Bolt—plate to axle. 38 Nut—bolt. 39 Shoe—lined—brake.
40 Spring—shoe pull-off. 41 Spring—shoe tension. 42 Spring—shoe steady. 43 Abutment strip—brake-shoe.
44 Nut—abutment strip. 45 Spring washer. 46 Adjuster. 47 Mask—adjuster. 48 Body—with abutment strip.
49 Piston with dust cover. 50 Piston—hydraulic. 51 Cup—piston. 52 Filler—cup. 53 Spring—filler. 54 Lever—hand brake.
55 Pin—lever. 56 Boot—hydraulic cylinder. 57 Banjo connection—wheel cylinder. 58 Bolt—banjo connection.
59 Gasket—banjo connection—large. 60 Gasket—banjo connection—small. 61 Screw—bleeder. 62 Body—master cylinder.
63 Cover—body—master cylinder. 64 Screw—body to cover. 65 Shakeproof washer—screw. 66 Gasket—cover to body.
67 Cap—filler assembly. 69 Body—valve. 70 Cup. 71 Seat. 72 Spring—piston return. 73 Retainer. 74 Piston.
75 Cup—piston—primary. 76 Cup—piston—secondary. 77 Washer—primary cup to piston. 78 Push-rod.
79 Boot—push-rod to cylinder. 80 Plate—boot fixing. 81 Screw—plate. 82 Shakeproof washer—screw. 83 Gasket—fixing plate.
84 Yoke—push-rod to pedal. 85 Locknut—yoke. 86 Pin—clevis—yoke. 87 Washer—plain—clevis pin.
88 Banjo connection—master cylinder—R.H.D. 89 Bolt—banjo connection—R.H.D. 90 Gasket—banjo connection—large.
91 Gasket—banjo connection—small. 92 Adaptor—master cylinder—clutch. 93 Gasket—clutch master cylinder.
94 Seal—master cylinder to dash. 95 Bracket—cylinder to dash. 96 Screw—bracket to dash. 97 Spring washer—screw.
98 Bolt—long—master cylinder to bracket. 99 Bolt—short—master cylinder to bracket. 100 Nut—bolts. 101 Spring washer—bolts.
102 Spacer—bolt. 103 Stay—support—master cylinder. 104 Screw—stay to valance. 105 Nut—screw. 106 Spring washer.
107 Washer—plain. 108 Plate—blanking—master cylinder hole. 109 Screw—plate to dash. 110 Spring washer—screw.
111 Body—clutch cylinder. 112 Piston. 113 Cup—piston. 114 Filler—piston cup. 115 Spring—cup filler. 116 Push-rod. 117 Boot.
118 Clip—boot to cylinder. 119 Clip—boot to push-rod. 128 Screw—bleeder. 132 Banjo connection—master cylinder—L.H.D.
133 Bolt—banjo connection—L.H.D. 134 Sealing ring. 135 Bolt—cylinder to brake plate ($\frac{7}{16}$ in). 136 Spring washer—bolt.
137 Bolt—cylinder to brake plate ($\frac{1}{4}$ in). 138 Spring washer—bolt. 139 Spring washer. 140 Seal. 141 Bolt—slave cylinder to
clutch housing. 142 Spring washer—bolt.

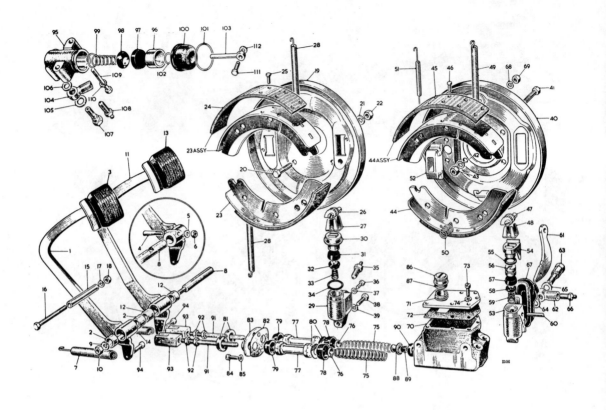

Fig 10:11 Brake components and twin Lockheed master cylinders on Oxfords.

Key to Fig 10:11 1 Pedal—clutch. 2 Bush. 3 Pad—rubber. 4 Cotter. 5 Washer—cotter. 6 Nut—cotter. 7 Spring—return. 8 Shaft—pedal. 9 Washer—spring—nut. 10 Nut. 11 Pedal—brake. 12 Bush. 13 Pad—rubber. 14 Spring—return. 15 Tube—distance stop. 16 Bolt—stop tube to frame. 17 Washer—spring—bolt. 18 Nut—bolt. 19 Plate—L/H front brake. 20 Bolt—to swivel pin. 21 Washer—spring—bolt. 22 Nut—bolt. 23 Shoe assembly—brake. 24 Liner. 25 Rivet—liner. 26 Adjuster. 27 Mask—adjuster. 28 Spring—pull-off. 29 Body—L/H. 30 Piston with dust cover. 31 Cup. 32 Filler—cup. 33 Spring—cup filler. 34 Ring—sealing. 35 Screw—bleeder. 36 Screw—to brake plate—small. 37 Washer—spring—screw. 38 Screw—to brake plate—large. 39 Washer—spring—screw. 40 Plate—L/H rear brake. 41 Bolt—to axle. 42 Washer—spring—bolt. 43 Nut—bolt. 44 Shoe assembly—brake. 45 Liner. 46 Rivet—liner. 47 Adjuster. 48 Mask—adjuster. 49 Spring—pull-off. 50 Spring—steady. 51 Spring—tension. 52 Block—abutment. 53 Body with abutment strip. 54 Piston with dust cover. 55 Seal—piston. 56 Piston—hydraulic. 57 Cup—piston. 58 Filler—cup. 59 Spring—cup filler. 60 Pin—hand brake lever pivot. 61 Lever—hand brake. 62 Connection—banjo. 63 Bolt—banjo. 64 Gasket—small—bolt. 65 Gasket—large—bolt. 66 Screw—bleeder. 67 Boot—rubber. 68 Washer—spring—nut. 69 Nut—to brake plate. 70 Body—cylinder and supply tank. 71 Cover—body. 72 Gasket—cover. 73 Screw—cover to body. 74 Washer—shakeproof—screw. 75 Spring—piston return. 76 Retainer—spring. 77 Piston. 78 Cup—primary—piston. 79 Cup—secondary—piston. 80 Washer—primary cup to piston. 81 Boot—push-rod. 82 Gasket—boot fixing plate. 83 Plate—boot fixing. 84 Screw—plate. 85 Washer—shakeproof—screw. 86 Cap—filler. 87 Seal. 88 Body—valve. 89 Cup. 90 Washer. 91 Push-rod. 92 Nut—locking. 93 Yoke. 94 Pin—clevis—yoke to pedal. 95 Body—clutch cylinder. 96 Piston. 97 Cup—piston. 98 Filler—piston cup. 99 Spring—cup filler. 100 Boot. 101 Clip—large—boot. 102 Clip—small—boot. 103 Push-rod. 104 Connection—banjo. 105—Gasket—connection—large. 106 Gasket—connection—small. 107 Bolt—connection. 108 Screw—bleeder. 109 Bolt—to gearbox. 110 Washer—spring—bolt. 111 Pin—clevis—push-rod to clutch lever. 112 Washer—pin.

Reassembling

Clean and check everything after reading 'Notes on dismantling'.

1 Stretch the secondary cup over the push-rod end of the piston with its lip facing forward or into the bore of the cylinder. Work the cup gently into the piston groove with the fingers until it is properly seated.

2 Press cup 70 into valve body 69 and insert the assembly into the spring. Retainer 73 must be in position at the other end. Push valve seat 71 down the bore, then the valve with the spring trailing.

3 Insert primary cup 75 lip first, pressing it down to the spring retainer. Drop in the cup washer 77, concave side forward, and insert the piston, taking special care of the lip on the secondary cup. Push the piston down the bore. Check that the clutch bore is complete and refit the cover 80. Fill the reservoir with approved fluid and push the pistons down the bores, allowing them to return. After one or two strokes, fluid should flow from the outlets.

4 If the adaptors 89 and 92 were removed, refit them and tighten down securely on the copper washers. Washer 90 is larger than washer 91. During this, set the banjo 88 in the correct position.

5 Replace the unit by reversing the removal instructions. Connect the brake and clutch pipe lines, check that the brakes are properly adjusted and bleed them by following the instructions given under that heading. As there will also be air in the clutch system it must be bled according to the instructions in the Clutch chapter. Note that the Wolseley '15/50' clutch slave cylinder differs from the one shown with body 111 in **FIG 10:10**.

Removing and dismantling the master cylinder – Wolseley '1500'

1 Remove the circlip and withdraw the clevis pin securing the master cylinder push-rod to the brake pedal lever.

2 Under the bonnet, disconnect the pipe union from the end of the master cylinder. Remove the two bolts securing the cylinder flange to the bulkhead and withdraw the unit complete. Look out for packing washers under the flange.

3 Dismantle the unit by following the instructions given for the twin-bore master cylinder in the preceding section for the 'Magnettes' and other models. Any reference to the check valve parts 69, 70 and 71 should be ignored. The Wolseley '1500' check valve is a dome drilled with holes and fitted with a rubber seal on the concave side, as can be seen on the left in **FIG 10:9**.

4 Clean and reassemble the parts after referring to the section called 'Notes on dismantling'. Replace the unit in the reverse order of dismantling, then adjust and bleed the brakes by following the instructions given in the appropriate sections.

Removing and dismantling the master cylinder – 'Oxfords' 11 and 111

1 Refer to **FIG 10:11** which shows the components of the 'Oxford' master cylinder and brakes. The master cylinder is located under the floor on the driver's side, beneath a plate which is held down by six or eight screws according to the model. A hole in the plate gives access for topping up.

2 Remove the plate, and then work under the car to remove the clevis pins 94. This will disconnect the push-rods 91 from the pedal levers. Disconnect the pipe lines from the rear of the master cylinder body 70.

3 Remove the bolts securing the cross-member and the master cylinder. Lift out the unit together with the push-rods.

To dismantle the master cylinder, refer to the section which gives instructions for a similar operation on the 'Magnettes' and Wolseley '15/50's'. Follow the removal procedure in reverse to replace the unit, checking the brake adjustment and bleeding both clutch and brake systems. Finally, check the system for leaks with the brake pedal hard down. The brake bore components are on the far side in **FIG 10:11,** hence the check valve parts 88, 89 and 90.

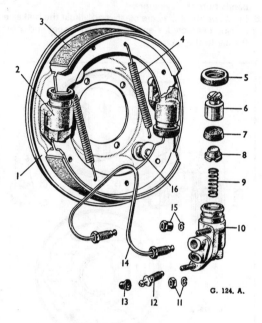

Fig 10:12 Front brake and cylinder components, Austins 'A40', 'A50' and 'A55'.

Key to Fig 10:12 1 Back plate. 2 Wheel cylinder. 3 Shoe lining. 4 Shoe return spring. 5 Rubber dust cover. 6 Piston. 7 Seal. 8 Seal support. 9 Spring. 10 Cylinder housing. 11 Washer and nut. 12 Bleed screw. 13 Bleed screw cover. 14 Cylinder connecting pipe. 15 Washer and nut. 16 Cam adjuster.

Removing and replacing brake shoes – Austins 'A40', 'A50' and 'A55'

Front brakes:

1 Jack up the car, remove the road wheels and brake drums. Pull one shoe outwards until the ends are clear of the two wheel cylinders. Remove the return spring 4 in **FIG 10:12,** noting that the end which fits into the hole in the backplate is 'swan-necked'. Repeat with the second shoe.

2 Fit a piece of wire or a rubber band round each cylinder to prevent the pistons from expanding, and refrain from operating the brake pedal.

3 Clean down the backplate, check that the cylinders are not leaking and try the adjusters for easy working. Turn anti-clockwise as seen from behind the backplate so that the adjusters are fully 'off'. Release the handbrake.

4 Smear the contact points of moving parts with Girling (White) Brake Grease but be most careful to keep this grease from touching the hydraulic cylinders, the pistons or the rubber parts. Also keep grease off the linings at all times and do not touch them with greasy hands.

5 Fit new return springs to the new shoes and place the hooked end of each spring through the hole in the web of the shoe. Place the 'swan-necked' end through the hole in the backplate near the adjuster 16 of the opposite shoe, as shown in **FIG 10:12**. Replace each shoe independently, after removing the wires or the rubber bands from the cylinders.

6 Fit the drums if they are clean, and adjust the brakes as already instructed. Replace the road wheel and lower the car to the ground.

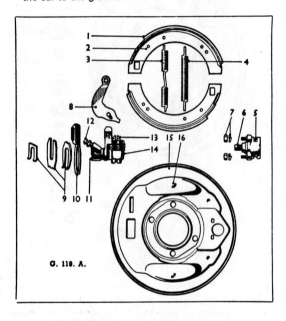

Fig 10:13 Austin rear brake components.

Key to Fig 10:13 1 Shoe lining. 2 Shoe. 3 Shoe return spring. 4 Shorter return spring. 5 Adjuster body. 6 Adjuster wedge. 7 Nut and washer. 8 Handbrake lever. 9 Cylinder securing clips. 10 Rubber washer. 11 Pipe orifice. 12 Bleed screw. 13 Slot for shoe. 14 Cylinder body. 15 Back plate. 16 Back plate dimple.

Rear brakes:

1 Follow the procedure for the front brakes but lift only one of the shoes out of the abutment slots. Both shoes can then be removed complete with springs.

2 When refitting the return springs, glance at **FIG 10:13**. Note that the springs must lie behind the shoe webs and next to the backplate. Fit the shorter spring 4 at the adjuster end. Now locate one shoe in the adjuster body 5, the other end fitting in the slot in the wheel cylinder piston 13. Prise the second shoe into position on the opposite side. Note that the linings are offset on the

shoes. This also can be seen in **FIG 10:13** where the top lining is some distance from the left-hand end, but is almost in line with the right-hand end or 'heel' of the shoe. Thus the top shoe has the lining towards the 'heel', or adjuster end, and the bottom shoe towards the cylinder end on both brakes.

3 Make several hard applications of the brake pedal to bed everything down and then adjust the brakes.

Removing and replacing brake shoes – 'Magnettes' ZA and ZB, Wolseley '15/50' and 'Oxfords' 11 and 111

Front:

1 After removing the road wheel and brake drum, pull the brake shoes apart and lift them away from the backplate. Wire the wheel cylinder pistons to prevent them moving, or use a rubber band. Do not depress the brake pedal until the shoes are replaced.

2 Check the cylinders for leaks and clean up the backplate and brake drum. Turn the adjusters fully off, especially when fitting new linings. Release the handbrake.

3 Fit the springs to the shoes remembering that they must lie behind the webs of the shoes and next to the backplate. The shoes are interchangeable but notice the semi-circular recess in one end. This recess is made to engage the adjuster 21 in **FIG 10:10**. The opposite shoe must be fitted with its recessed end against the second adjuster. Remove the wire or rubber band from each cylinder.

4 Fit one shoe, pull on the other to stretch the springs and let it return into position. Replace the drum and adjust the brakes.

Rear:

1 Remove the road wheel and brake drum. Press in, turn, and withdraw the brake steady springs 42. Draw the shoes apart and remove from the backplate.

2 The shoes are interchangeable but there is a semi-circular recess in one end of each web which fits over the pin of adjuster 46. The 'Oxford' cylinder is fitted with the piston uppermost, so that the adjuster is on top. The recessed end of the second shoe abuts the cylinder.

3 Both pull-off springs are fitted behind the shoes, the lighter spring 41 being farthest from the cylinder.

4 With the adjuster backed right off and the handbrake released, fit the brake drum and then adjust the brakes when the other wheel has been serviced.

Removing and replacing brake shoes – Wolseley '1500'

Front:

1 Follow the instructions in the preceding section, but when it comes to replacing the pull-off springs, fit the rear spring in the rear hole in the upper shoe and the inner of the two holes in the lower shoe. The front spring is fitted in the front hole of the lower shoe and the inner of the two holes in the upper shoe.

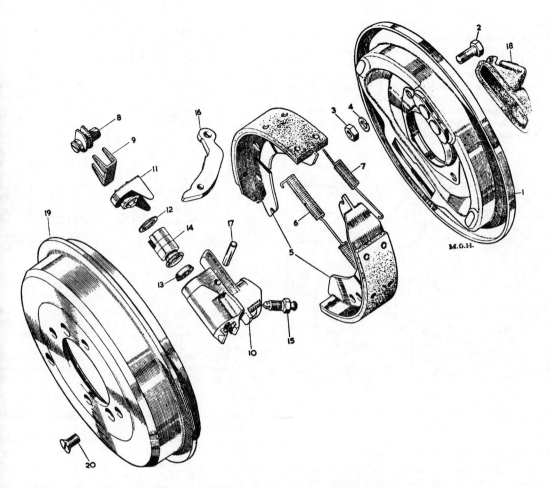

Fig 10:14   Right-hand rear brake assembly on Wolseley '1500's'.

ear:

FIG 10:14 shows the components of a right-hand rear brake, from which it is seen that there are no steady springs through the shoe webs. The cylinder fits in the rectangular hole on the far side of the backplate, the brake shoe abutment being on the nearside. Remove and replace the shoes by following the 'Magnette' instructions, apart from the sentence about the steady springs.

Again, the shoes are interchangeable, but the recess in the rear shoe web fits on the adjuster end of the wheel cylinder. The front shoe is fitted with the recess against the abutment plate. Both springs are fitted behind the shoes, the lighter spring 7 being fitted nearest to the abutment and hooked into the inner of the two holes in the rear shoe. Heavier spring 6 is fitted at the cylinder end and hooked into the outer hole in the front shoe.

Removing and replacing brake shoes – Riley '1.5'

Front:

1 Follow the instructions given for The Austins 'A40', '50' and '55'. If replacement shoes are fitted or if there is any sign of uneven wear across the surface of the original linings, it will be necessary to adjust the steady posts. These are shown dotted behind the shoe webs on the vertical centre line in **FIG 10:15**.

2 Fit the brake drum and adjust the brakes, then slacken the steady post locknut behind the backplate. Unscrew the post three or four turns. Apply the brakes hard and keep the pedal down while a second operator turns the post clockwise until it contacts the shoe web. The post must be held in this position while the locknut is tightened.

Rear:

1 Follow the instructions given for the Austins 'A40', '50' and '55'. **FIG 10:16** shows the brake assembly details and the steady posts are dotted in on the horizontal centre line. Adjust these in the manner suggested for the front brakes. The diagram clearly shows how the leading shoe on the left, which is the one operated by the piston, has its lining fitted towards the trailing or adjuster end. The other lining is fitted more towards the cylinder end.

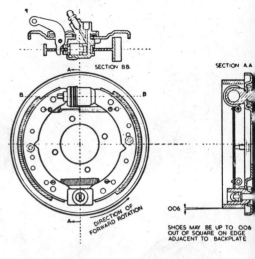

Fig 10:16   Rear brake details on Riley '1.5'.

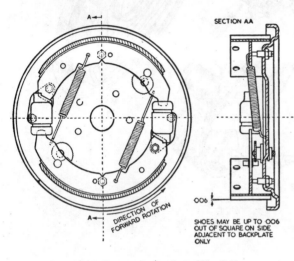

Fig 10:15   Front brake details on Riley '1.5'.

Removing flexible hoses – all models

Before describing the operation of removing wheel cylinders, it is essential to stress the great importance of knowing how to remove flexible hoses in the correct sequence. **FIG 10:17** shows, in the bottom left-hand corner, the inner end of a front hose on the 'Oxford'. The bracket is shown dotted, a method of mounting which is common to all the cars in this book. This is the starting point for removing a hose. **Never** begin by trying to unscrew the hose at the backplate end. Refer again to the left-hand corner of the illustration. Unscrew the union to release the metal pipe line 47. Prevent hose 53 from twisting by using a spanner on the hexagon, and unscrew the large nut 56. Note the shakeproof washer. The inner end being free, the other end of the hose can be unscrewed from the backplate, taking care to retrieve the small copper gasket washer.

Replace a flexible hose in the reverse sequence.

Removing and replacing wheel cylinders – Austins 'A40', 'A50' and 'A55', Riley '1.5'

Front:

1 Remove the road wheel and brake drum. Referring to **FIG 10:12,** detach the link pipe 14 from both cylinders. It is behind the backplate. Remove the flexible hose by following the preceding instructions.
2 Remove the brake shoes as already described. Detach the cylinders by unscrewing nuts 11 and 15.

3 Dismantle each cylinder by first peeling off the du[...] cover 5. Air pressure at the inlet will be useful whe[...] trying to extract the internal parts. They will come o[...] in the order shown.
4 Service the cylinder after reading 'Notes on dismantling[...] Reassemble and replace in the reverse order and ble[...] the brakes.

Rear:

1 After the brake shoes have been removed, work behir[...] the backplate to disconnect the fluid pipe line and th[...] cable from the handbrake lever. Refer to **FIG 10:13** an[...] prise apart the retainer and spring plates 9, using [...] screwdriver. Tap the retaining plate from below th[...] neck of the wheel cylinder.
2 Withdraw the handbrake lever from between th[...] cylinder and the backplate. Remove the spring pla[...] and distance piece and the cylinder will be free.
3 Service the cylinder in the manner described in the se[...] tion 'Notes on dismantling'. The dust cover is held [...] with a spring clip and the seal fits on the neck of th[...] piston without a support or spring. Assemble the se[...] so that the lip enters the bore first.
4 Reassemble in the reverse order. Smear the backpla[...] and the cylinder with Girling White Brake Grease ar[...] mount the cylinder on the backplate with the ne[...] through the large slot. **FIG 10:13** shows the order ar[...] position for replacing the items 9. The right-hand di[...] tance piece goes between the cylinder neck and th[...] backplate with the open end away from the handbra[...] lever. The two cranked lips must face away from th[...] backplate. Replace the lever. Locate the central re[...] taining plate between the distance piece and the ou[...] spring plate with its open end towards the lever. Ta[...] it into place until the two cranked lips of the sprir[...] plate locate in the retaining plate. When the remainir[...] parts are replaced, bleed and adjust the brakes. No[...] that the cylinder is intended to slide in the backplat[...] When the piston moves outwards to apply one sho[...] reaction of the cylinder causes it to slide the other wa[...] to apply the second shoe.

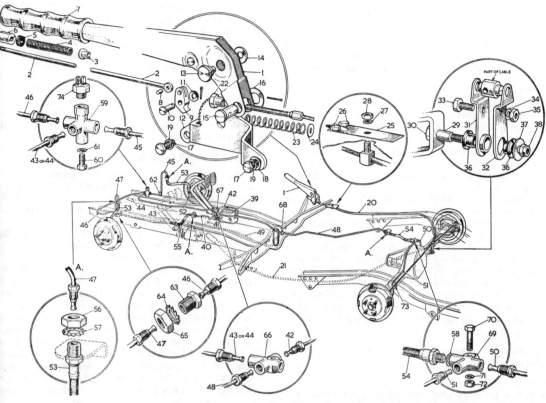

Fig 10:17 Handbrake details and pipe connections on Oxfords.

emoving and servicing wheel cylinders—
Magnettes' ZA and ZB, Wolseley '15/50'

ront:

Dismantle the brake to the point where the shoes have
been removed. Work behind the backplate and release
the flexible hose from its bracket at the inner end, using
the method described under the heading 'Removing
flexible hoses'. Unscrew the hose from the wheel
cylinder. On some early models the hose screws into a
banjo bolt. In this case remove the bolt instead, noting
that the small copper washer goes next to the cylinder.

On the same models remove the banjo bolt from the
second cylinder, which will release the link pipe joining
the cylinders hydraulically. On later models, unscrew
the link pipe unions from the wheel cylinders.

2 Remove the two setscrews 135 and 137 in **FIG 10:10**.
These hold the cylinders to the backplate, and once
they are removed the cylinders can be lifted off.

3 Service the cylinders according to 'Notes on dismantling'. Reassemble in the order shown in **FIG 10:10**,
noting that the spring 27 seats in a recess in filler 26.
The cup 25 faces into the bore with its plain side seating
on the flat face of piston 24. Replace the cylinders in

the reverse order, noting that the cylinders are interchangeable.

4 The flexible hose is connected to the rear cylinder and the bleeder screw goes into the front one. On those models with banjo fittings, the link pipe passes over the stub axle. When the link pipe unions screw directly into the wheel cylinders the pipe passes under the axle.

Rear:

1 After the brake shoes have been taken off, detach the pipe line behind the backplate. Remove the hollow banjo bolt 58. Note that the small copper washer 60 goes next to the wheel cylinder boss. Remove the clevis pin connecting the handbrake cable to lever 54. Peel off rubber boot 56 and withdraw the lower piston 49 from the cylinder. Extract the cylinder from the backplate.

2 Tap out pivot pin 55 to release lever 54. If there is any difficulty in extracting the internal parts from the cylinder bore, some air pressure applied to the inlet hole will blow them out.

3 Clean and reassemble the cylinders by following 'Notes on dismantling'. Fit the cylinder on the forward side of the axle casing, with the bleeder screw vertical. Replace the brake shoes with the linings offset as shown, and the recess in the web of the lower shoe fitted over the pin of adjuster 46. The cylinder is designed to slide in the backplate slot. When reassembly is complete, bleed the brakes.

Removing and replacing wheel cylinders – Wolseley '1500'

Front:

1 Follow the 'Magnette' instructions, but note that the bleed screw and the pipe fittings screw directly into the wheel cylinders where they project through the backplate.

2 The piston seal fits over a spigot without a retainer or spring. Do not remove the seal unless it is intended to fit a new one.

3 The cylinders are interchangeable from front to rear on a given backplate, but they cannot be fitted on the opposite front backplate. The cylinders are marked 'L' for a left-hand, and 'R' for a right-hand backplate. The link pipe passes below the stub axle, the flexible hose is connected to the front cylinder and the bleed screw goes into the rear one.

Rear:

1 Follow the 'Magnette' instructions, referring to **FIG 10:14** for details. The piston and seal are similar to those in the front brake cylinders.

2 There is a tapered slot in the piston 14. Replace it with the longer side facing lever 16. With the cylinder at the top of the slot in the backplate, press the base of the cylinder inwards to replace it. It must lie to the rear of the axle casing with the bleed screw at the bottom. Bleed the brakes when everything has been replaced.

Removing and replacing wheel cylinders – 'Oxfords' 11 and 111

Front:

1 Follow the Magnette instructions but use **FIG 10:11** to refer to details. It is important to note that the cylinders

are not interchangeable on the same backplate, so ma them lightly before removal.

2 When replacing the fittings behind the backplate, link pipe banjo unions must be arranged so that flexible hose is connected to the front cylinder and bleed screw goes in the rear cylinder. The link pi passes under the axle centre.

Rear:

1 Dismantle according to the 'Magnette' instructions.

2 When reassembling fit the cylinder to the rear of axle casing with the bleed screw horizontal. Final bleed the brakes.

Pipe lines – all models

Generally speaking, the layout of connecting pipes similar on all the cars covered by this manual. A typi system is shown by **FIG 10:17** which is the one fitted the 'Oxfords'. From this it can be seen that small-bo metal pipes run from the master cylinder to the inner en of flexible hoses 53 and 54. These hoses carry the flu to the brakes and accommodate the movements of suspension systems. The rear hose 54 is connected metal transverse pipes which are clipped to the a: casing and lead to the rear wheel cylinders. One of pipe connectors 59, (top left), carries a stop-light swit 74. This is a pressure operated device which closes electrical circuit to the lamps when the brakes are appli Note that the ends of the pipes are flared to make pressure-tight connection when the union nuts tightened. It is unlikely that the pipe lines will give troub but if there is a persistent need for topping-up the mas cylinder and it is known that the wheel cylinders are leaking, then every pipe connection should be check

Fig 10:18 Handbrake adjustment on Austins 'A40', 'A5 and 'A55'.

Key to Fig 10:18 1 Sleeve nut. 2 Locknut. 3 Bra lever. 4 Longitudinal rod. 5 Lever pivot.

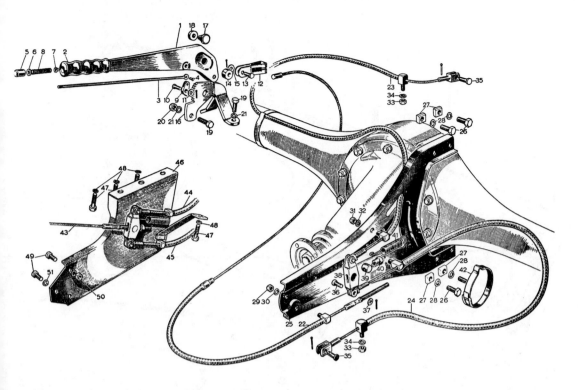

Fig 10:19 Handbrake details, early and late Magnettes.

Key to Fig 10:19 1 Lever. 2 Grip—lever. 3 Rod—pawl. 4 Pin—rod. 5 Knob—pawl rod. 6 Washer—knob. 7 Bush—pawl rod guide. 8 Spring—pawl rod. 9 Pawl. 10 Pin—clevis—pawl. 11 Washer—anti-rattle—pawl. 12 Fork end—cable. 13 Pin—clevis—fork end to lever. 14 Spacer—clevis pin. 15 Washer—plain—clevis pin. 16 Ratchet. 17 Pin—fulcrum—ratchet. 18 Washer—fulcrum pin. 19 Screw—ratchet to body tunnel. 20 Nut—screw—to bracket on tunnel. 21 Spring washer—screw. 22 Cable—brake—front—to balance link. 23 Cable—brake—rear R/H. 24 Cable—brake—rear L/H. 25 Bracket—abutment— brake cables. 26 Screw—bracket to axle. 27 Tapping plate—screw. 28 Spring washer—screw. 29 Nut—front cable to abutment bracket. 30 Spring washer—nut. 31 Nut—rear cable to abutment bracket. 32 Spring washer—nut. 33 Nut—rear cable to axle bracket. 34 Spring washer—nut. 35 Pin—clevis—cable to brake lever. 36 Pin—clevis—cable to balance link. 37 Washer—plain—clevis pin. 38 Link—balance—cables—rear. 39 Trunnion—balance link. 40 Nut—cable adjusting. 41 Spring—pull-off—cables. 42 Strap—cables to rear axle. 43 Cable—brake—front—to balance link. 44 Cable—brake—rear R/H. 45 Cable—brake—rear L/H. 46 Bracket—abutment—brake cables. 47 Screw—bracket to seat pan. 48 Spring washer—screw. 49 Screw—bracket to tunnel. 50 Nut—screw. 51 Spring washer—screw.

Handbrake – Austins 'A40', 'A50' and 'A55'

This operates on the rear wheels only and is applied by a pull-up lever alongside the steering column. The linkage is a long rod under the car to a relay lever in front of the rear axle as shown in **FIG 10:1**. From this lever a cable runs back to a compensator on the rear axle. This can be seen in **FIG 10:2**. From the compensator, transverse rods go to levers on the rear brake backplates. The linkage is set at the works and normally does not need adjusting. When the rear brakes are correctly adjusted, the handbrake is automatically set too. If a complete overhaul makes it necessary to adjust the handbrake linkage, first lock the rear shoes to the drums and slightly apply the handbrake. **FIG 10:18** shows the forward end of the control rod under the car. Slacken the locknut and turn sleeve nut 1 until any slackness in the wire cable at the rear is just removed. Lock the sleeve nut again when finished.

Handbrake – 'Magnettes' ZA and ZB

Details of the handbrake layout are shown in **FIG 10:19**. The bracket 25 is an early type and it is more likely

that bracket 46, (inset left), will be found bolted under the floor. The central handbrake lever 1 is connected by cable 43 to a balance link which ensures an even pull on the cables 44 and 45. These go to the rear brake levers. Correct adjustment of the rear brake shoes is normally all the adjustment which is required. If there is undue slackness in the cables, leading to excessive movement of the handbrake lever, turn the nut behind the balance link. It is shown as item 40 in the earlier layout. This will tighten the main cable 43.

Handbrake – Wolseley '15/50'

The system is shown in exploded form in **FIG 10:20**. The pistol-grip handle is connected by cable to a relay lever 28 which, in turn, is connected by another cable to lever 44. The fulcrum of this lever is a slot in bracket 51. Fibre pads 45 are riveted to the lever to stop rattles. Balance link 55 is connected to the lever by pin 56 and is attached to the two cables 58 which run to the rear brake levers. If these cables have been disconnected or put out of adjustment, readjust in the following manner. Fully

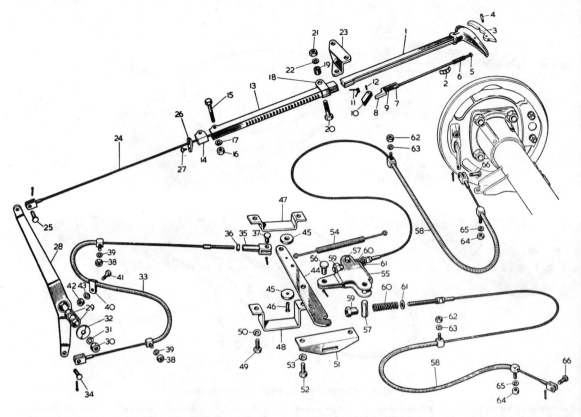

Fig 10:20   Handbrake mechanism on Wolseley '15/50'.

Key to Fig 10:20   1 Sleeve and handle—inner.   2 Spring—handle retaining.   3 Trigger.   4 Pivot—trigger.   5 Push-rod—trigger.
6 Spring—push-rod.   7 Nut—push-rod.   8 Wedge—pawl operating.   9 Spring—wedge.   10 Pawl—hand brake.   11 Spring—pawl.
12 Rivet—pawl.   13 Sleeve—outer.   14 Distance-piece—control outer sleeve.   15 Bolt—outer sleeve.   16 Nut—outer sleeve bolt.
17 Washer—spring—outer sleeve bolt.   18 Clip—control support bracket.   19 Distance-piece—clip.   20 Bolt—clip.   21 Nut—clip bolt.
22 Washer—spring—clip bolt.   23 Bracket—control support.   24 Cable—control to relay.   25 Pin—clevis—cable to relay lever.
26 Guide—cable through dash.   27 Screw—guide to dash.   28 Lever—relay.   29 Bush.   30 Nut—lever to pivot.
31 Washer—spring—pivot nut. 32 Washer—plain—pivot nut. 33 Cable—relay to hand brake lever. 34 Pin—clevis—cable to relay lever.
35 Yoke—cable to hand brake.   36 Locknut—yoke.   37 Pin—clevis—yoke to hand brake lever.   38 Nut—cable to body.
39 Washer—spring—cable nut. 40 Clip—cable to body. 41 Screw—clip to body. 42 Nut—clip screw. 43 Washer—spring—clip screw.
44 Lever—hand brake.   45 Pad—fibre.   46 Rivet—pad to lever.   47 Bracket—top—lever guide.   48 Bracket—bottom—lever guide.
49 Screw—guide bracket to body. 50 Washer—spring—guide bracket screw. 51 Bracket—lever fulcrum. 52 Screw—fulcrum bracket
to body.   53 Washer—spring—bracket screw.   54 Spring—hand brake lever return.   55 Link—balance.   56 Pin—clevis—link to
hand brake lever.   57 Trunnion—balance link.   58 Cable—rear.   59 Nut—cable adjusting.   60 Spring—cable adjusting.
61 Washer—plain—adjusting spring.   62 Nut—cable to body.   63 Washer—spring—cable nut.   64 Nut—cable to rear axle.
65 Washer—spring—cable nut.   66 Pin—clevis—cable to brake-drum lever.

release the handbrake at the fascia. Adjust the brake shoes
correctly. From behind the rear backplates, detach the
brake cables from the levers. Turn nuts 59 at the cable
ends in the balance link 55 by equal amounts until the
clevis pins will push freely into the cable forks and levers
without moving the levers. Replace the split pins. Stretching of cables 24 and 33 can be rectified by screwing fork
35 farther on to cable 33.

Handbrake – Riley '1.5'

Do not attempt to adjust the brakes by interfering with
the cables. Remove slackness in the handbrake mechanism
by adjusting the brake shoes correctly. Then turn the brass
nut on the front end of the rear longitudinal cable at the
intermediate lever. Move it clockwise until the handbrake

is hard on when the lever is pulled up three or four notches.
Afterwards, check that the rear wheels are free to rotate
when the handbrake is off.

Handbrake – Wolseley '1500'

Adjustment is needed if the handbrake lacks power or
the lever ratchet has reached the end of its travel. To
adjust, chock the front wheels, remove the rear ones and
adjust the rear brake shoes. If there is still excessive travel
on the handbrake, examine the brake linings. If they are
thin, replace them. If the excessive travel is still present
after this, take it out by adjusting the cable through the
balance link. Apply the handbrake so that the pawl drops
into the third serration on the ratchet. Adjust the nut on

the relay lever to compensating link cable, until it is just possible to rotate the wheels by hand under heavy pressure. Return the lever to the 'off' position. If there is any stiffness present, check that the pull-off springs are correctly fitted, and that the piston in the wheel cylinder has not seized. The cylinder must also be free to slide in the brake backplate. Having cured any stiffness, readjust and check again.

Handbrake – 'Oxfords' 11 and 111

The lever and its fittings can be seen at the top of **FIG 10:17**. Balanced braking results from the use of a compensating lever 31 and 32, which is pivoted on the rear axle casing. This eliminates the need for two adjusters on the handbrake cables. Normally the only adjustment for the handbrake is automatically achieved when the rear brake shoes are correctly adjusted. There is, however, an adjuster for the condition where the handbrake lever has excessive movement or there is slackness in the cables. This can be taken out by turning nut 22. Before moving it, check the adjustment of the rear brake shoes. After setting the handbrake, make sure the wheels are free to rotate with the handbrake off. Remember that there will be some resistance to turning caused by the drag of the differential gear in the rear axle.

Removing brake backplates – all models

In all cases it will be necessary to draw off the wheel hubs to free the backplates from the front swivel pins or the rear axle casing flange. The backplates are secured by four nuts and bolts with spring washers.

Setting brake pedal clearance – Austins 'A40', 'A50' and 'A55' Wolseley '1500' and Riley '1.5'

These cars have separate master cylinder units with flanges bolted to the bulkhead. Clearance of the brake pedal push-rod is set by using packing pieces under the flange during manufacture. If there is not about $\frac{1}{2}$ in of free movement of the pedal pad before the push-rod contacts the master cylinder piston, then adjustment can be made by altering the thickness of the packing. On the Wolseley '1500' at car No. 10514, the push-rod length was increased to between 5.10 in and 5.12 in. This longer push-rod may be fitted in place of the shorter rod if packing washers 21G.5163 and 21G.5164 are fitted as required between the flange and the bulkhead.

Setting brake pedal clearance – 'Magnettes' ZA and ZB, Wolseley '15/50' and 'Oxfords' 11 and 111

The correct amount of free movement between the master cylinder push-rod and piston is set during manufacture and should not need adjustment. If the parts have been disturbed, reset the length of the push-rod until there is about $\frac{1}{2}$ in of free movement of the pedal pad before the piston starts to move. Adjustment is made by unlocking push-rod 78 from fork 84 and turning it as shown in **FIG 10:10**, or by unlocking and screwing push-rod 91 in or out of fork 93 in **FIG 10:11**. The last illustration shows the 'Oxford' arrangement.

Note: Before making an alteration it is important to ensure that the pedal is not obstructed by the floorboard or the floor cover. In either case a false impression will be given even though the pedal clearance is correct.

Unbalanced braking – all models

A brake which is binding can be found by running the car without using the brakes and coasting to a standstill. An immediate check of the brake drum temperatures by a quick dab of the fingers will soon find the one which is rubbing. After using the brakes on the road, this is also an effective check on the brake which is causing unbalanced braking, but be careful not to burn the fingers on an overheated drum. Front brakes will normally be hotter than rear ones as they do more work.

Modifications

On 'Magnettes' ZA and ZB, Wolseley '15/50's'

On later models the front flexible hose brackets were repositioned on the suspension upper pivot bolts. This happened on 'Magnettes' from Chassis No. ZA 1868, and on Wolseleys from car No. 6891. There were new metal pipes too. From 'Magnette' ZA 9800 all brake shoes were fitted with DM.12 linings instead of MR.19. The new lining has blue and yellow code colours on the edge.

On 'Oxfords' 11 and 111

Beginning at chassis No. 165742, a fully floating brake pedal mounting was introduced. The cotter pin method of locking the pedals to shaft 8, as shown inset in **FIG 10:11**, was discontinued. The new shaft and bushes are shown just below the cotter pin inset. From car No. 187433, seals were fitted to the brake drum holes to stop the entry of dust and water. They are in two sizes, $\frac{1}{2}$ in and $\frac{3}{4}$ in. The seals may be fitted to earlier cars. They do not prevent the use of a screwdriver to adjust the brake shoes.

Fault diagnosis

(a) Pedal needs pumping

1 Brake shoes want adjusting.
2 Leaking joints or connections.
3 Worn cylinder cups or seals.

(b) Pedal feels springy

1 System needs bleeding.
2 Linings not bedded in.
3 Master cylinder loose.
4 Master cylinder cups worn.

(c) Brakes inefficient

1 Shoes incorrectly adjusted.
2 Wrong type of linings.
3 Linings wet or greasy.
4 Drums or linings badly worn.
5 Cup fillers wrongly fitted.
6 Linings not bedded in.

(d) Brakes grab or pull to one side

1 Check 1 and 3 in (c).
2 Drums scored or distorted.
3 Broken or loose road spring.
4 Worn suspension linkage.
5 Mixed grades of linings fitted.
6 Backplate loose on axle.
7 Tyres unevenly inflated.

(e) Brakes drag

1 Check 1 in (c).
2 Shoe springs weak or broken.
3 Pedal spring weak or broken.
4 Handbrake mechanism seized.
5 Wheel cylinder piston seized.
6 Vent hole in filler cap choked.
7 Too little pedal free movement.

(f) Brakes remain on

1 Check 7 in (e).
2 Shoes over-adjusted.
3 Handbrake over-adjusted.
4 Master cylinder by-pass port restricted.
5 Swollen wheel cylinder cups or seals.
6 Blocked flexible hose.

CHAPTER ELEVEN

THE ELECTRICAL EQUIPMENT

*Battery   Testing electrolyte   Generator   Fault testing   Servicing   Starter motor   Servicing
Pinion drive   Control box regulator setting   Cut-out setting   Fuses   Headlamp adjustment
Horn adjustment   Indicators   Wiper motor   Fault diagnosis*

Every model has a twelve-volt electrical system in which the positive battery terminal is earthed. The battery charging circuit incorporates a control box containing a cut-out and a regulator. The latter gives compensated voltage control of the charging rate according to the condition of the battery. The mechanical features of the generator and the starter motor are relatively simple, and a competent owner should have no difficulty in servicing them. If serious electrical faults develop, or there is extensive wear in a unit, it is hardly worth the trouble of trying to recondition it. The defective part should be replaced by a new or re-built one on an exchange basis.

For the operator with a knowledge of electricity and the ability to follow circuits, there are comprehensive wiring diagrams in Technical Data towards the end of this book. Also, he will find that most of the electrical tests are within his powers, presuming of course, that he has access to the necessary precision measuring instruments. Accurate readings are essential and it is hopeless to expect these from a cheap and unreliable meter.

The battery is an important part of the electrical supply system and it has to cope with heavy demands for current when starting an engine, especially in the winter. As it is easily accessible under the bonnet, the owner should feel encouraged to give it the regular attention which it must have if it is to meet those demands and also last a long time before renewal.

The battery

The exterior of a battery must always be clean and dry if there is to be no trouble with corrosion or electrical leakage. Dilute sulphuric acid is used as an electrolyte, and any which 'creeps' or is spilled on the outside of a battery must be wiped off without delay. The top must also be wiped clean and dry if distilled water is spilled during the process of topping up. High electrical resistance is caused by acid corrosion of the battery terminals and this will prevent adequate charging and discharging. The corrosion must be removed and the contacting surfaces scraped bright and clean. Smear the terminal post and the socket with petroleum jelly before fitting together and press some into the hole where the securing screw goes. Paint adjacent metal parts such as the battery tray, the strap and the bolts with anti-sulphuric paint.

Topping up

Preferably use a properly designed battery filler for this operation as it eliminates the chance of spilling water on the battery top. Always use distilled water, and never at any time add neat acid. Fill to a level just above the tops of the separators. Never overfill, or there will be trouble with an escape of electrolyte through the filler plug vent holes. When topping up, check the Specific Gravity of the electrolyte with an hydrometer. The method is shown in **FIG 11:1**. The following table shows how the reading varies with the state of charge of a battery.

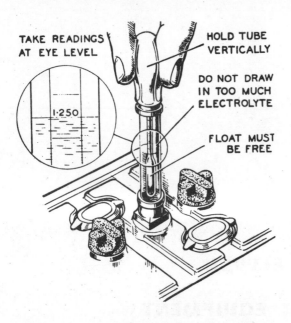

Fig 11:1   Correct method of using hydrometer to check specific gravity.

For climates below 32°C (90°F):
Cell fully charged.........Specific Gravity 1.270 to 1.290
Cell about half discharged.................1.190 to 1.210
Cell fully discharged ....1.110 to 1.130

These figures apply to an electrolyte temperature of 16°C (60°F). For every rise of 2.7°C (5°F) add .002 to the hydrometer reading. Subtract .002 if the temperature is the same amount below. All six cells should read approximately the same. If one cell differs radically from the rest it may be due to an internal fault or there might have been spilling or leakage of the electrolyte. When electrolyte has been lost, topping up with distilled water will lower the

Specific Gravity, so the loss must be made good by adding more electrolyte with the same Specific Gravity. This can be done by adding sulphuric acid to distilled water, **never** by adding water to the acid, which is highly dangerous.

If the battery is in a low state of charge, take the car for a long daylight run or put it on a charger at 4 amps DC until it gasses freely, removing the vent plugs before switching on. The gas is inflammable so keep naked lights away. A battery which is unused for long periods must be given a freshening-up charge every month. Left in a discharged condition the battery plates will become sulphated and the battery ruined. It must be pointed out that a battery may seem to be quite healthy and yet be unable to maintain the high rate of discharge needed when starting up from cold. Most garages have instruments which will check the performance of a battery at high rates of discharge.

The generator

Early- and late-type generators were fitted to the cars under review, the first type having 'windows' in the yoke for access to the brushgear. This is shown in **FIG 11:2** as the Lucas C.39.PV.2. The armature shaft runs in a plain bush in the commutator end bracket and a ball-bearing in the driving end bracket. There are two brushes. The later generator is the Lucas C.40/1 shown in **FIG 11:3** and it can be seen from this that the general design is much the same, but it is necessary to remove the commutator end bracket to get at the two brushes. The latest generators have a Lucar tag connector instead of the field terminal screw illustrated. The servicing instructions for both C.39.PV.2 and C.40/1 generators are almost identical and will be covered in one section, but with reference to any small points of difference. The output from the generator passes through a compensated voltage control regulator unit which gives a high rate of charge to a low battery. When the battery is fully charged the regulator prevents overcharging by controlling the output, holding it down to a rate which will keep the battery in good condition. Output is automatically increased to balance the current required by lamps and accessories.

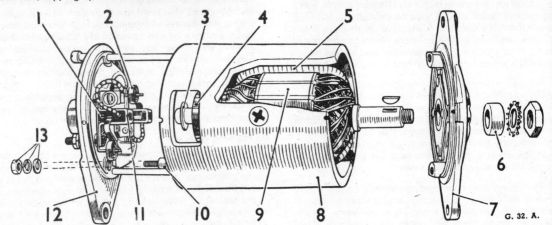

Fig 11:2   Exploded view of early generator with 'windows'.

Key to Fig 11:2   1 Brush.   2 Brush spring.   3 Thrust collar.   4 Commutator.   5 Field coil.   6 Distance collar.   7 Driving end bracket.   8 Yoke.   9 Armature.   10 Field terminal.   11 Brush holder.   12 Commutator end bracket.   13 Field terminal nut and washers.

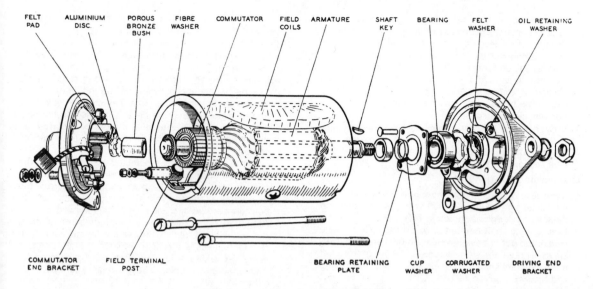

FELT PAD | ALUMINIUM DISC. | POROUS BRONZE BUSH | FIBRE WASHER | COMMUTATOR | FIELD COILS | ARMATURE | SHAFT KEY | BEARING | FELT WASHER | OIL RETAINING WASHER

COMMUTATOR END BRACKET | FIELD TERMINAL POST | BEARING RETAINING PLATE | CUP WASHER | CORRUGATED WASHER | DRIVING END BRACKET

Fig 11:3   The later 'windowless' generator.

Routine maintenance

Adjust the driving belt until there is about one inch of sideways movement in the middle of the longest run. **FIG 4:2** in the Cooling chapter shows the generator fixings which must be slackened to make an adjustment. The front ball-bearing is packed with grease on assembly. Lubricate the rear end bush by injecting two or three drops of thin oil, (20W), every 12,000 miles. The oil hole is in the end of the central boss. At approximately the same distance check the brushgear and commutator. Remove the metal band covering the 'windows' of the early generator and check that the brushes are not worn too short. Hook back each spring in turn and pull on the flexible lead to see if the brush moves freely in its holder. **FIG 11:4** shows this operation. On the later generator it will be necessary to remove the end bracket to expose the brush-gear and the commutator. If the brushes are removed it is important to replace them in their original positions where they have become 'bedded-in'. Rub the sides of a brush on a smooth file if it is tight in its holder. Brushes which have worn shorter than $\frac{11}{32}$ in on the early, and $\frac{1}{4}$ in on the later generator, must be renewed. Clean the commutator with a petrol-soaked rag, turning the engine by hand. Spring tension is tested with a spring balance, the correct figure for the early generator being 20–25 oz, and 18–26 oz for the C.40/1. Fit a new spring if the original one proves to be weak.

Generator not charging

1 Check for slipping belt. Do not over-tighten or the generator bearings may be damaged.
2 Check the connections. Generator terminal D should be connected to terminal D on the control box, and generator terminal F to control box terminal F. The control box is illustrated in **FIG 11:8.**
3 Switch off all lights and accessories and disconnect the cables from generator terminals D and F. Connect the two terminals with a piece of stout wire.

4 Clip the negative lead of a 20-volt moving coil volt-meter to one generator terminal and the other to a good earth on the generator body. Start the engine at idling speed and gradually increase speed. The voltmeter reading should rise rapidly and without fluctuation. Do not let the reading rise to 20 volts and do not race the engine in an attempt to increase the voltage. 1000 rpm is sufficient.
5 If there is no reading check the brushgear. If in the region of one volt the field winding may be faulty. If approximately five volts the armature winding may be defective.

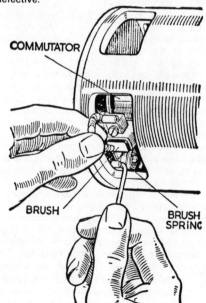

COMMUTATOR

BRUSH

BRUSH SPRING

Fig 11:4   Lifting the brush spring with a wire hook.

6 If the generator is in good order, restore the original cable connections but leave the temporary link in place. Disconnect the lead from the D terminal on the control box and connect the voltmeter between the lead and a good earth on the car. Run the engine as before, when the reading should be the same as that measured directly at the generator. If there is no reading it indicates a broken cable. Repeat the operation on the disconnected F lead.

7 If the readings are correct remove the temporary link. If there is still no indication of charging current, test the control box, a proceeding which is covered in a later section.

Dismantling the generator

1 Remove the generator from the engine by disconnecting the cables and taking out the two top pivot bolts and the lower link bolt as shown in **FIG 4:2**.

2 Unscrew the shaft nut and draw off the pulley, taking care not to put too much weight on the flanges as they are easily bent. Prise the Woodruff key out of the shaft if the armature shaft is to be pressed out of the driving end bracket. Refer to **FIG 11:2**.

3 Unscrew the two long bolts which secure the end brackets to the yoke 8. The heads may be at either end according to the model. Lift off the driving end bracket 7 complete with armature 9. When the armature is partly out the brushes spring forward in their holders as they clear the commutator. Do not let the armature drop back again as it will trap and possibly break the brushes. Remove the field terminal nuts and washers 13 and lift off the commutator end bracket 12. There is no need to remove the driving end bracket from the armature shaft unless the bearing is worn. Replacement of the bearing, and of the plain bush at the commutator end, is best left to an electrical service station.

Servicing the generator

1 Check the brushes and springs 1 and 2 by following the instructions in the earlier section on Maintenance. If the working face of a new brush is preformed to the curvature of the commutator, 'bedding-in' is not necessary. To 'bed-in' a brush not so formed, prepare a strip of fine glasspaper the width of the commutator. Fit the armature to the commutator end bracket and wrap the glasspaper partly round the commutator. Fit the brush in its holder so that it presses on the abrasive surface of the paper and work the strip to and fro. This will quickly produce the same curvature on the end of the brush as that of the commutator. Check that the brushes are free to slide by pulling on the flexible leads. Brush away all traces of dirt and carbon dust from the inside face of the end bracket.

2 Clean the commutator with a cloth moistened in petrol. When in good condition it will be smooth and free from burned spots. If only discoloured, it can be polished with fine glasspaper, **not** emery cloth. If badly worn or scored the commutator can be skimmed in a lathe, taking very light cuts with a keen tool, finally polishing with glasspaper. The mica must then be undercut as shown in **FIG 11:5**. Grind the sides of a piece of hacksaw blade until it is the width of the mica adjoining copper segments. Use this tool to and fro until the mica is $\frac{1}{32}$ in below the copper. Badly burnt copper segments are a sign of broken armature windings.

Short-circuited windings cause darkening of the over-heated coils and burnt commutator segments.

3 Test the field coils 5 without removing them from the yoke by means of a resistance meter. The reading should be between 6.0 and 6.3 ohms. If such a meter is not available use an ammeter. Connect it in series with a 12-volt battery and put one lead on the field terminal 10 and the other on the yoke. The meter should read approximately 2 amps. If there is no reading the field coils have a break in them and must be replaced, an operation which should be entrusted to a service station.

Earthed field coils are detected by unsoldering the field winding from the earth terminal on the yoke. A battery-operated test lamp is connected across the field terminal and the yoke. If the lamp lights the field coils are earthed and will have to be renewed.

4 Armature testing requires special equipment which is not normally available to the average owner, but he can substitute a suspect with an armature which is known to be in working order. The shaft can be checked for true running by rotating it between lathe centres, but a bent shaft must not be straightened, neither is it permissible to machine the armature core. Leave bearing replacement to an agent.

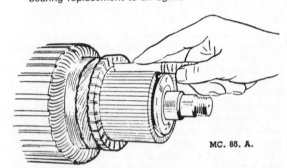

MC. 86. A.

Fig 11:5 Method of undercutting commutator insulation.

Reassembling

1 Fit the brushes and connect the flexible leads. Keep the brushes well up in the holders and hold them in position by letting the springs rest on the sides instead of on the top. The working surfaces of the brushes must not project below the holders.

2 Replace the armature and driving end bracket, locating the dowel on the bracket in the recess in the end face of the yoke. Drop the commutator end bracket into place on the type of generator which has 'windows', line up the dowel and replace the two long through-bolts. Lift the brush springs with a piece of hooked wire, push the brushes inwards and let the springs come to rest on the top faces. If it is a 'windowless' generator this cannot be done, so feed the end bracket on to the armature shaft until it is half-an-inch clear of the yoke. Release the brushes on to the commutator so that the springs are correctly positioned and then press the end bracket fully home. When all is secure, inject a few drops of 20W oil into the centre hole in the commutator end bracket.

3 At the driving end, replace the distance collar 6 and the Woodruff key, fit the driving pulley and tighten the shaft nut securely on a shakeproof washer. Replace the generator on the engine, adjusting the belt to the correct tension. Lastly, connect the cables.

The starter motor

This is shown exploded in **FIG 11:6,** the pinion components below being illustrated as if they were drawn off the armature shaft to the right.

Testing 'in situ'

If the starter will not operate make sure that the battery is well charged. If the lights go dim but there is no sound from the starter motor it is likely that the pinion is jammed. Refer to **FIG 11:7** where it will be seen that there is a squared end to the armature shaft, sometimes covered by a removable cap. Turn the shaft with a spanner. If it is tight at first, and then comes free, it shows that the pinion has been released from the flywheel starter ring. Another method is to engage bottom gear and rock the car gently backwards and forwards until the pinion is released. If the lights remain bright when the starter switch is operated, check the switch and all cable connections. If the cables are sound, the connections clean and tight and the switch effective, the starter must be removed for inspection. A sluggish starter is often due to poor connections or corroded terminals which produce a high resistance into the circuit. If the starter runs freely without the drive engaging, the pinion must be examined, but a reluctant pinion can sometimes be freed by washing the assembly with a brush and paraffin without removing the starter. Never oil the pinion assembly in an attempt to improve matters. It is intended to run dry. Another reason for the drive not engaging is that the shaft has been bent through operating the starter switch while the engine is running.

Removing the starter

'A40', 'A50' and 'A55'. Remove the battery and its mounting platform. Remove the oil filter casing as instructed in the Engine chapter. Remove the cable from the starter terminal, the two bolts from the flange and withdraw the starter forwards.

'Magnettes' and Wolseley '15/50'. Remove the windscreen washer container and the cable from the starter. Take out the two fixing bolts and manoeuvre the starter forward below the oil filter, then backwards and up.
Wolseley '1500' and Riley '1.5'. After removing the starter cable follow the 'Magnette' instructions.
'Oxfords' 11 and 111. Follow the Austin instructions but do not disturb the battery. In every case disconnect one of the battery leads.

Testing starter

Hold the body of the starter in a vice and connect it to a 12-volt battery using heavy cables. The starter should run at a very high speed. Poor performance may be improved by removing the cover band A in **FIG 11:6** and holding a petrol-soaked cloth on the commutator while the armature is revolved. Check the brushes by hooking

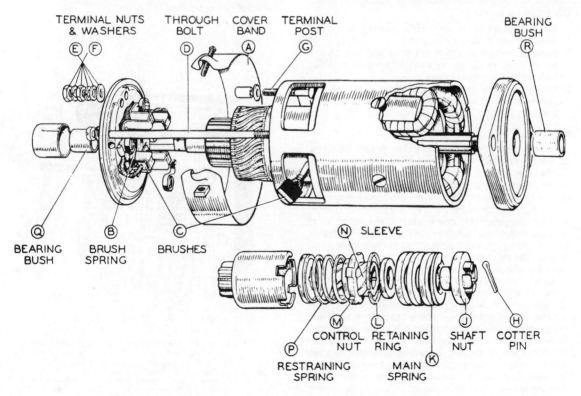

Fig 11:6 Components of starter motor and pinion drive.

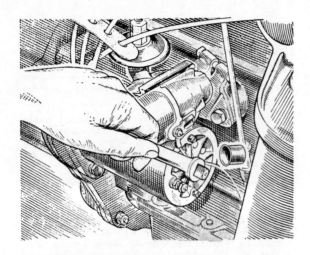

Fig 11:7 Releasing a jammed starter pinion by turning the squared end of the armature shaft.

back the springs with a piece of wire. Pull gently on the flexible leads to see if the brushes move freely. If sluggish, ease the sides of a brush by rubbing on a smooth file. If the bushes are worn so that they do not touch the commutator, or if the flexible lead is exposed on the running face, the brushes must be renewed. Always replace used brushes in their original position.

Dismantling starter

1 Remove cover band A, hook back springs B and with-draw brushes C from their holders.
2 Remove the two long through-bolts and pull on the pinion drive, which will draw out the armature together with the flanged end bracket.
3 Remove terminal nuts E and washers F so that the commutator end bracket can be lifted off the starter body.

Servicing

To renew worn brushes, unsolder the flexible leads one at a time and solder into a new brush. As each one is finished place it in the correct holder so that there is no doubt about the right position. Starter brushes do not require 'bedding-in'. Deal with the commutator by following the instructions given for the generator. **Note: Unlike the generator commutator, the mica must not be undercut.** The field coils are tested for breaks by connecting a 12-volt battery lead to the field terminal post G. The other lead should have a test lamp in series, with a prod going to the tapping point of the field coils to which two of the brushes are connected. If the lamp does not light there is a break in the field coils. Even if the lamp lights there is still the chance that one of the coils may be earthed to the yoke. This is checked by removing the prod from the brush connector and holding it on a clean part of the yoke. If the lamp lights up it shows that the field coils are earthed. Renewing field coils is a job for an electrical service station. The renewal of worn bearings must also be entrusted to a competent agent. The armature is often damaged when the starter control is operated with the engine running. This leads to exces-

sive speed which is shown by the lifting of the conductors secured to the commutator segments. Renewal is the only cure for a damaged armature. No attempt should be made to machine the core or to straighten a bent shaft.

Dismantling pinion drive

1 Remove split pin H, grip the squared end of the armature shaft in a vice and unscrew nut J.
2 Lift off main spring K and prise out retaining ring L from the pinion barrel. This will enable control nut M, sleeve N and restraining spring P to be slid off the shaft.
3 Withdraw the splined washer from the shaft and remove the pinion and barrel assembly.

Note: In the case of damage to the control nut or the screwed sleeve do not fit individual spare parts. The correct replacement is an assembly of the two together. Re-assemble the starter in the reverse order of dismantling, using the same technique for replacing the brushes as the one suggested for the generator.

The control box

The latest control box, type RB.106/2 is shown in **FIG 11:8**, the regulator being on the left and the cut-out on the right. The earlier box has lock-nutted screws for parts 1 and 2, and terminal posts along the bottom instead of tags. The regulator controls the generator output according to the load on the battery and its state of charge. The cut-out is an automatic switch for connecting the battery to the generator. It also disconnects the battery from the generator when the engine is stationary or running slowly, otherwise the battery would discharge through the generator.

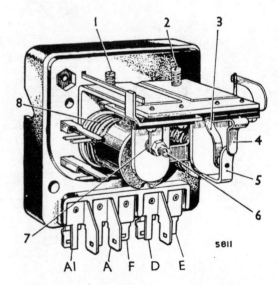

Fig 11:8 The modified control box in its latest form.

Key to Fig 11:8 1 Regulator adjusting screw. 2 Cut-out adjusting screw. 3 Fixed contact blade. 4 Stop arm. 5 Armature tongue and moving contact. 6 Regulator fixed contact screw. 7 Regulator moving contact. 8 Regulator series windings.

Adjustment of regulator

Before altering the regulator setting it is as well to check the simpler causes of trouble in the charging circuit. These could be a defective battery, corroded terminals and cables, or a slipping belt. If these are eliminated and the battery is still not being charged or if the generator output does not fall when the battery is fully charged, the regulator setting can be checked and adjusted if necessary.

Electrical setting of regulator

1 Preliminary checking can be done without removing the cover and with the unit cold. All adjustments must be completed within 30 seconds, otherwise heating of the shunt winding will affect the meter readings.
2 Disconnect the cables from control box terminals A and A1, joining them together. Use a good-quality 20-volt moving coil voltmeter and connect its negative lead to terminal D, the other lead going to terminal E.
3 Start the engine and speed it up slowly until the meter needle 'flicks' and then steadies at a reading within the limits given below. These will vary according to the surrounding temperature.

Control box	Ambient temperature	Voltage reading
RB. 106/2	20°C (68°F)	15.4–16.4 at 1500 rev/min
Modified RB. 106/2	20°C (68°F)	16.0–16.7 at 3000 rev/min

For every 10°C (18°F) above or below this temperature, subtract or add 0.1 volt. If the reading becomes steady outside the above limits the regulator must be adjusted.
4 Stop the engine and remove the control box cover. Turn adjusting screw 1 in a clockwise direction to raise the voltage setting and anti-clockwise to lower it. Do this a fraction of a turn at a time, tightening the locknut, (if one is fitted) and checking the meter reading at each adjustment until the correct setting is obtained. When satisfied, connect the cables.

False settings may be made if the generator is run at high speeds on an open circuit, as it will build up a high voltage. Therefore increase the engine speed slowly until the regulator operates. Remember to work quickly to avoid undue temperature rise.

Mechanical setting of regulator

FIGS 11:9 and **11:10** will determine the type of regulator to be adjusted. The location of the fixed contact is the deciding factor, as there is an adjusting screw in front on the later type. Note however, that the coil is actually horizontal and not vertical as illustrated.

1 Adjust the early type in **FIG 11:9** by slackening the two fixing screws E. Insert a .018 in feeler gauge between the back of the armature A and the frame B.
2 Hold the gauge in position and press the armature back against the frame and down onto the bobbin core C. Lock in this position by tightening screws E
3 The gap between the armature and the bobbin core should be between .012 in and .020 in. If outside these limits correct by adding or removing shims F. Remove the gauge and press the armature down. The gap between the fixed and moving contacts should be between .006 in and .017 in. When satisfied, re-check the electrical setting.

Regulator contacts can be cleaned with fine emery cloth or a fine carborundum stone. Wipe away all traces of dust with methylated spirits.

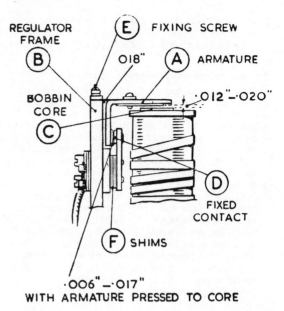

Fig 11:9 Mechanical adjustment of early regulator.

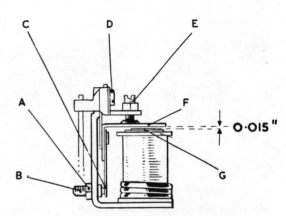

Fig 11:10 Mechanical setting of later regulator.

Key to Fig 11:10 A Locknut. B Voltage adjusting screw. C Armature tension spring. D Armature securing screws. E Fixed contact adjustment screw. F Armature. G Core face and shim.

Adjust the later type in **FIG 11:10** as follows:
1 Slacken the locknut on screw E if one is fitted. Undo the screw until it is well clear of the armature contact on F. Repeat with screw B, slackening it until it is quite clear of tension spring C. Slacken the securing screws D.
2 Insert a .015 in feeler gauge, which is wide enough to cover the core face, between the armature F and the core shim G. Be careful not to damage or turn up the edge of the shim. Press the armature squarely down against the gauge and tighten the securing screws.
3 Leave the gauge in the same position and screw down the adjustable contact E until it just touches the con-

tact on armature F. Reset the voltage adjusting screw by following the instructions for electrical setting.

Clean the contacts in the manner suggested for the early type of regulator.

Cut-out adjustment – electrical setting

If the regulator is correctly adjusted but the battery is still not being charged, the cut-out may be at fault. Check the operation of it as follows:

1 Use **FIG 11:11** as a guide to the construction of the cut-out. Remove the control box cover and connect the voltmeter between terminals D and E. Start the engine and slowly increase its speed until the cut-out points are seen to close. This should be at a voltage of 12.7 to 13.3 volts.

2 If the cut-out operates outside these limits it must be reset. Turn screw A in a clockwise direction to raise the voltage setting and anti-clockwise to reduce it, turning only a fraction at a time. Tighten the locknut if one is fitted and test as before with the engine running. Work quickly as a rapid temperature rise will affect the setting.

3 If the cut-out does not operate there may be an open circuit in the wiring of the control box. This can be checked against the diagram in **FIG 11:12**.

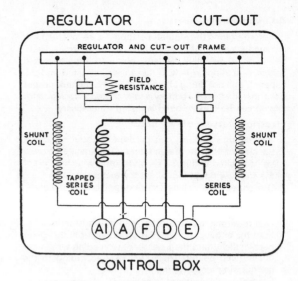

REGULATOR   CUT-OUT

CONTROL BOX

Fig 11:12   Wiring diagram of control box.

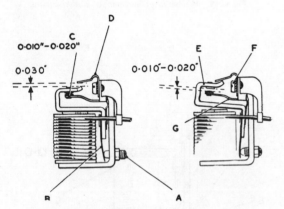

Fig 11:11   Mechanical setting of the cut-out.

Key to Fig 11:11   A Cut-out adjusting screw.   B Armature tension spring. C 'Follow through' .010 to .020 in. D Stop arm. E Armature tongue and moving contact.   F Armature securing screws.   G Fixed contact blade.

Mechanical setting

1 Slacken the adjusting screw A until it is well clear of armature tension spring B. Slacken securing screws F.

2 Press the armature down squarely against the core face as shown on the left and retighten the securing screws. With the armature still down, check the gap between the tip, and stop arm D. It should be .030 in and adjustment is made by bending the stop arm with some thin-nosed pliers.

3 In the same way, fixed contact blade G is bent so that when the armature is squarely down on the core the 'follow through' or deflection of the blade is .010 in to .020 in as shown at C. After this, reset the cut-out adjusting screw by following the notes on electrical setting.

Cleaning contacts

Do **not** use emery cloth or carborundum stone on the soft cut-out points. If the contact faces are dirty or burnt, pass a strip of fine glass-paper between them while they are closed by hand, but disconnect the battery first. Draw the glass-paper through two or three times with the abrasive side towards each point in turn. Moisten a clean non-fluffy cloth with methylated spirits and wipe away all dust when the operation is completed.

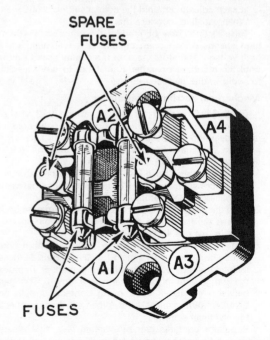

SPARE FUSES

FUSES

Fig 11:13   The fuse unit.

Ignition warning light

The red light which appears when the ignition switch is turned on should slowly fade as the generator begins to produce current with rising engine speed. The lamp will go out completely when the cut-out points close. If the lamp burns out it will not affect the ignition system, but it is wise to renew it so that it can give warning that the ignition switch has been left on with the engine stationary.

Fuses

These are mounted on a separate block away from the control box, as shown in **FIG 11:13**. The fuse between terminal blocks A1 and A2 protects the general auxiliary circuits which are independent of the ignition switch, e.g. the horn. The other fuse protects the ignition circuit and those auxiliaries which operate only when the ignition is switched on, e.g. the fuel gauge, wiper motor and flashers. The wiring diagrams in Technical Data will give a clear idea of the circuitry. Before renewing a blown fuse check the wiring, and units which have failed, for evidence of short circuits or other faults which caused the trouble. Both fuses are 35 amps in all cases except the Austins. These have a 50 amp fuse for protecting the auxiliaries which are independent of the ignition switch.

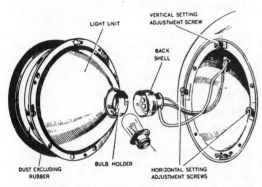

Fig 11:14 Headlamp removed to show bulb holder and adjusting screws.

Headlamps

All the cars with the exception of late Wolseley '1500's' and Riley '1.5's' have headlamps of the type shown in **FIG 11:14**. These have bulbs which do not need focussing. To renew a bulb take out the single fixing screw from the plated lamp rim and lift both rim and dust-excluding rubber. The heads of the vertical and horizontal setting screws will now be seen. Press the light unit inwards and turn it anti-clockwise until the heads of the setting screws are released from the keyhole slots. The back shell has a bayonet fixing of the back shell to the bulb holder. Remove it and lift out the bulb, noting the locating notch in the flange.

Accurate headlamp beam setting should be entrusted to a garage which uses proprietary equipment. The owner who decides to make his own adjustments must find a stretch of level ground where he can set his loaded car square with a wall at least 25 feet away. The lamp rims must be removed to reveal the setting screws. Turning the

top screw in and out will set the beam vertically. Turning one of the horizontal screws in and other out will set the beam horizontally, the object of both settings being to achieve the result shown by **FIG 11:15**. It is an advantage to cover one lamp while setting the other.

Sealed-beam light units

These were introduced on Wolseley and Riley cars from Series WHS 2 and RHS 2 respectively. To remove the unit undo the single fixing screw and lift off the rim. see **FIG 11:16**. Remove light unit rim 5 and lift out the unit from seating 7. Disconnect the three-pin socket 6. The seating rim contains the screws for vertical and horizontal beam setting, the method being the one described in the previous section.

Horn adjustment

On the type of horn without a flared trumpet, look for the serrated adjustment screw on the back near the fixing bracket. Operate the horn push and turn the screw anti-clockwise until the horn just stops sounding. Release the horn push at once and turn the screw clockwise for six notches. This should restore the original performance.

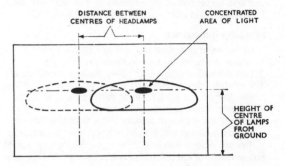

Fig 11:15 Headlamp beam setting.

Key to Fig 11:15 A Front of the vehicle to be square with the wall. B Vehicle to be loaded and on level ground. C Recommended distance for setting is at least 25 ft. (7.6 m).

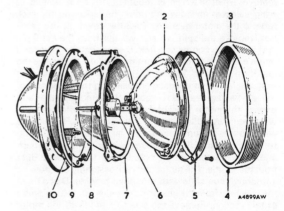

Fig 11:16 The sealed beam light unit.

Key to Fig 11:16 1 Vertical adjustment screw. 2 Light unit. 3 Front rim. 4 Front rim fixing screw. 5 Light unit rim. 6 Three-pin socket. 7 Seating rim. 8 Horizontal adjustment screw. 9 Tensioning spring. 10 Back-shell.

On Windtone horns with trumpets, adjustment does not alter the pitch of the note. Before adjusting an unsatisfactory horn check all wiring and connections. Try mounting bolts with a spanner, see that the horn is not touching some object in the vicinity and check neighbouring fittings which might be vibrating in sympathy. Horns under adjustment take heavy current so short circuit fuse A1 to A2. Disconnect the supply lead from one horn, taking care that it cannot short-circuit on some part of the car. Remove the other horn cover to reveal a pair of contacts just inside. Slacken the locknut on the inner contact and screw the contact down until the horn just fails to sound. Turn the adjusting nut half a turn in the opposite direction and tighten the locknut. The current consumption should not exceed $7\frac{1}{2}$ to $8\frac{1}{2}$ amps when the horn is sounded. If incorrect, turn the adjusting screw clockwise to decrease, and the other way to increase the current. Adjust the other horn in a similar manner.

Trafficators

Do not try to prise up an arm to get at the bulb. Switch on the ignition and operate the trafficator switch, hold up the arm and switch off: Remove the screw from the outer end and lift up the cover, unhooking it at the inner end. The replacement bulb is a 12-volt, 3 watt festoon.

Flashing indicators

In the event of failure proceed as follows:
1 Check the bulbs for broken filaments.
2 Use the wiring diagram to check flasher connections.
3 Switch on the ignition and check that terminal 'B' on the flasher unit is at 12-volts with respect to earth.
4 Connect together flasher unit terminals 'B' and 'L' and operate the indicator switch. If the flasher lights now work, the flasher unit is defective and must be renewed.

Do not drop a flasher unit as it will be thrown out of adjustment. For the unit to operate correctly it is important to use the specified bulbs.

Windscreen wiper motor

Before dismantling an apparently defective motor, check the wiring for faults and loose connections. To remove a motor which is mounted on the bulkhead or wing valance, unscrew the union nut securing the rack tube to the motor gearbox. Take the cover off the gearbox, remove the split pin and washer from the crankpin and lift off the connecting link. Disconnect the cable and remove the unit from its mounting bracket. To remove the motor on 'Oxfords' 11 and 111, take off the finisher strip from the left-hand windscreen pillar and the outer side of the left-hand glove box. Disconnect the motor cables and release the motor bracket and earth cable. Remove the wiper arms by pulling them off the spindles. Release the wheel boxes by unscrewing the large nuts surrounding the wiper arm spindles. Remove the instrument panel mask and the ventilator control knob. Detach the demister duct from the scuttle. The motor and rack assembly can now be withdrawn complete with mounting bracket. Disconnect the rack tube from the gearbox as detailed at the beginning of this section. Remove the screws and lift off the motor cover to service the brushgear and commutator. Clean the commutator with a cloth soaked in petrol. If the brushes do not bear on the commutator they are worn or need new tension springs. If the brush levers are not free on their pivots apply a tiny trace of thin oil and work the levers with the fingers. If the motor runs when replaced but does not work the wiper spindles, remove the cover of the gearbox. A push-pull motion should be transmitted to the inner cable of the flexible rack. If the cross-head is sluggish drop a small amount of 30W oil in the groove in the housing. Pack the gearbox with approved grease.

There is a thrust screw on top of the cross-head housing. To adjust it, slacken the locknut and turn the screw inwards until it contacts the armature. Turn it back a fraction of a turn, hold it stationary with a screwdriver and tighten the locknut.

Fault diagnosis

(a) Battery discharged

1 Terminals loose or dirty.
2 Lighting circuit shorted.
3 Generator not charging.
4 Regulator or cut-out unit not working.
5 Battery defective internally.

(b) Insufficient charging current

1 Loose or corroded battery terminals.
2 Generator belt slipping.

(c) Battery will not hold charge

1 Level of electrolyte low.
2 Battery plates sulphated.
3 Electrolyte leaking from cracked case or top sealing.
4 Plate separators defective.

(d) Battery overcharged

1 Voltage regulator needs adjusting.

(e) Generator output low or nil

1 Belt broken or slipping.
2 Regulator unit out of adjustment.
3 Worn bearings, loose pole pieces.
4 Commutator worn, burned or shorted.
5 Armature shaft bent or worn.
6 Insulation proud between commutator segments.
7 Brushes sticking, springs weak or broken.
8 Field coils shorted, broken or burned.

(f) Starter motor inoperative or sluggish

1 Battery discharged, loose cable connections.
2 Starter pinion jammed in mesh with flywheel gear
3 Starter switch faulty.
4 Brushes worn or sticking, leads detached or shorting.
5 Commutator worn or dirty.
6 Starter shaft bent.
7 Engine abnormally stiff.

(g) Starter motor runs without turning engine

1 Pinion sticking on screwed sleeve.
2 Broken teeth on pinion or flywheel gears.

(h) Noisy starter pinion when engine is running

1 Restraining spring weak or broken.

(j) Starter motor inoperative

1 Battery discharged, loose cable connections.
2 Armature or field coils faulty.
3 Brushes worn or stuck.

(k) Starter motor rough or noisy

1 Mounting bolts loose.
2 Damaged pinion or flywheel gear teeth.
3 Main pinion spring broken.

(l) Lamps do not work, or flicker

1 Battery low, bulbs burned out.
2 Faulty earthing of lamps or battery.
3 Lighting switch faulty, loose or broken wiring.

(m) Wiper motor sluggish, taking high current

1 Faulty armature.
2 Bearings out of alignment.
3 Commutator dirty or short-circuited.
4 Wheelbox spindle binding, cable rack tight in housing.

(n) Wiper motor operates but does not drive arms

1 Wheelbox gear and spindle worn.
2 Cable rack faulty.
3 Gearbox components worn.

(o) Fuel gauge does not register

1 No battery supply to gauge.
2 Gauge casing not earthed.
3 Cable between gauge and tank unit earthed.

(p) Fuel gauge registers 'FULL'

1 Cable between gauge and tank unit broken or disconnected.

Note: Do not connect the battery direct to the terminal on the fuel gauge tank unit.

CHAPTER TWELVE

BODYWORK

Minor re-touching   Removing door trim   Removing and replacing door glass   Removing ventilators
Servicing door locks   Removing external handles   Removing fascia panels   Heater servicing
Modifications

Panel beating and sheet-metal welding are specialized skills which are normally outside the powers of the average car owner. For this reason, instructions in this chapter will be confined mainly to the mechanical details of parts such as doors, fascia panels and heaters. There are, however, a few preliminary hints on touching up minor paint damage which will be inserted here because they may be found quite useful. Small dents and abrasions may be filled with primer surfacer or paste stopper, but first it will be necessary to remove any wax polish with a solvent. When the filler is dry, it must be rubbed down with 300, and then 400 grade 'Wet and Dry' paper until the surface is perfectly smooth and flush with the surrounding areas. Apply the re-touching paint by spray, keeping it wet in the centre of the patch, and light and dry round the edges. After leaving the paint to dry for a few hours, use a cutting compound to remove the dry spray, and then finish off with a liquid polish. Paint changes colour with age, so that it may not be possible to match the original colour exactly. For this reason, it is better to spray a complete wing than attempt to touch-up a small area which may be very noticeable when dry. The adjustment and dismantling of mechanical details will follow.

Removing door trim panel – Austins 'A40', 'A50' and 'A55'

Remove the interior handles by pushing in the escutcheon ring against spring pressure to reveal the cross-pin shown in **FIG 12:1**. Push out the pin and pull off the handles. On a rear door, take off the armrest by removing the cushion pad, thus enabling the two large screws holding the bracket in place to be extracted. Use a screwdriver to prise away the spring clips holding the trim panel to the door, as shown in **FIG 12:2**. Pull the top edge of the panel downwards to clear the lip of the window frame.

'Magnettes' and Wolseley '15/50'

Remove the interior handles in the manner described for the Austins and prise off the panel as shown in **FIG 12:2**.

Wolseley '1500' and Riley '1.5'

Undo the two screws and remove the door capping, then remove the three self-tapping screws to release the front door pull. On rear doors, take off the armrest by unscrewing the two slotted barrel nuts under the rest.

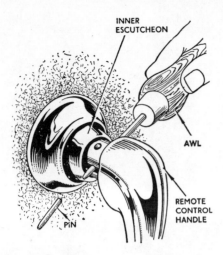

Fig 12:1 Pushing out an interior handle cross-pin.

Remove the ashtray and the two self-tapping screws inside the holder. Remove the interior handles and the trim panel in the manner described for the Austins, with the exception of the remarks about the top edge.

'Oxfords' 11 and 111

Remove the door pull. On rear doors, the bolts securing the armrest are accessible after releasing the top edge of the trim panel. Take away the interior handles, escutcheons and fibre washers after removing the securing screws. Prise off the panel as shown in **FIG 12:2**.

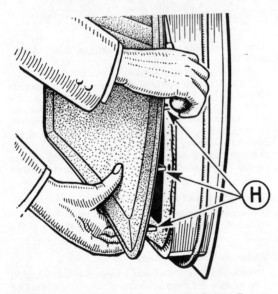

H

Fig 12:2 Levering off a door trim panel. Spring clips are shown at H.

Removing and replacing door window glasses— Austins 'A40', 'A50' and 'A55'

On the balanced type front door window, remove the trim and lower the window. Remove the four screws embedded in the lining of the window rear channel, one in the vertical and three in the top part. Lift the glass clear and remove its rest bracket. Withdraw the two screws which hold the window regulator frame to the door panel, pull down the window and spring out the regulator from its channel at the foot of the glass. Look carefully for a small steel ball which may fall out of a hole in the end of the regulator arm. Slacken the half-bolt at the bottom of the rear channel and pull the channel upwards through the window aperture. If there is any difficulty, use two wooden wedges to increase the space between the inner and outer door skins. This will also help when passing the window handle downwards, so that the glass can be taken out through the large hole in the base of the door panel. To replace a window glass, reverse the procedure, but when the regulator is in place, stick the steel ball on the tip of a finger with a little grease. It will then be possible to locate the ball in the end of the regulator arm as it passes into the window channel.

On the winding-type window, remove the front one by taking off the trim. Detach the window stop and slacken the two exposed bolts at the bottom of each vertical window channel. Wind down the window and spring the regulator out of its channel in the runner at the bottom of the glass. Withdraw the glass downwards. During replacement, grease the regulator so that it will slide freely. The rear door window is removed in the same way, but in addition the window moulds inside and out must be removed, and also the ventilator. This will allow the main glass to be lifted upwards and out through the main aperture.

'Magnettes' and Wolseley '15/50'

Remove the interior handles and the trim panel. Remove the nuts from the lower ends of the two vertical glass channels, and the screw, covered by felt, at the upper front corner of the window frame. Remove the lower glass stop, lower the glass and withdraw the quadrant arm from the window lift channel. Lower the glass to the bottom of the door. Prise the two felt strips, retained by spring clips, from the lower edge of the window frame. Extract the two channels, turn the glass through 90° and withdraw it from the door. Reverse the procedure to replace the glass. Rear door glasses are removed and replaced in the same way.

Wolseley '1500' and Riley '1.5'

Remove the trim panel and the door lock. The last operation is covered in a later section. From then on, follow the 'Magnette' instructions just given.

'Oxfords' 11 and 111

Raise the glass to within 3 in of the top, remove the interior handles, the door pull and the trim panel. Remove the front window channel by taking out the screw at the lower end. Remove four bolts to release the regulator assembly, sliding the arm out of the channel along the lower edge of the glass. Lift the assembly out at the bottom of the door. Remove the rear window channel, which is held by two screws. Slide the cover pieces along and remove the inner, door glass, finisher. Release the window contour strip from the frame by cutting the heads off the rivets. Remove the lower window stop. Turn the glass and lift it from the door. When reassembling in the reverse order, ensure that the top end of the front channel is correctly engaged, and that the regulator mechanism and lifting channel are well greased.

Removing ventilator windows – Austins 'A40', 'A50' and 'A55'

The front one is lifted out after the door is stripped of its trim and the main window glass removed, but slacken the half-bolt at the bottom end of the front guide channel and withdraw the channel from the rear of the ventilator, into which it clips. Tip the top of the ventilator rearwards and lift out of the door, using great care so that the chrome and coloured mouldings on each side of the window frame are not damaged. It may be necessary to use wooden wedges to increase the space between the two skins of the door shell. To remove a rear door ventilator, strip the door of its trim, main window front guide channel, regulator and window stop bracket. Lower the main window to its full extent. wedging the aperture wider to allow the window glass handle to pass through. Pull the main window channel out of the groove of the ventilator after freeing the lower half-bolt at the base of the channel. Tip the top of ventilator away from the door frame and lift out. Replace in the reverse order.

Magnettes and Wolseley '15/50', Wolseley '1500' and Riley '1.5'

Remove the window channels as already described. Remove the two screws securing the ventilator assembly to the door, slide the assembly to the rear and withdraw.

Oxfords' 11 and 111

Remove the door glass as previously instructed. Remove the screw which secures the ventilator to the front of the door frame. Take out the screw located between the bottom edge of the ventilator frame and the door lock remote control and then withdraw the assembly from the door. To adjust the ventilator tensioner, slacken the locknut on the lower pivot and turn the tensioner spring nut until the lower end of the spring is $\frac{7}{8}$ in from the face of the mounting bracket.

Removing and replacing door locks – Austin 'A40' and 'A50'

Remove the door trim, when it will be seen that the lock mechanism is secured at the edge of the door by three cross-head screws. Do not fully extract the lower one from the lock as it also holds in place the rotary catch. The lock mechanism is connected to the remote control by a long flat bar. The remote control is removed by extracting three securing screws. Replace in the reverse order. The barrel-type private lock, which is turned by the ignition key, is secured to the door panel on the inside by a nut. Under the nut is a packing piece. This nut can be reached through an aperture in the door panel.

Magnettes' and Wolseley '15/50'

Remove the trim panel and the window as already detailed. Detach the remote control and swing it to the bottom of the door, passing the connecting link between the front channel bracket and the inner door panel. Turn

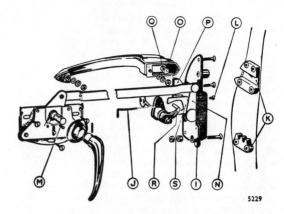

5229

Fig 12:3 Door lock mechanism—Wolseley '1500', Riley '1.5' and Austin 'A55'.

Key to Fig 12:3 I Rotor.   J Lock retaining clip.   K Door lock striker.   L Lock case retaining screw.   M Locating peg (remove after fitting).   N Operating lever.   O Push-button bolt. P Lock contractor.   Q Push-button bolt locknut.   R Private lock operating arm.   S Frame plate.

the outside latch to the fully locked position, remove the lock fixing screws and slide the lock down until it is clear of the actuating lever. Raise the lock again, ensuring that the actuating lever does not re-engage with the contactor. Work the outside latch inwards through the door shut-face. Feed the remote control through the front lower aperture and slide the lock down between the channel and the shut-face until it can be withdrawn through the rear aperture. To refit all locks except that of the driver, pre-set the lock and remote control. Turn the outside latch to the fully locked position. Use the remote control handle to turn the remote control cam in the direction of the lock until the cam clicks into the 'on safety' position. Grease the mechanism and refit, feeding the outside latch through the cut-out. Slide the lock down until stopped by the edge of the cut-out, then slide it up, guiding the actuating lever into the contactor. Insert the lock fixing screws and guide the cut-out trim plate into position. Tighten the screws. Refit the remote control with the cam still in the 'on safety' position, push the control as far as it will go towards the lock and tighten the screws. Check the action of the lock. The driver's remote control is fitted with a stop to prevent the cam from being turned to the 'on safety position. Refit the driver's remote control so that the lock fires when the remote control handle is moved in the appropriate direction and so that the outside push button is free to operate.

Wolseley '1500' and Riley '1.5', Austin 'A55'

Refer to **FIG 12:3**. Remove the trim panel and then release the remote control. Take out the three screws securing the lock to the edge of the door and withdraw the lock and remote control assembly. The lock is detached from its backplate by taking out screw L. This screw also seals the oil hole and **must not be overtightened** on replacement. Later cars have a separate oil hole so that the screw need not be disturbed. Remove the private lock by withdrawing the retaining spring clip J. Do not disturb the striker assembly K except when making adjustments or fitting a replacement, when all six screws must be slackened. When refitting, the remote control must be in the locked position. The locating peg M, supplied with new control assemblies, must be removed after fitting. Fit the assembly loosely and tighten the lock securing screws first, the longest screw passing through the rotor. Slide the remote control assembly as far as possible towards the lock until the lever N is touching the lock case and then tighten the screws. If the outside handle was removed, hold it in position, with its seating washers in place, and check the clearance between push-button bolt O and lock contactor P. It should be $\frac{1}{32}$ in and is adjusted by releasing locknut Q. After the handle is refitted, insert the private lock so that arm R projects through locking frame plate S. The arm is spring-loaded and can be turned through 180 deg if necessary. Secure the lock with spring clip J. Lubricate with 20W oil after assembly is completed. Adjustment of the striker K is only necessary when it has been renewed. Check the door closing action and the position of the door. Adjust the striker by slackening the screws slightly and tapping it into a different position, tightening the screws again to check the result.

'Oxfords' 11 and 111

Remove the trim panel as already described. Remove the sealing pads from the apertures inside the door. Remove the two screws holding the window channel guide to the inner side of the door and remove the guide. Take out the three screws securing the catch to the edge of the door and remove the assembly. When replacing the lock, turn the latch to the locked position so that it will readily engage with the handle press button assembly. Grease everything thoroughly before refitting.

Removing external door handles– Austins 'A40', 'A50' and 'A55'

The two fixing points are inside the door shell. Raise the window fully so that the fixing nut and the set-screw can be reached with a box spanner passed through holes in the inner shell.

'Magnettes' and Wolseley '15/50'

Spring the plated waist rail from the spring clips which secure it to the door. This will allow the removal of a cross-head screw from the front end of the handle. The rear end is secured by a set-screw through the outer door panel.

Wolseley '1500' and Riley '1.5'

Remove the trim panel. From inside the door, remove the cross-head screw which secures the front of the handle. Unscrew the 2 BA nut and spring washer from the stud locating the rear of the handle.

'Oxfords' 11 and 111

There is only one screw holding the handle and this is to be found under the rubber sealing strip down the edge of the door. Take out this screw and slide the handle to the rear to disengage a spring-loaded locating ball.

Removing fascia– Austins 'A40', 'A50' and 'A55'

Take off the steering column covers below the fascia as described in the 'Steering' chapter. Release the steering column from the fascia bracket. Remove the side fillets covering the windscreen pillars. Release the starter pull-cable under the fascia by slackening the clamping screw near the bulkhead, and release the outer cable from the bulkhead bracket. Disconnect the choke cable from the carburetter and the outer cable from the bulkhead bracket under the bonnet. Remove the screws from the top corners of the fascia and the set-screws from the lower corners underneath. Lift the fascia slightly so that its rear flange clears five clips welded to the frame. To remove the fascia completely, disconnect the speedometer cable and all electrical leads. Spring out the bulb holders, disconnect the heater cables from the heater unit and release the demister pipes. To attend to the instruments alone, there is no need to remove the fascia. The instrument board is held to the fascia by two wing nuts, and so is the control panel. When replacing the fascia, lift up the lip of the windscreen rubber so that it will rest on top of the fascia.

'Magnettes' ZA and ZB

Remove the 'L' and 'W' knobs from the right-hand end section of the fascia panel. The panel section is secured by spring clips. Withdraw the section. Spring the radio speaker grille from the panel. The four bolts securing the instrument panel may now be removed and the panel pulled away to give access to the instruments.

Wolseley '1500'

Disconnect the battery leads. Remove the fascia capping by unscrewing the three fixing screws. Remove the four screws at the top of the panel and the single screw above the radio aperture blanking piece. Take out the two screws under each end of the fascia adjacent to the doors and remove the four nuts and bolts securing the radio and fascia side supports. Pull the panel forward. To remove the instrument board from the fascia panel, remove the control knobs and disconnect all electrical leads and cables from the heater controls. Remove the screws which hold the controls to the fascia and remove the controls and escutcheons. Disconnect the choke cable from the carburetter and remove the control. Disconnect the speedometer cable, oil pipe, all electrical leads, and pull out the bulb holders. Remove the six securing nuts and washers and lift the instrument board away from the fascia. To remove the remaining switch knobs, depress the spring-loaded pin in each one. The instruments can be removed by releasing the fixing clamps. Replacement is a reversal of the dismantling procedure.

Riley '1.5'

Disconnect the battery leads and the choke control at the carburetter. Separate the oil pipe from the gauge and the speedometer cable from the instrument. Remove the fillets from the windscreen pillars. Unscrew the two screws from the top of the fascia panel just below the top rail. Remove the screws holding the fascia to the side support brackets by the doors. Remove the radio or the blanking piece. Disconnect the windscreen washer pipes from the switch, ease the panel forward and disconnect the heater control cables. Pull out the bulb holders, disconnect the tachometer drive and detach all electrical leads. The panel and instruments can now be removed complete. Release the fixing clamps to remove the instruments. Knobs are removed by depressing the spring-loaded pin in each one. Reverse the dismantling order to replace the parts.

Release of control panel– 'Oxfords' 11 and 111

The panel carrying the controls is secured to the under

156

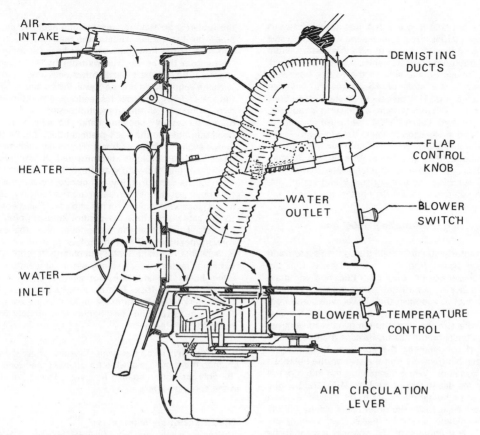

Fig 12:4 Heater system of Oxford 11 from car No. 215304 until the Oxford 111 was introduced.

side of the instrument panel by two hinge bolts and wing nuts. Removal of the nuts allows the panel to be lowered to give access to the control pulls and switch connections.

Heater control adjustment – Austins 'A40', 'A50' and 'A55'

Move the ventilating lever on the fascia to 'OFF'. The air valve lever on the heater unit should now be right forward and little air should enter the car with the fan motor running. There might be the slightest leakage past the valve. Move the lever to 'HOT'. The lever on the heater unit should now be right back, with slight movement of the water valve lever towards the closed position. Adjust the operation by altering the control cables at either end, slackening the clamping screw and sliding the cable through by the required amount and then re-checking. Move the lever to 'COLD'. The lever on the water valve should now be vertical, the valve will be closed and there will be no water flow to the heater. After two or three minutes with the fan motor and engine running, the air entering the car should be cold. If not, water is still entering the heater. This is checked by removing the top water connection hose. Close the end manually and see whether water issues from the heater core with the engine running not too fast. If the water is not entirely cut off, keep the control lever in the 'COLD' position, and slacken

the screw which clamps the water valve rod. This rod is below the cable attachment. Move the valve lever. Slight resistance should be felt as the lever approaches and passes the vertical position, which shows that the valve is seating properly. If this resistance is not felt, turn the centre screw on the water lever one quarter of a turn clockwise and check again. Make slight adjustments until satisfied and then re-clamp the valve rod with the lever vertical. Adjust the Demist control by turning the lever to 'OFF'. The demist valve lever on the heater unit should now be right forward with no air coming out of the demist nozzles with the fan motor running. Move the lever to 'DEFROST' and see whether the lever on the heater unit is right back. If not, adjust the cable length as before.

Heater servicing on 'Magnettes' and Wolseley '15/50'

To remove the heater, drain the radiator, disconnect the heater hoses and drain as much water as possible from the heater. Remove the pedal and heater masks. Disconnect the inner and outer cables and control wires from the left-hand side of the heater. Unscrew the two bolts securing the heater and heater strap to the bulkhead, and remove the heater. When replacing the heater in the reverse order, ensure that the cables are correctly set. With the temperature control lever at 'HOT', position the short side lever on the heater so that it is just at the end of its first movement and is about to close the water inlet valve to the heater. Adjust the cable to give this setting. From car No. ZA.9800 a new heater unit assembly was fitted. The control levers on the side of the heater box were re-positioned to an angle of 45 degrees to give an improved cable run. The preceding heater instructions remain the same. When maximum de-misting is required, set the temperature lever to 'HOT', with the air lever at 'DEFROST' and the air scoop lever in the glove box in the central position. Failure to obtain cold air through the blower can be rectified as follows. With the temperature lever at 'COLD', set the water regulating valve in the 'OFF' position by releasing the locking screw and setting the lever into a vertical position. Re-tighten the screw and check for correct operation.

Heater servicing on Wolseley '1500' and Riley '1.5'

To remove the heater unit, drain the cooling system and remove both hoses from the unit. Slacken the clip securing the inlet hose to the heater duct and withdraw the hose. Release the control cable from the clamps on the heater inlet duct. Disconnect the blower wires, one from the snap connector and the other from the earth terminal on the box. Slacken the clips and remove the hoses from the demister ducts on the heater. Release the heater from the bulkhead by removing the six cross-head screws. When reassembling ensure that the seal on the bulkhead is in good condition. When connecting the inlet control cable place the dashboard control to 'MIN' and put the flap lever on the heater inlet duct in the closed position with the lever adjacent to the outer cable clamp. Fill the cooling system and check for leaks after running the engine for a few minutes. If the controls appear to be incorrectly set, place the temperature and air levers to 'MAX'. Fully open the water valve by turning it anti-clockwise after releasing the cable clamping device. Re-connect the cable. Release the air control cable and turn the air flap valve anti-clockwise until it is fully open, and then re-connect the cable.

Heater servicing on 'Oxford' 11, see FIG 12:4

To remove the blower motor, disconnect the battery. Remove the two wing bolts, cups and rubber washers to lower the control panel. Disconnect the wires from the motor switch and the windscreen wiper switch. Unthread the wires from the rubber grommet. Remove the deflector plate screws and the five which secure the motor mounting plate to the underside of the control panel. Slacken the fan spindle nut and pull off the fan. Take out the three nuts and bolts to release the motor from its rubber mountings. To remove the ventilator casing, drain the radiator and disconnect the battery. Remove the ventilator control knob from the centre of the instrument panel. Remove the instrument panel cover by taking out two screws from each side. Release the ventilator shutter control from the underside of the scuttle. Disconnect the speedometer cable and oil gauge pipe from the instruments and push the rubber grommets forward. Disconnect the oil gaug[e] pipe from the engine. Detach the generator control bo[x] and fuse carrier from the ventilator box. Disconnect th[e] hoses from the heater. Remove the bolts securing th[e] ventilator box to the bulkhead and withdraw it, togethe[r] with the ventilating shutter control, the oil gauge pipe an[d] the water drain. Release the speedometer cable and th[e] two grommets. If the ventilator casing is dismantle[d] during reassembly coat the flange liberally with sealin[g] compound before the back-plate is fitted. Secure the to[p] flange sealing rubber with suitable rubber cement. If th[e] heater control cable is disconnected at any time, re[-] connect in the following way. Push the knob right in an[d] connect the cable to the water control valve lever in th[e] fully open position. When clamping the cable, twist it ha[lf] a turn clockwise looking on the end of it. This gives a bia[s] to the cable and stops the control knob slipping off i[ts] ratchets. Check that the valve lever is in the extrem[e] forward position and that the full range of valve openin[g] is available. Correct water circulation throughout th[e] system is indicated by a steady rise in temperature of th[e] water hoses. If water does not seem to circulate it ma[y] be due to an air-lock. This is released by disconnectin[g] the heater outlet hose from the outlet pipe assembly whil[e] the engine is running. Re-connect immediately water i[s] pumped from the hose.

Important: In all the heater systems covered by this chapter, there is no provision for draining the heater unit. The only protection against freezing is to use anti-freeze in the cooling system.

Modifications – 'Magnettes'

Starting with car No. ZA.6501 a new fascia wa[s] introduced. To remove it, disconnect the battery. Remov[e] the right- and left-hand cappings. Disconnect the o[il] gauge pipe and all the wiring from the instruments[.] Disconnect the cables from the heater controls and th[e] blower switch wire. Remove the four nuts and washers[,] one on the outside edge of the glove box, one each to th[e] right- and left-hand of the radio mounting brackets and th[e] fourth close to the outer edge of the oil gauge. Ease th[e] fascia away and withdraw it through the passenger's doo[r.] To reach the back of the instrument panel without re[-] moving the complete fascia, take off the 'S', 'C' and '[F]' knobs and the two heater control knobs. Remove the tw[o] panel fixing screws and withdraw the panel, exposin[g] the back of the instruments and the panel lights. A furthe[r] modification to the fascia was made at car No. ZB.18577[.] To remove it, follow the previous instructions but do no[t] detach all the pipes, wiring and cables. Instead, withdra[w] the control knobs by pressing in the spring-loade[d] plunger under each one, keeping a note of the correc[t] positions. Also remove the instrument panel and the nu[t] and bolt from the upper support bracket for the steerin[g] column. Ease the column down and to the left. Pull th[e] fascia forward away from the dash and upwards to clea[r] the speedometer.

APPENDIX

SPECIFICATIONS

        Engine   Carburetters and fuel systems   Ignition system
        Gearbox   Rear axle   Steering gear   Front suspension
        Rear suspension   Electrical system   Capacities
        Torque wrench figures

WIRING DIAGRAMS

        FIG 13:1   Austin A40 and A50 (trafficators)
        FIG 13:2   Austin A40 and A50 (flashers)
        FIG 13:3   Austin A55
        FIG 13:4   Early 'Magnettes' ZA and ZB
        FIG 13:5   Later 'Magnette' ZB, starting Car No. ZB 18577
        FIG 13:6   Early Wolseley 15/50
        FIG 13:7   Later Wolseley 15/50, starting Car No. 31901
        FIG 13:8   Wolseley 1500 and Riley 1.5
        FIG 13:9   Morris 'Oxford' II
        FIG 13:10   Morris 'Oxford' III (trafficators)
        FIG 13:11   Morris 'Oxford' III (flashers)
        FIG 13:12   Morris 'Oxford' III, half-ton van

HINTS ON MAINTENANCE AND OVERHAUL

GLOSSARY OF TERMS

TECHNICAL DATA

ENGINE

Dimensions are in inches unless otherwise stated

Bore and stroke (mm):
- 1200 cc ... ... 65.48×89
- 1489 cc ... ... 73.025×89

Compression ratio (low):
- 'A40' 7.2:1
- 'A50', 'A55' Wolseley '1500' and 'Oxfords' (engine types BP.15M and BP. 15ML) 7.2:1
- 'Oxford' up to Engine No. BP.15M.21644 ... ... 7.43:1
- 'Magnette' prior to Car No. ZA.18101 and Wolseley '15/50' ... 7.15:1

Compression ratio (high):
- Wolseley '15/50' 8.2:1
- 'A55', Wolseley '1500', Riley '1.5', 'Magnette' starting at Car No. ZA.18101 and 'Oxford' (engine type BP.15MH) 8.3:1

Main bearings, journal diameter 2.0005–2.001

Main journals, minimum regrind diameter—all models except Wolseley '15/50' 1.960

Minimum regrind diameter—Wolseley '15/50' 1.937

Main bearing liners:
- Material ... ... White-metal
- Running clearance 0.0005–0.002

Crankpin diameter 1.8759–1.8764

Crankpin, minimum regrind diameter—except Wolseley '15/50' ... 1.8359–1.8364

Minimum regrind diameter—Wolseley '15/50' 1.812

Crankshaft end-float 0.002–0.003

Connecting rod centres 6.5

Big-end bearing liners:
- Material—'A40', 'A50', 'Magnette' before Car No. ZA.18101 and early Wolseley '15/50' ... ... White-metal
- 'Oxford', engine type BP.15M ... ... White-metal or lead-tin-lined
- 'Magnette' starting at Car No. ZA.18101 and Wolseley '15/50' (later BP.15WL and BP. 15WH) ... ... Lead-indium
- Wolseley '1500' and Riley '1.5' ... ... Lead-bronze, lead-indium or lead-tin-plated
- 'A55' and 'Oxford' (engines BP.15ML and BP.15MH) ... Lead-indium or lead-tin-lined
- Side clearance 0.008–0.012
- Running clearance—all except 'A55', Wolseley '1500' and Riley '1.5' 0.001–0.0016
- Running clearance—'A55', Wolseley '1500' and Riley '1.5' ... 0 001–0.0025

Pistons ... ... Aluminium alloy
- Clearance, bottom of skirt at right-angles to gudgeon-pin—
  - 'A40' and 'A50' 0.0006–0.0012
  - 'A55' 0.0007–0.0013
  - 'Magnette' prior to Car No. ZA.18101, Wolseley '15/50' and 'Oxford' 0.0008–0.0014
  - 'Magnette', starting at Car No. ZA. 18101 ... ... 0.0017–0.0023
  - Wolseley '1500', Part No. 1H.583 ... ... 0.0008–0.0014
  - Wolseley '1500', Part No. 1H.581 ... ... 0.0007–0.0013
  - Wolseley '1500', Part No. 1H.700 ... ... 0.0006–0.0012
  - Riley '1.5' 0.0017–0.0023
  - Oversizes ... ... +0.010, +0.020 +0.030, +0.040

Piston rings:

Top	Compression, plain
2nd and 3rd	Compression, tapered
4th	Oil-control, scraper
Gap, fitted	0.008–0.013
Clearance in groove, compression	0.0015–0.0035
Clearance in groove, oil-control	0.0018–0.0038

Valves:

Seat angle	45 deg
Lift, 'A40', 'A50' and 'A55'	0.325
Lift, 'Magnette', Wolseleys '1500' and '15/50', Riley '1.5'	... 0.322
Lift, 'Oxford'	... 0.312
Head diameter, inlet: 'A40', 'A50', 'A55', Wolseleys '1500' and '15/50', 'Oxford'	... 1.375
Head diameter, inlet: Riley '1.5', 'Magnette'	... 1.5
Head diameter, exhaust: 'A40', 'A50', 'A55', Wolseleys '1500' and '15/50', 'Oxford'	1.1875
Head diameter, exhaust: Riley '1.5', 'Magnette'	1.281
Stem diameter, inlet	0.3422–0.3427
Stem diameter, exhaust	0.34175–0.34225
Stem clearance in guide, inlet	0.0015–0.0025
Stem clearance in plain guide, exhaust	0.002–0.003
Stem clearance in stepped guide, exhaust, top	0.0015–0.0025
Stem clearance in stepped guide, exhaust, bottom	0.0035–0.0045
Rocker clearance, running	0.015
Rocker clearance for timing purposes only	0.021

Valve guides:

Length, inlet: 'A40', 'A50', 'A55', Wolseley '1500' and '15/50', Riley '1.5' (engine types R and RB)	1.875
Length, exhaust: 'A40', 'A50', 'A55', Wolseley '1500', and Riley '1.5' (engine type R)	2.20
Length, exhaust: Wolseley '15/50'	2.281
Length, exhaust: Riley '1.5' (engine type RB)	1.875
Fitted height above head	0.625

Valve springs:

Free length, single	2.0156
Pressure, valve closed	77.5 ± 2 lb
Free length, double, inner	1.9687
Free length, double, outer	2.047
Pressure, valve closed, inner	30 ± 2 lb
Pressure, valve closed, outer	60.5 ± 2 lb

Camshaft:

Journal diameter, front	1.78875–1.78925
Journal diameter, centre	1.72875–1.72925
Journal diameter, rear	1.62275–1.62325
Bearing clearance	0.001–0.002
Bearing liner material	White-metal
End-float	0.003–0.007
Timing chain	Double roller, 0.375 pitch 52 pitches

Valve timing with cold clearance of 0.021:

Inlet opens	5 deg before tdc
Inlet closes	45 deg after bdc
Exhaust opens	40 deg before bdc
Exhaust closes	10 deg after tdc
On Wolseley '1500's from engine No. 15WC.U.L12316 and Riley '1.5's from 15RB.U.H5623 only:	
Inlet opens	tdc

Inlet closes	50 deg after bdc
Exhaust opens	35 deg before bdc
Exhaust closes	15 deg after tdc
Restore to correct running clearance after checking	

Oil pump:

Relief valve lifting pressure (see below)	50 lb/sq in
Relief valve lifting pressure, later Riley '1.5's', type RB ...	75 lb/sq in
Relief valve spring, free length (see below)	2.875
Relief valve spring, free length, Wolseley '1500' and early Riley '1.5'	2.859
Relief valve spring, free length, Riley '1.5' type RB	3.0
Oil pressure, normal running (see below)	50 lb/sq in
Oil pressure, normal running, Riley '1.5' type RB	75 lb/sq in

Oil filter type:

'A40', 'A50', 'Magnette' prior to Car No. ZA.18101, Wolseley '15/50' prior to Engine No. 4209 and early 'Oxfords' ...	By-pass
'A55', 'Magnette' starting at Car No. ZA.18101, Wolseley '15/50' starting at engine No. 4209, Wolseley '1500', Riley '1.5' and later 'Oxfords'	Full-flow

CARBURETTERS AND FUEL SYSTEMS

Carburetter:

Type, 'A40'	Zenith 30.VIG

Jets, Zenith 30.VIG:

Main	67
Correction	95
Pilot	50
Choke tube	25
Type, 'A50', 'A55'	Zenith 30.VIG.10

Jets, Zenith 30.VIG.10:

Main	72
Correction	95
Pilot	50
Choke tube	27
Type, 'Magnette' prior to Car No. ZA.18101	Twin SU, H2
Needle, standard	GM
Type, Magnette starting at Car No. ZA. 18101	Twin SU, H4
Needle, standard	EQ
Type, Wolseley '15/50' up to engine Nos. 8538(H) and 7301(L)	SU, H2

Needle, (BP.15.W and BP.15.W/L):

Standard	EB
Weak	GG
Rich	HA

Needle, (BP.15.W/H):

Standard	M
Weak	CF
Rich	AH2
Type, Wolseley '15/50' from engine Nos. 8539(H) and 7302(L)	SU, HS2
Needle (high compression), Standard	M
Needle (low compression, Standard	EB
Type, Wolseley '1500' prior to car No. 37633	SU, H2

Needle:

Standard	EB
Weak	GG
Rich	HA
Type, Wolseley '1500' from car No. 37633	SU, HS2

Needle, (WC engines):
- Standard ... ... M
- Weak ... ... EB
- Rich AH2

Needle, (WD engines):
- Standard ... ... GY
- Weak ... ... GG
- Rich ... ... M

Piston spring, Wolseley '1500' ... ... Green, (later models, red)

Type, Riley '1.5' ... ... SU, H4 (twin)

Needle:
- Standard ... ... AD
- Weak ... ... HA
- Rich ... ... AR

Piston spring, Riley '1.5' ... ... Red

Type, 'Oxford' ... ... SU, H2

Needle (high compression):
- Standard ... ... M
- Weak ... ... CF
- Rich AH2

Needle (low compression) and Half-ton van, Series III:
- Standard ... ... EB
- Weak ... ... GG
- Rich ... ... HA

Piston spring, 'Oxford' (high compression) ... ... Yellow

Piston spring, 'Oxford' (low compression) ... ... Green

Fuel pump:
- Type, 'A40', 'A50' and 'A55' ... ... AC-Sphynx 'U' type, mechanical
- Type, Wolseley '1500' and Riley '1.5' (early to late) ... ... SU, SP, HP and AUF 200
- Type, 'Magnette', Wolseley '15/50' prior to car No. 40088, and 'Oxford' ... ... SU, HP
- Type, Wolseley '15/50' starting at car No. 40088 ... ... SU, PD

Air cleaner:
- Type, early 'Magnette' and 'Oxford' ... ... Oil-wetted
- Type, later 'Magnette' and 'Oxford', Wolseley '15/50', early Wolseley '1500', Riley '1.5' ... ... Oil-bath
- Type, later Wolseley '1500' ... ... Paper element

IGNITION SYSTEM

Distributor:
- Type, 'A40', 'A50', 'A55', early 'Magnette' and Wolseley '15/50', Riley '1.5' (type 15R) and early 'Oxford' ... ... Lucas DM2
- Type, Wolseley '1500' (WA engine), later 'Magnette' and Wolseley '15/50', later Oxford ... ... Lucas DM2.P4
- Type, Wolseley '1500' (WC and WD engines) and Riley '1.5' (type 15RB) ... ... Lucas 25.D/4

Static ignition timing:
- Given for Premium fuels. Crankshaft degrees are also shown as measurements round the crankshaft pulley O/D.
- 'Magnette' from car No. ZA.18101 and 'Oxford' 11 ... ... 4 deg before tdc—$\frac{3}{16}$ in
- 'Oxford' 111 (BP.15MH), 'A55' (high compression), Wolseley '15/50' (BP.15WH) and Wolseley '1500' (high compression WD engine) ... ... 5 deg before tdc—$\frac{15}{64}$ in
- 'Oxford' 111 (BP.15ML), '15/50' (BP15W and BP.15W/L), Wolseley '1500' (WA engine) and Riley '1.5' ... ... 6 deg before tdc—$\frac{9}{32}$ in

'Magnette' prior to ZA.18101 ...	...	...	...	...	8 deg before tdc—$\frac{3}{8}$ in
'A50', 'A55' (low compression)	...	...	...	...	10 deg before tdc—$\frac{15}{32}$ in
'A40' ...	...	...	...	...	12 deg before tdc—$\frac{9}{16}$ in

Contact breaker gap ... ...   0.014—0.016

Sparking plug type:

  'A40', 'A50', 'A55', Wolseley '1500', Riley '1.5' and

    'Magnette', starting car No. ZA.18101 ... ...   Champion N5, long reach

  'Magnette prior to car No. ZA.18101, Wolseley '15/50', 'Oxford'   Champion N8, long reach

  Gap 0.025

GEARBOX

Overall ratios—'A40'

Top	5.125:1
3rd	7.64:1
2nd	12.31:1
1st	20.22:1
Reverse	26.44:1

Overall ratios—'A50', 'A55' Half-ton van and 'Oxford'

Top	4.875:1
3rd	7.26:1
2nd	11.714:1
1st	19.233:1
Reverse	25.15:1

Overall ratios—'Magnette' prior to car No. ZA.18101, Wolseley '15/50' (starting at car No. 35858), and 'A55' Half-ton van

Top	4.875:1
3rd	6.698:1
2nd	10.793:1
1st	17.745:1
Reverse	23.205:1

Overall ratios—'Magnette' starting at car No. ZA.18101

Top	4.55:1
3rd	6.252:1
2nd	10.074:1
1st	16.562:1
Reverse	21.658:1

Overall ratios—'A55'

Top	4.3:1
3rd	6.4:1
2nd	10.328:1
1st	16.96:1
Reverse	22.183:1

Overall ratios—Wolseley '1500' and Riley '1.5'

Top	3.73:1
3rd	5.12:1
2nd	8.25:1
1st	13.56:1
Reverse	17.73:1

REAR AXLE

Type—all models except Wolseley '15/50' prior to car No. 35858	Three-quarter floating
Type—Wolseley '15/50' prior to car No. 35858	Semi-floating
Ratio:	
'A40', Wolseley '15/50' prior to car No. 35858 and	
'Oxford' Half-ton van	5.125:1
'A50', 'Magnette' prior to car No. ZA.18101, Wolseley '15/50'	
starting at car No. 35858, 'Oxfords', and	
'A55' Half-ton van	4.875:1
'A55'	4.3:1
'Magnette' starting at car No. ZA.18101	4.55:1
Wolseley '1500' and Riley '1.5'	3.727:1

STEERING GEAR

Type—'A40', 'A50', 'A55'	Cam and lever
Camber angle	1 deg
Castor angle	$1\frac{1}{2}$ deg
Swivel pin inclination	7 deg
Toe-in	$0-\frac{1}{8}$ in
Type—'Magnette', Wolseley '1500' and '15/50', Riley '1.5' and	
'Oxford'	Rack and pinion
Camber angle—Wolseleys '1500' and '15/50', Riley '1.5' ...	$\frac{3}{4}$ deg
Camber angle—'Magnette'	1 deg
Camber angle—'Oxford'	$\frac{1}{2}$ deg
Castor angle—'Magnette', Wolseley '1500', Riley '1.5' and Oxford	3 deg
Castor angle—Wolseley '15/50'	2 deg, 40 min
Swivel pin inclination—'Magnette'	6 deg
Swivel pin inclination—Wolseley '15/50'	$6\frac{1}{4}$ deg
Swivel pin inclination—Wolseley '1500', Riley '1.5'	9 deg
Swivel pin inclination—'Oxford'	$8\frac{1}{4}$ deg
Toe-in—'Magnette', Wolseleys '1500' and '15/50', and Riley '1.5'	Nil
Toe-in—'Oxford'	$\frac{3}{32}$

FRONT SUSPENSION

Type—'A40', 'A50', 'A55', 'Magnette' and Wolseley '15/50' ...	Independent, coil spring
Spring length, free:	
'A40' and 'A50' (new)	10.69—10.89
'A55' (nominal)	10.27—10.47
'Magnette' prior to chassis No. 1826	13.375
'Magnette' from chassis No. 1826 and Wolseley '15/50'	14.156
Type—Wolseley '1500', Riley '1.5' and 'Oxford'	Independent, torsion bar

REAR SUSPENSION

Type	Semi-elliptic, leaf
Number of leaves, with free camber in brackets:	
'A55'	5 (4.5)
'A40', 'A50' and Wolseley '15/50'	6 (4.8)
'Magnette'	7 (3.8)
Wolseley '1500' and Riley '1.5'	7 (4.375)
'Oxford' prior to car No. 182993	7 (3.17)
'Oxford' starting car No. 182993	7 (3.67)
'Oxford' Traveller up to car No. 274458	7 (4.77)
'Oxford' Traveller from car No. 274458	7 (3.77)
'Oxford' Half-ton van	10 (4.315)

ELECTRICAL SYSTEM

Battery type—'A40', 'A50', 'A55'	Lucas GTW.7A/2
Battery type—'Magnette' and 'Oxford'	Lucas GTW.9A/2
Battery type—Wolseley '15/50'	Lucas GTW.9A
Battery type—Wolseley '1500', Riley '1.5' (early)	Lucas GTW.7A/2
Battery types—Wolseley '1500', Riley '1.5' (later)	Lucas BT.7/A and BT.9/A
Generator type (early)	Lucas C39.PV/2
Generator type (later 'windowless')	Lucas C40/1
Generator:	
Minimum brush length—C39.PV/2 and C40/1	$\frac{1}{4}$ in
Brush spring tension—C39.PV/2	20–25 oz
Brush spring tension—C40/1	18–26 oz
Regulator (early RB.106/2), open circuit setting at 20°C ...	15.4–16.4 volts at 1500 generator rev/min
Regulator (later RB.106/2), open circuit setting at 20°C ...	16.0–16.6 volts at 3000 generator rev/min
Add or subtract 0.3 volt for every 10°C below or above 20 deg ambient temperature (early type)	
Add or subtract 0.1 volt for every 10°C below or above 20 deg ambient temperature (later type)	
Cut-out, cut-in voltage	12.7–13.3
Cut-out, drop-off voltage	8.5–11

CAPACITIES

Sump—all models except Wolseley '1500' and Riley '1.5' (including filter)	8 pints
Sump—Wolseley '1500' and Riley '1.5'	$7\frac{1}{2}$ pints
Gearbox	$4\frac{1}{2}$ pints
Rear axle—'A40', 'A50' and 'A55'	2 pints
Rear axle—'Magnette', Wolseley '15/50', 'Oxford'	$2\frac{3}{4}$ pints
Rear axle—Wolseley '1500' and Riley '1.5'	$1\frac{3}{4}$ pints
Rear axle—'Oxford' half-ton van	$3\frac{3}{4}$ pints
Cooling system—'A40', 'A50', 'A55', Wolseley '1500' ...	12 pints
Cooling system—Riley '1.5', 'Oxford' half-ton van	13 pints
Cooling system—'Magnette' and Wolseley '15/50'	$10\frac{1}{2}$ pints
Cooling system—'Oxford'	14 pints

TORQUE WRENCH FIGURES

Engine:

Cylinder head nuts	40 lb/ft
Rocker shaft bracket nuts (inner)	25 lb/ft
Rocker shaft bracket nuts (outer)	40 lb/ft
Main bearing nuts	70 lb/ft
Big-end bolts	35 lb/ft
Gudgeon pin clamping bolt	25 lb/ft
Timing cover, $\frac{1}{4}$ in screws	6 lb/ft
Timing cover, $\frac{5}{16}$ in screws	14 lb/ft
Rear mounting plate, $\frac{5}{16}$ in screws	20 lb/ft
Rear mounting plate, $\frac{3}{8}$ in screws	30 lb/ft
Flywheel to crankshaft	40 lb/ft

Clutch to flywheel	...	...	...	...	...	...	25 lb/ft
Tappet cover screws	...	...	...	...	...	...	2 lb/ft
Rocker cover nuts	...	...	...	...	...	...	4 lb/ft
Sump bolts	...	...	...	...	...	...	6 lb/ft
Manifold nuts ...	...	...	...	...	...	...	25 lb/ft

Rear axle:

Bevel pinion nut	...	...	...	...	...	135–140 lb/ft
Differential bearing cap nuts	...	...	...	...	...	60–65 lb/ft
Crown wheel to differential carrier	...	...	...	...	55–60 lb/ft
Hub bearing retaining nut	...	...	...	...	...	180 lb/ft

Road wheel nuts—all models except Wolseley '1500' and Riley '1.5' 60–62.5 lb/ft
Road wheel nuts—Wolseley '1500' and Riley '1.5' ... ... 37–39 lb/ft

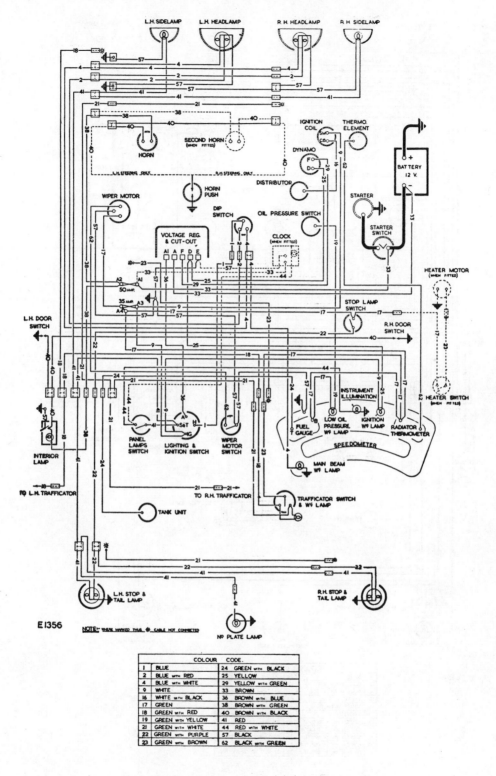

Fig 13:1 Wiring diagram—Austin A40 and A50 (Trafficators).

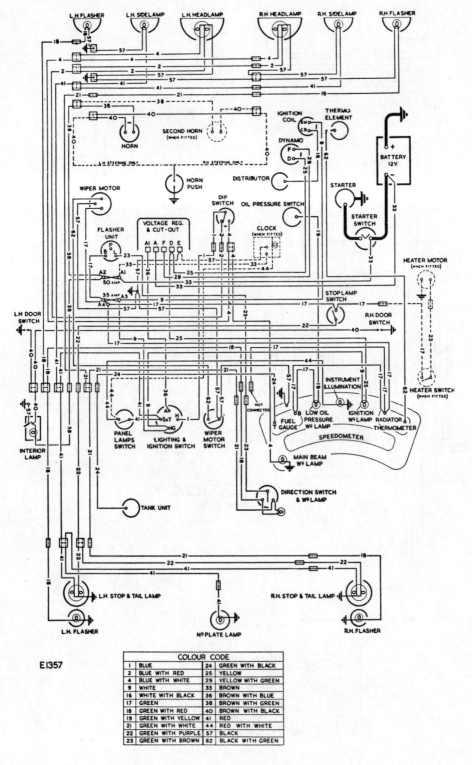

Fig 13:2 Wiring diagram—Austin A40 and A50 (Flashers).

COLOUR CODE			
1	BLUE	24	GREEN WITH BLACK
2	BLUE WITH RED	25	YELLOW
4	BLUE WITH WHITE	29	YELLOW WITH GREEN
9	WHITE	33	BROWN
16	WHITE WITH BLACK	36	BROWN WITH BLUE
17	GREEN	38	BROWN WITH GREEN
18	GREEN WITH RED	40	BROWN WITH BLACK
19	GREEN WITH YELLOW	41	RED
21	GREEN WITH WHITE	44	RED WITH WHITE
22	GREEN WITH PURPLE	57	BLACK
23	GREEN WITH BROWN	62	BLACK WITH GREEN

E1357

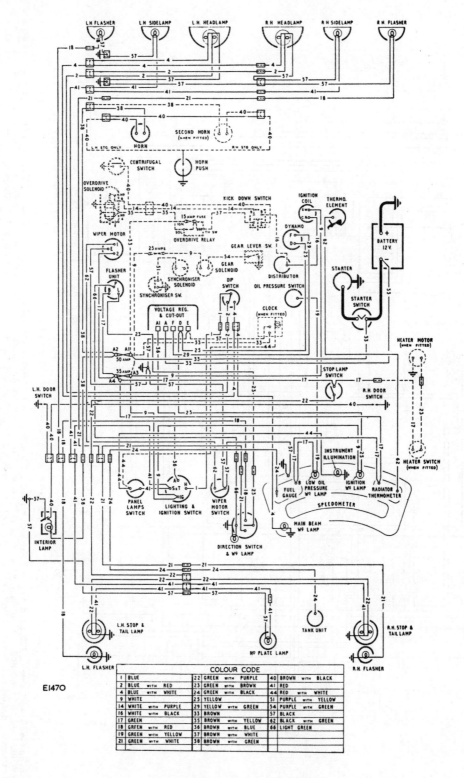

Fig 13:3 Wiring diagram—Austin A55.

E1470

	COLOUR CODE				
1	BLUE	22	GREEN with PURPLE	40	BROWN with BLACK
2	BLUE with RED	23	GREEN with BROWN	41	RED
4	BLUE with WHITE	24	GREEN with BLACK	44	RED with WHITE
9	WHITE	25	YELLOW	51	PURPLE with YELLOW
14	WHITE with PURPLE	29	YELLOW with GREEN	54	PURPLE with GREEN
16	WHITE with BLACK	33	BROWN	57	BLACK
17	GREEN	35	BROWN with YELLOW	62	BLACK with GREEN
18	GREEN with RED	36	BROWN with BLUE	66	LIGHT GREEN
19	GREEN with YELLOW	37	BROWN with WHITE		
21	GREEN with WHITE	38	BROWN with GREEN		

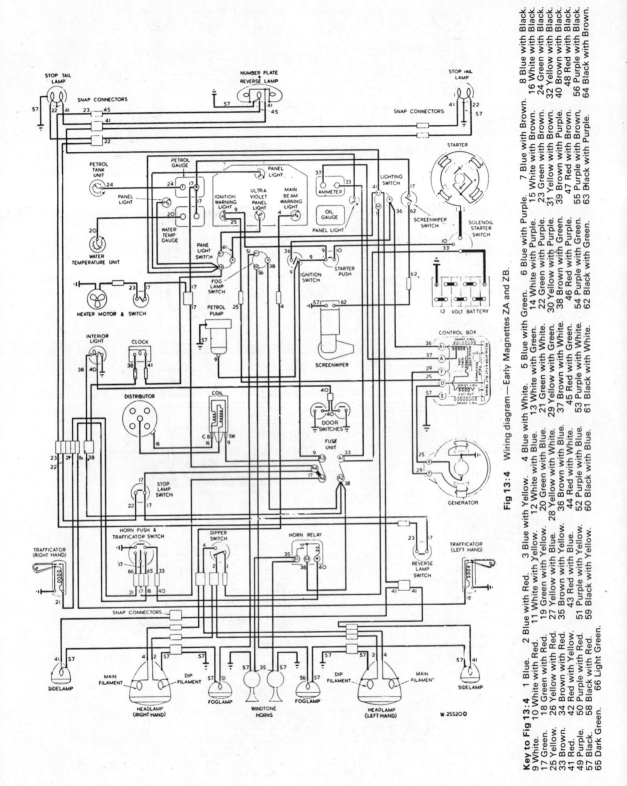

Fig 13:4 Wiring diagram—Early Magnettes ZA and ZB.

Key to Fig 13:4
1 Blue.
2 Blue with Red.
3 Blue with Yellow.
4 Blue with White.
5 Blue with Green.
6 Blue with Purple.
7 Blue with Brown.
8 Blue with Black.
9 White.
10 White with Red.
11 White with Yellow.
12 White with Blue.
13 White with Green.
14 White with Purple.
15 White with Brown.
16 White with Black.
17 Green.
18 Green with Red.
19 Green with Yellow.
20 Green with Blue.
21 Green with White.
22 Green with Purple.
23 Green with Brown.
24 Green with Black.
25 Yellow.
26 Yellow with Red.
27 Yellow with Blue.
28 Yellow with White.
29 Yellow with Green.
30 Yellow with Purple.
31 Yellow with Brown.
32 Yellow with Black.
33 Brown.
34 Brown with Red.
35 Brown with Blue.
36 Brown with White.
37 Brown with Green.
38 Brown with Purple.
39 Brown with White.
40 Brown with Black.
41 Red.
42 Red with Yellow.
43 Red with Blue.
44 Red with White.
45 Red with Green.
46 Red with Purple.
47 Red with Brown.
48 Red with Black.
49 Purple.
50 Purple with Red.
51 Purple with Yellow.
52 Purple with Blue.
53 Purple with White.
54 Purple with Green.
55 Purple with Brown.
56 Purple with Black.
57 Black.
58 Black with Red.
59 Black with Yellow.
60 Black with Blue.
61 Black with White.
62 Black with Green.
63 Black with Purple.
64 Black with Brown.
65 Dark Green.
66 Light Green.

172

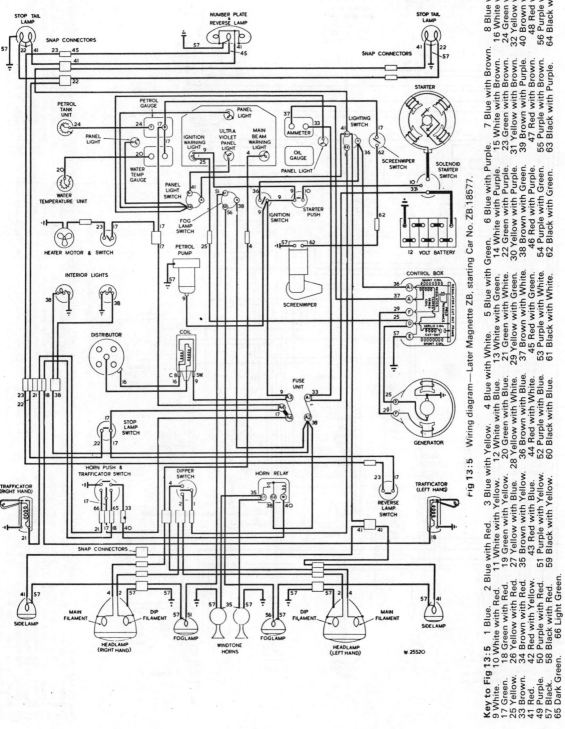

Fig 13:5   Wiring diagram—Later Magnette ZB, starting Car No. ZB.18577.

Key to Fig 13:5   1 Blue.   2 Blue with Red.   3 Blue with Yellow.   4 Blue with White.   5 Blue with Green.   6 Blue with Purple.   7 Blue with Brown.   8 Blue with Black.
9 White.   10 White with Red.   11 White with Yellow.   12 White with Blue.   13 White with Green.   14 White with Purple.   15 White with Brown.   16 White with Black.
17 Green.   18 Green with Red.   19 Green with Yellow.   20 Green with Blue.   21 Green with White.   22 Green with Purple.   23 Green with Brown.   24 Green with Black.
25 Yellow.   26 Yellow with Red.   27 Yellow with Blue.   28 Yellow with White.   29 Yellow with Green.   30 Yellow with Purple.   31 Yellow with Brown.   32 Yellow with Black.
33 Brown.   34 Brown with Red.   35 Brown with Yellow.   36 Brown with Blue.   37 Brown with White.   38 Brown with Green.   39 Brown with Purple.   40 Brown with Black.
41 Red.   42 Red with Yellow.   43 Red with Blue.   44 Red with White.   45 Red with Green.   46 Red with Purple.   47 Red with Brown.   48 Red with Black.
49 Purple.   50 Purple with Red.   51 Purple with Yellow.   52 Purple with Blue.   53 Purple with White.   54 Purple with Green.   55 Purple with Brown.   56 Purple with Black.
57 Black.   58 Black with Red.   59 Black with Yellow.   60 Black with Blue.   61 Black with White.   62 Black with Green.   63 Black with Purple.   64 Black with Brown.
65 Dark Green.   66 Light Green.

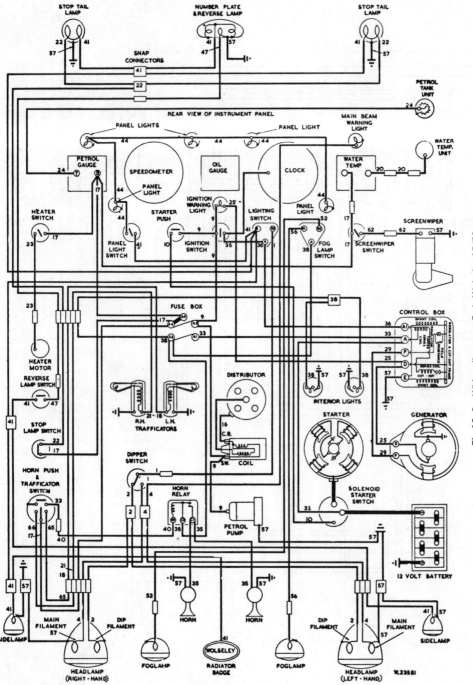

Fig 13:.6   Wiring diagram—Early Wolseley 15/50.

Key to Fig 13:6

1 Blue.	2 Blue with Red.	3 Blue with Yellow.	4 Blue with White.	5 Blue with Green.	6 Blue with Purple.	7 Blue with Brown.	8 Blue with Black.
9 White.	10 White with Red.	11 White with Yellow.	12 White with Blue.	13 White with Green.	14 White with Purple.	15 White with Brown.	16 White with Black.
17 Green.	18 Green with Red.	19 Green with Yellow.	20 Green with White.	21 Green with Blue.	22 Green with Purple.	23 Green with Brown.	24 Green with Black.
25 Yellow.	26 Yellow with Red.	27 Yellow with Blue.	28 Yellow with White.	29 Yellow with Green.	30 Yellow with Purple.	31 Yellow with Brown.	32 Yellow with Black.
33 Brown.	34 Brown witn Red.	35 Brown with Yellow.	36 Brown with Blue.	37 Brown with White.	38 Brown with Green.	39 Brown with Purple.	40 Brown with Black.
41 Red.	42 Red with Yellow.	43 Red with Blue.	44 Red with White.	45 Red with Green.	46 Red with Purple.	47 Red with Brown.	48 Red with Black.
49 Purple.	50 Purple with Red.	51 Purple with Yellow.	52 Purple with Blue.	53 Purple with White.	54 Purple with Green.	55 Purple with Brown.	56 Purple with Black.
57 Black.	58 Black with Red.	59 Black with Yellow.	60 Black with Blue.	61 Black with White.	62 Black with Green.	63 Black with Purple.	64 Black with Brown.
65 Dark Green.	66 Light Green.						

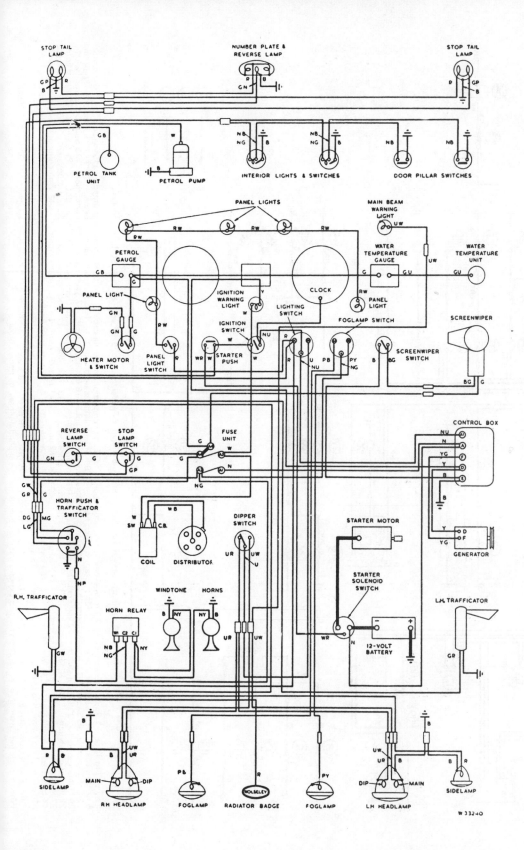

Fig 13:7 Wiring diagram—Later Wolseley 15/50, starting Car No. 31901.

Key to Fig 13:7 CABLE COLOUR CODE. B Black. N Brown. G Green. U Blue. P Purple. R Red. S Slate. W White. Y Yellow. L Light. D Dark. M Medium.
When a cable has two-colour code letters the first denotes the main colour and the second denotes the tracer colour.

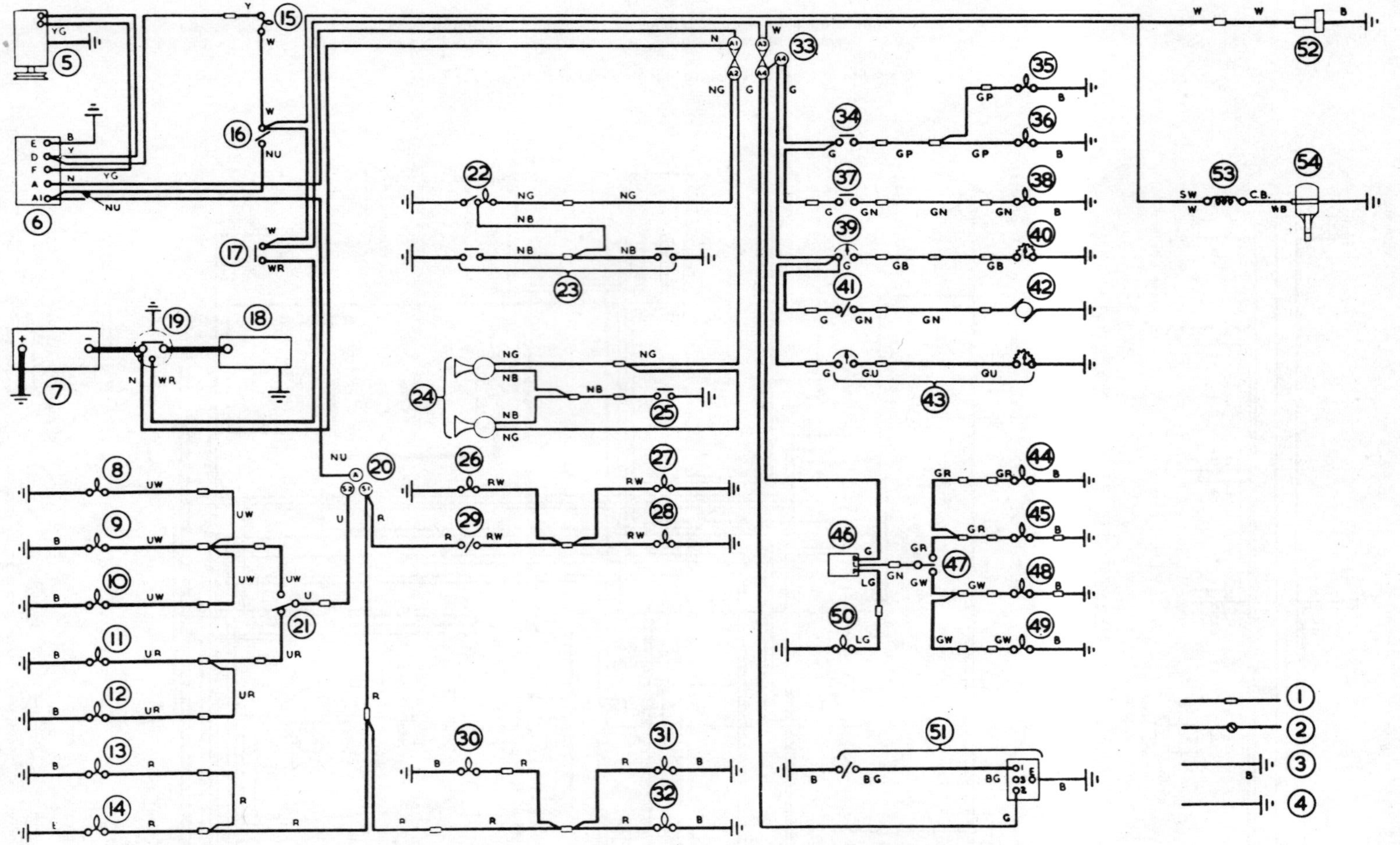

Fig 13:8　Wiring diagram—Wolseley 1500 and Riley 1.5 (Wolseley, not 26, 37 and 38. Read BG for GU in 43).

Key to Fig 13:8　1 Snap connectors.　2 Terminal blocks or junction box.　3 Earth connections made via cable.　4 Earth connections made via fixing bolt.　5 Generator.
6 Control box.　7 12-volt battery.　8 Main-beam warning light.　9 R.H. headlamp main beam.　10 L.H. headlamp main beam.　11 R.H. headlamp dip beam.
12 L.H. headlamp dip beam.　13 L.H. pilot lamp.　14 R.H. pilot lamp.　15 Ignition warning light.　16 Ignition switch.　17 Starter push.　18 Starter motor.　19 Solenoid starter switch.
20 Lighting switch.　21 Dipper switch.　22 Interior light and switch.　23 Interior light door switches.　24 Horns.　25 Horn-push.　26 Panel light.　27 Panel light.　28 Panel light.
29 Panel light switch.　30 L.H. tail lamp.　31 R.H. tail lamp.　32 Number-plate lamp.　33 Fuse unit.　34 Stop lamp switch.　35 L.H. stop lamp.　36 R.H. stop lamp.
37 Reverse lamp switch.　38 Reverse lamp.　39 Fuel gauge.　40 Fuel tank unit.　41 Heater switch.　42 Heater motor.　43 Water temperature gauge and unit.
44 L.H. rear flasher.　45 L.H. front flasher.　46 Flasher unit.　47 Flasher switch.　48 R.H. front flasher.　49 R.H. rear flasher.　50 Flasher warning light.
51 Screen wiper switch and motor.　52 Fuel pump.　53 Ignition coil.　54 Distributor.

CABLE COLOUR CODE　B Black.　U Blue.　N Brown.　G Green.　P Purple.　R Red.　S Slate.　W White.　Y Yellow.　L Light.　D Dark.　M Medium.
When a cable has two-colour code letters the first denotes the main colour and the second denotes the tracer colour.

176

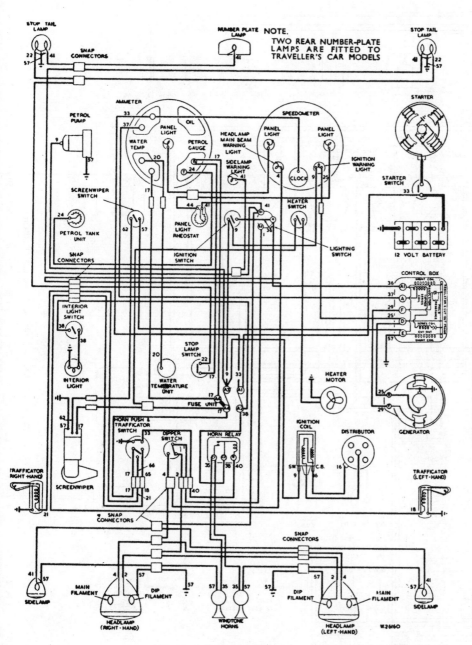

Fig 13:9   Wiring diagram — Morris Oxford 11.

Key to Fig 13:9 1 Blue. 2 Blue with Red. 3 Blue with Red. 4 Blue with White. 5 Blue with White. 6 Blue with Purple. 7 Blue with Brown. 8 Blue with Black.
9 White. 10 White with Red. 11 White with Yellow. 12 White with Blue. 13 White with Green. 14 White with Purple. 15 White with Brown. 16 White with Black.
17 Green. 18 Green with Red. 19 Green with Yellow. 20 Green with Blue. 21 Green with White. 22 Green with Purple. 23 Green with Brown. 24 Green with Black.
25 Yellow. 26 Yellow with Red. 27 Yellow with Yellow. 28 Yellow with Blue. 29 Yellow with White. 30 Yellow with Green. 31 Yellow with Brown. 32 Yellow with Black.
33 Brown. 34 Brown with Red. 35 Brown with Yellow. 36 Brown with Blue. 37 Brown with White. 38 Brown with Green. 39 Brown with Purple. 40 Brown with Black.
41 Red. 42 Red with Yellow. 43 Red with Blue. 44 Red with White. 45 Red with Green. 46 Red with Purple. 47 Red with Brown. 48 Red with Black.
49 Purple. 50 Purple with Red. 51 Purple with Yellow. 52 Purple with Blue. 53 Purple with White. 54 Purple with Green. 55 Purple with Brown. 56 Purple with Black.
57 Black. 58 Black with Red. 59 Black with Yellow. 60 Black with Blue. 61 Black with White. 62 Black with Green. 63 Black with Purple. 64 Black with Brown.
65 Dark Green. 66 Light Green.

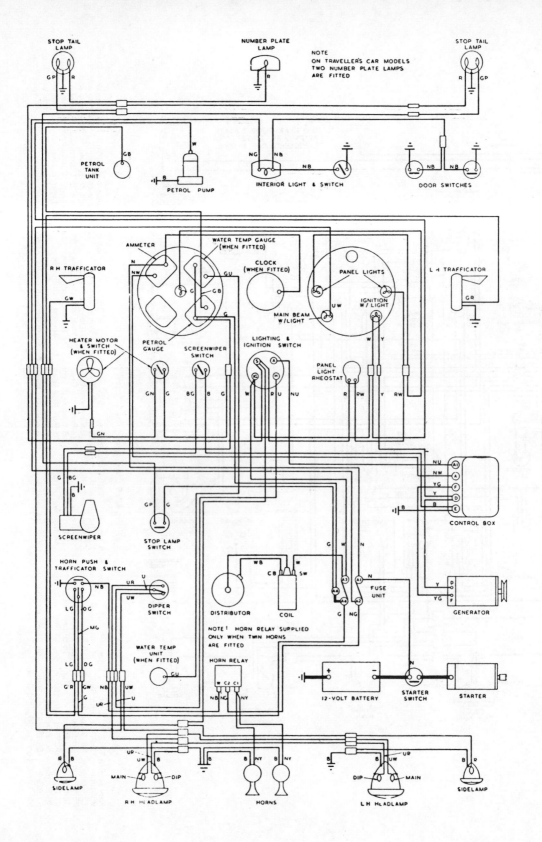

Fig 13:10 Wiring diagram—Morris Oxford 111 (Trafficators).

Key to Fig 13:10 CABLE COLOUR CODE B Black. U Blue. N Brown. G Green. P Purple. R Red. S Slate. W White. Y Yellow. L Light. D Dark. M Medium.

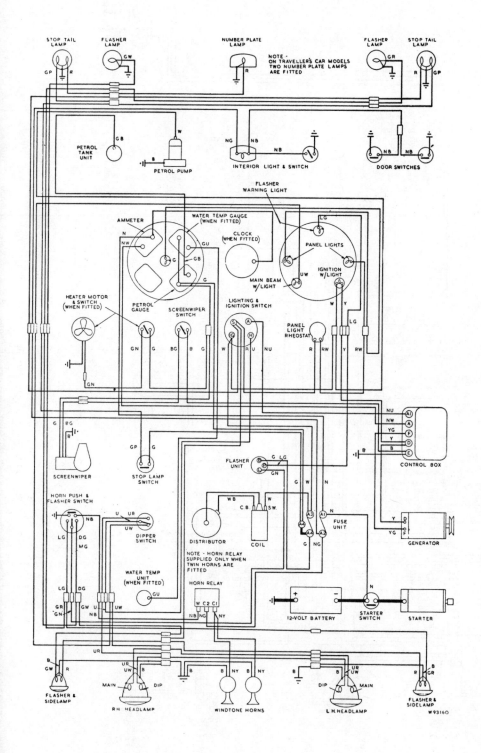

Fig 13:11 Wiring diagram—Morris Oxford 111 (Flashers).

Key to Fig 13:11 CABLE COLOUR CODE B Black. U Blue. N Brown. G Green. P Purple. R Red. S Slate. W White. Y Yellow. L Light. D Dark. M Medium.

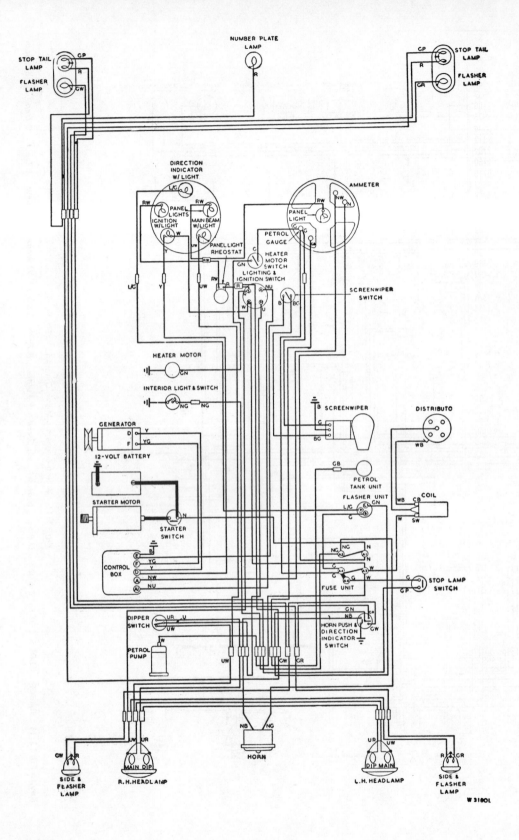

Fig 13:12 Wiring diagram—Morris Oxford 111, Half-ton van.

Key to Fig 13:12 CABLE COLOUR CODE. B Black. U Blue. N Brown. G Green. P Purple. R Red. S Slate. W White. Y Yellow. L Light. D Dark. M Medium.

Inches	Decimals	Milli-metres	Inches to Millimetres — Inches	Inches to Millimetres — mm	Millimetres to Inches — mm	Millimetres to Inches — Inches
$\frac{1}{64}$	.015625	.3969	.001	.0254	.01	.00039
$\frac{1}{32}$	.03125	.7937	.002	.0508	.02	.00079
$\frac{3}{64}$	.046875	1.1906	.003	.0762	.03	.00118
$\frac{1}{16}$	.0625	1.5875	.004	.1016	.04	.00157
$\frac{5}{64}$	.078125	1.9844	.005	.1270	.05	.00197
$\frac{3}{32}$	.09375	2.3812	.006	.1524	.06	.00236
$\frac{7}{64}$	.109375	2.7781	.007	.1778	.07	.00276
$\frac{1}{8}$	.125	3.1750	.008	.2032	.08	.00315
$\frac{9}{64}$	.140625	3.5719	.009	.2286	.09	.00354
$\frac{5}{32}$	.15625	3.9687	.01	.254	.1	.00394
$\frac{11}{64}$	.171875	4.3656	.02	.508	.2	.00787
$\frac{3}{16}$	.1875	4.7625	.03	.762	.3	.01181
$\frac{13}{64}$	.203125	5.1594	.04	1.016	.4	.01575
$\frac{7}{32}$	.21875	5.5562	.05	1.270	.5	.01969
$\frac{15}{64}$	.234375	5.9531	.06	1.524	.6	.02362
$\frac{1}{4}$	.25	6.3500	.07	1.778	.7	.02756
$\frac{17}{64}$	.265625	6.7469	.08	2.032	.8	.03150
$\frac{9}{32}$	.28125	7.1437	.09	2.286	.9	.03543
$\frac{19}{64}$	.296875	7.5406	.1	2.54	1	.03937
$\frac{5}{16}$	.3125	7.9375	.2	5.08	2	.07874
$\frac{21}{64}$	.328125	8.3344	.3	7.62	3	.11811
$\frac{11}{32}$	.34375	8.7312	.4	10.16	4	.15748
$\frac{23}{64}$	.359375	9.1281	.5	12.70	5	.19685
$\frac{3}{8}$	.375	9.5250	.6	15.24	6	.23622
$\frac{25}{64}$	.390625	9.9219	.7	17.78	7	.27559
$\frac{13}{32}$	.40625	10.3187	.8	20.32	8	.31496
$\frac{27}{64}$	.421875	10.7156	.9	22.86	9	.35433
$\frac{7}{16}$	.4375	11.1125	1	25.4	10	.39370
$\frac{29}{64}$	.453125	11.5094	2	50.8	11	.43307
$\frac{15}{32}$	.46875	11.9062	3	76.2	12	.47244
$\frac{31}{64}$	.484375	12.3031	4	101.6	13	.51181
$\frac{1}{2}$	.5	12.7000	5	127.0	14	.55118
$\frac{33}{64}$	.515625	13.0969	6	152.4	15	.59055
$\frac{17}{32}$	.53125	13.4937	7	177.8	16	.62992
$\frac{35}{64}$	.546875	13.8906	8	203.2	17	.66929
$\frac{9}{16}$	.5625	14.2875	9	228.6	18	.70866
$\frac{37}{64}$	.578125	14.6844	10	254.0	19	.74803
$\frac{19}{32}$	.59375	15.0812	11	279.4	20	.78740
$\frac{39}{64}$	.609375	15.4781	12	304.8	21	.82677
$\frac{5}{8}$	.625	15.8750	13	330.2	22	.86614
$\frac{41}{64}$	.640625	16.2719	14	355.6	23	.90551
$\frac{21}{32}$	.65625	16.6687	15	381.0	24	.94488
$\frac{43}{64}$	.671875	17.0656	16	406.4	25	.98425
$\frac{11}{16}$	.6875	17.4625	17	431.8	26	1.02362
$\frac{45}{64}$	.703125	17.8594	18	457.2	27	1.06299
$\frac{23}{32}$	.71875	18.2562	19	482.6	28	1.10236
$\frac{47}{64}$	.734375	18.6531	20	508.0	29	1.14173
$\frac{3}{4}$	.75	19.0500	21	533.4	30	1.18110
$\frac{49}{64}$	.765625	19.4469	22	558.8	31	1.22047
$\frac{25}{32}$	.78125	19.8437	23	584.2	32	1.25984
$\frac{51}{64}$	.796875	20.2406	24	609.6	33	1.29921
$\frac{13}{16}$	.8125	20.6375	25	635.0	34	1.33858
$\frac{53}{64}$	.828125	21.0344	26	660.4	35	1.37795
$\frac{27}{32}$	.84375	21.4312	27	685.8	36	1.41732
$\frac{55}{64}$	.859375	21.8281	28	711.2	37	1.4567
$\frac{7}{8}$	.875	22.2250	29	736.6	38	1.4961
$\frac{57}{64}$	.890625	22.6219	30	762.0	39	1.5354
$\frac{29}{32}$	.90625	23.0187	31	787.4	40	1.5748
$\frac{59}{64}$	.921875	23.4156	32	812.8	41	1.6142
$\frac{15}{16}$	.9375	23.8125	33	838.2	42	1.6535
$\frac{61}{64}$	.953125	24.2094	34	863.6	43	1.6929
$\frac{31}{32}$	.96875	24.6062	35	889.0	44	1.7323
$\frac{63}{64}$	.984375	25.0031	36	914.4	45	1.7717

UNITS	Pints to Litres	Gallons to Litres	Litres to Pints	Litres to Gallons	Miles to Kilometres	Kilometres to Miles	Lbs. per sq. In. to Kg. per sq. Cm.	Kg. per sq. Cm. to Lbs. per sq. In.
1	.57	4.55	1.76	.22	1.61	.62	.07	14.22
2	1.14	9.09	3.52	.44	3.22	1.24	.14	28.50
3	1.70	13.64	5.28	.66	4.83	1.86	.21	42.67
4	2.27	18.18	7.04	.88	6.44	2.49	.28	56.89
5	2.84	22.73	8.80	1.10	8.05	3.11	.35	71.12
6	3.41	27.28	10.56	1.32	9.66	3.73	.42	85.34
7	3.98	31.82	12.32	1.54	11.27	4.35	.49	99.56
8	4.55	36.37	14.08	1.76	12.88	4.97	.56	113.79
9		40.91	15.84	1.98	14.48	5.59	.63	128.00
10		45.46	17.60	2.20	16.09	6.21	.70	142.23
20				4.40	32.19	12.43	1.41	284.47
30				6.60	48.28	18.64	2.11	426.70
40				8.80	64.37	24.85		
50					80.47	31.07		
60					96.56	37.28		
70					112.65	43.50		
80					128.75	49.71		
90					144.84	55.92		
100					160.93	62.14		

UNITS	Lb ft to kgm	Kgm to lb ft	UNITS	Lb ft to kgm	Kgm to lb ft
1	.138	7.233	7	.967	50.631
2	.276	14.466	8	1.106	57.864
3	.414	21.699	9	1.244	65.097
4	.553	28.932	10	1.382	72.330
5	.691	36.165	20	2.765	144.660
6	.829	43.398	30	4.147	216.990

182

HINTS ON MAINTENANCE AND OVERHAUL

There are few things more rewarding than the restora-
n of a vehicle's original peak of efficiency and smooth
rformance.

The following notes are intended to help the owner to
ch that state of perfection. Providing that he possesses
e basic manual skills he should have no difficulty in
rforming most of the operations detailed in this manual.
must be stressed, however, that where recommended in
e manual, highly-skilled operations ought to be entrusted
experts, who have the necessary equipment, to carry out
e work satisfactorily.

uality of workmanship:

The hazardous driving conditions on the roads to-day
mand that vehicles should be as nearly perfect,
echanically, as possible. It is therefore most important
at amateur work be carried out with care, bearing in
nd the often inadequate working conditions, and also
e inferior tools which may have to be used. It is easy to
unsel perfection in all things, and we recognize that it
ay be setting an impossibly high standard. We do,
wever, suggest that every care should be taken to ensure
at a vehicle is as safe to take on the road as it is humanly
ssible to make it.

fe working conditions:

Even though a vehicle may be stationary, it is still
tentially dangerous if certain sensible precautions are
t taken when working on it while it is supported on
cks or blocks. It is indeed preferable not to use jacks
one, but to supplement them with carefully placed
ocks, so that there will be plenty of support if the car
lls off the jacks during a strenuous manoeuvre. Axle
ands are an excellent way of providing a rigid base which
not readily disturbed. Piles of bricks are a dangerous sub-
tute. Be careful not to get under heavy loads on lifting
ckle, the load could fall. It is preferable not to work
one when lifting an engine, or when working under-
ath a vehicle which is supported well off the ground.
be trapped, particularly under the vehicle, may have
pleasant results if help is not quickly forthcoming. Make
me provision, however humble, to deal with fires.
ways disconnect a battery if there is a likelihood of
ectrical shorts. These may start a fire if there is leaking
el about. This applies particularly to leads which can
rry a heavy current, like those in the starter circuit.
hile on the subject of electricity, we must also stress the
nger of using equipment which is run off the mains
d which has no earth or has faulty wiring or connections.
many workshops have damp floors, and electrical
ocks are of such a nature that it is sometimes impossible
let go of a live lead or piece of equipment due to the
uscular spasms which take place.

ork demanding special care:

This involves the servicing of braking, steering and
spension systems. On the road, failure of the braking
stem may be disastrous. Make quite sure that there can
e no possibility of failure through the bursting of rusty
ake pipes or rotten hoses, nor to a sudden loss of pres-
re due to defective seals or valves.

Problems:

The chief problems which may face an operator are:
1 External dirt.
2 Difficulty in undoing tight fixings.
3 Dismantling unfamiliar mechanisms.
4 Deciding in what respect parts are defective.
5 Confusion about the correct order for reassembly.
6 Adjusting running clearance.
7 Road testing.
8 Final tuning.

Practical suggestions to solve the problems:

1 Preliminary cleaning of large parts—engines, trans-
missions, steering, suspensions, etc.,—should be
carried out before removal from the car. Where road
dirt and mud alone are present, wash clean with a high-
pressure water jet, brushing to remove stubborn
adhesions, and allow to drain and dry. Where oil or
grease is also present, wash down with a proprietary
compound (Gunk, Teepol etc.,) applying with a stiff
brush—an old paint brush is suitable—into all crevices.
Cover the distributor and ignition coils with a poly-
thene bag and then apply a strong water jet to clear the
loosened deposits. Allow to drain and dry. The
assemblies will then be sufficiently clean to remove and
transfer to the bench for the next stage.

On the bench, further cleaning can be carried out,
first wiping the parts as free as possible from grease
with old newspaper. Avoid using rag or cotton waste
which can leave clogging fibres behind. Any remaining
grease can be removed with a brush dipped in paraffin.
If necessary, traces of paraffin can be removed by
carbon tetrachloride. Avoid using paraffin or petrol in
large quantities for cleaning in enclosed areas, such as
garages, on account of the high fire risk.

When all exteriors have been cleaned, and not before,
dismantling can be commenced. This ensures that dirt
will not enter into interiors and orifices revealed by
dismantling. In the next phases, where components
have to be cleaned, use carbon tetrachloride in preference to petrol and keep the containers covered
except when in use. After the components have been
cleaned, plug small holes with tapered hard wood
plugs cut to size and blank off larger orifices with grease-
proof paper and masking tape. Do not use soft wood
plugs or matchsticks as they may break.

2 It is not advisable to hammer on the end of a screw
thread, but if it must be done, first screw on a nut to
protect the thread, and use a lead hammer. This applies
particularly to the removal of tapered cotters. Nuts and
bolts seem to 'grow' together, especially in exhaust
systems. If penetrating oil does not work, try the
judicious application of heat, but be careful of starting
a fire. Asbestos sheet or cloth is useful to isolate heat.

Tight bushes or pieces of tail-pipe rusted into a
silencer can be removed by splitting them with an
open-ended hacksaw. Tight screws can sometimes be
started by a tap from a hammer on the end of a suitable
screwdriver. Many tight fittings will yield to the judicious
use of a hammer, but it must be a soft-faced hammer if
damage is to be avoided, use a heavy block on the
opposite side to absorb shock. Any parts of the

steering system which have been damaged should be renewed, as attempts to repair them may lead to cracking and subsequent failure, and steering ball joints should be disconnected using a recommended tool to prevent damage.

3 It often happens that an owner is baffled when trying to dismantle an unfamiliar piece of equipment. So many modern devices are pressed together or assembled by spinning-over flanges, that they must be sawn apart. The intention is that the whole assembly must be renewed. However, parts which appear to be in one piece to the naked eye, may reveal close-fitting joint lines when inspected with a magnifying glass, and, this may provide the necessary clue to dismantling. Left-handed screw threads are used where rotational forces would tend to unscrew a right-handed screw thread.

Be very careful when dismantling mechanisms which may come apart suddenly. Work in an enclosed space where the parts will be contained, and drape a piece of cloth over the device if springs are likely to fly in all directions. Mark everything which might be reassembled in the wrong position, scratched symbols may be used on unstressed parts, or a sequence of tiny dots from a centre punch can be useful. Stressed parts should never be scratched or centre-popped as this may lead to cracking under working conditions. Store parts which look alike in the correct order for reassembly. Never rely upon memory to assist in the assembly of complicated mechanisms, especially when they will be dismantled for a long time, but make notes, and drawings to supplement the diagrams in the manual, and put labels on detached wires. Rust stains may indicate unlubricated wear. This can sometimes be seen round the outside edge of a bearing cup in a universal joint. Look for bright rubbing marks on parts which normally should not make heavy contact. These might prove that something is bent or running out of truth. For example, there might be bright marks on one side of a piston, at the top near the ring grooves, and others at the bottom of the skirt on the other side. This could well be the clue to a bent connecting rod. Suspected cracks can be proved by heating the component in a light oil to approximately 100°C, removing, drying off, and dusting with french chalk, if a crack is present the oil retained in the crack will stain the french chalk.

4 In determining wear, and the degree, against the permissible limits set in the manual, accurate measurement can only be achieved by the use of a micrometer. In many cases, the wear is given to the fourth place of decimals; that is in ten-thousandths of an inch. This can be read by the vernier scale on the barrel of a good micrometer. Bore diameters are more difficult to determine. If, however, the matching shaft is accurately measured, the degree of play in the bore can be felt as a guide to its suitability. In other cases, the shank of a twist drill of known diameter is a handy check.

Many methods have been devised for determining the clearance between bearing surfaces. To-day the best and simplest is by the use of Plastigage, obtainable from most garages. A thin plastic thread is laid between the two surfaces and the bearing is tightened, flattening the thread. On removal, the width of the thread is compared with a scale supplied with the thread and th clearance is read off directly. Sometimes joint face leak persistently, even after gasket renewal. The fau will then be traceable to distortion, dirt or burrs. Stud which are screwed into soft metal frequently raise bur at the point of entry. A quick cure for this is to chamf the edge of the hole in the part which fits over the stu

5 **Always check a replacement part with th original one before it is fitted.**

If parts are not marked, and the order for reassemb is not known, a little detective work will help. Look f marks which are due to wear to see if they can b mated. Joint faces may not be identical due to manu facturing errors, and parts which overlap may b stained, giving a clue to the correct position. Mo fixings leave identifying marks especially if they wer painted over on assembly. It is then easier to decid whether a nut, for instance, has a plain, a spring, or shakeproof washer under it. All running surface become 'bedded' together after long spells of work an tiny imperfections on one part will be found to have le corresponding marks on the other. This is particularl true of shafts and bearings and even a score on cylinder wall will show on the piston.

6 Checking end float or rocker clearances by feeler gaug may not always give accurate results because of wea For instance, the rocker tip which bears on a valve ste may be deeply pitted, in which case the feeler w simply be bridging a depression. Thrust washers ma also wear depressions in opposing faces to mak accurate measurement difficult. End float is then easi to check by using a dial gauge. It is common practice adjust end play in bearing assemblies, like front hub with taper rollers, by doing up the axle nut until the hu becomes stiff to turn and then backing it off a little. D not use this method with ballbearing hubs as th assembly is often preloaded by tightening the axle n to its fullest extent. If the splitpin hole will not line u file the base of the nut a little.

Steering assemblies often wear in the straight-ahea position. If any part is adjusted, make sure that remains free when moved from lock to lock. Do not b surprised if an assembly like a steering gearbox, whic is known to be carefully adjusted outside the ca becomes stiff when it is bolted in place. This will be du to distortion of the case by the pull of the mountin bolts, particularly if the mounting points are not a touching together. This problem may be met in othe equipment and is cured by careful attention to th alignment of mounting points.

When a spanner is stamped with a size and A/F means that the dimension is the width between th jaws and has no connection with ANF, which is th designation for the American National Fine threa Coarse threads like Whitworth are rarely used on car to-day except for studs which screw into soft aluminiu or cast iron. For this reason it might be found that th top end of a cylinder head stud has a fine thread and th lower end a coarse thread to screw into the cylinde block. If the car has mainly UNF threads then it i likely that any coarse threads will be UNC, which ar not the same as Whitworth. Small sizes have the sam number of threads in Whitworth and UNC, but in th $\frac{1}{2}$ inch size for example, there are twelve threads to th inch in the former and thirteen in the latter.

7 After a major overhaul, particularly if a great deal of work has been done on the braking, steering and suspension systems, it is advisable to approach the problem of testing with care. If the braking system has been overhauled, apply heavy pressure to the brake pedal and get a second operator to check every possible source of leakage. The brakes may work extremely well, but a leak could cause complete failure after a few miles.

Do not fit the hub caps until every wheel nut has been checked for tightness, and make sure the tyre pressures are correct. Check the levels of coolant, lubricants and hydraulic fluids. Being satisfied that all is well, take the car on the road and test the brakes at once. Check the steering and the action of the handbrake. Do all this at moderate speeds on quiet roads, and make sure there is no other vehicle behind you when you try a rapid stop.

Finally, remember that many parts settle down after a time, so check for tightness of all fixings after the car has been on the road for a hundred miles or so.

8 It is useless to tune an engine which has not reached its normal running temperature. In the same way, the tune of an engine which is stiff after a rebore will be different when the engine is again running free. Remember too, that rocker clearances on pushrod operated valve gear will change when the cylinder head nuts are tightened after an initial period of running with a new head gasket.

Trouble may not always be due to what seems the obvious cause. Ignition, carburation and mechanical condition are interdependent and spitting back through the carburetter, which might be attributed to a weak mixture, can be caused by a sticking inlet valve.

For one final hint on tuning, never adjust more than one thing at a time or it will be impossible to tell which adjustment produced the desired result.

GLOSSARY OF TERMS

Allen key   Cranked wrench of hexagonal section for use with socket head screws.

Alternator   Electrical generator producing alternating current. Rectified to direct current for battery charging.

Ambient temperature   Surrounding atmospheric temperature.

Annulus   Used in engineering to indicate the outer ring gear of an epicyclic gear train.

Armature   The shaft carrying the windings, which rotates in the magnetic field of a generator or starter motor. That part of a solenoid or relay which is activated by the magnetic field.

Axial   In line with, or pertaining to, an axis.

Backlash   Play in meshing gears.

Balance lever   A bar where force applied at the centre is equally divided between connections at the ends.

Banjo axle   Axle casing with large diameter housing for the crownwheel and differential.

Bendix pinion   A self-engaging and self-disengaging drive on a starter motor shaft.

Bevel pinion   A conical shaped gearwheel, designed to mesh with a similar gear with an axis usually at 90 deg. to its own.

bhp   Brake horse power, measured on a dynamometer.

bmep   Brake mean effective pressure. Average pressure on a piston during the working stroke.

Brake cylinder   Cylinder with hydraulically operated piston(s) acting on brake shoes or pad(s).

Brake regulator   Control valve fitted in hydraulic braking system which limits brake pressure to rear brakes during heavy braking to prevent rear wheel locking.

Camber   Angle at which a wheel is tilted from the vertical.

Capacitor   Modern term for an electrical condenser. Part of distributor assembly, connected across contact breaker points, acts as an interference suppressor.

Castellated   Top face of a nut, slotted across the flats, to take a locking splitpin.

Castor   Angle at which the kingpin or swivel pin is tilted when viewed from the side.

cc   Cubic centimetres. Engine capacity is arrived at by multiplying the area of the bore in sq cm by the stroke in cm by the number of cylinders.

Clevis   U-shaped forked connector used with a clevis pin, usually at handbrake connections.

Collet   A type of collar, usually split and located in a groove in a shaft, and held in place by a retainer. The arrangement used to retain the spring(s) on a valve stem in most cases.

Commutator   Rotating segmented current distributor between armature windings and brushes in generator or motor.

Compression   The ratio, or quantitative relation, of the total volume (piston at bottom of stroke) to the unswept volume (piston at top of stroke) in an engine cylinder.

Condenser   See capacitor.

Core plug   Plug for blanking off a manufacturing hole in a casting.

Crownwheel   Large bevel gear in rear axle, driven by a bevel pinion attached to the propeller shaft. Sometimes called a 'ring wheel'.

'C'-spanner   Like a 'C' with a handle. For use on screwed collars without flats, but with slots or holes.

Damper   Modern term for shock-absorber, used in vehicle suspension systems to damp out spring oscillations.

Depression   The lowering of atmospheric pressure as in the inlet manifold and carburetter.

Dowel   Close tolerance pin, peg, tube, or bolt, which accurately locates mating parts.

Drag link   Rod connecting steering box drop arm (pitman arm) to nearest front wheel steering arm in certain types of steering systems.

Dry liner   Thinwall tube pressed into cylinder ball.

Dry sump   Lubrication system where all oil is scavenged from the sump, and returned to a separate tank.

Dynamo   See Generator.

Electrode   Terminal, part of an electrical component, such as the points or 'Electrodes' of a sparking plug.

Electrolyte   In lead-acid car batteries a solution of sulphuric acid and distilled water.

End float   The axial movement between associated parts, end play.

EP   Extreme pressure. In lubricants, special grades for heavily loaded bearing surfaces, such as gear teeth in a gearbox, or crownwheel and pinion in a rear axle.

Fade	Of brakes. Reduced efficiency due to overheating.
Field coils	Windings on the polepieces of motors and generators.
Fillets	Narrow finishing strips usually applied to interior bodywork.
First motion shaft	Input snaft from clutch to gearbox.
Fullflow filter	Filters in which all the oil is pumped to the engine. If the element becomes clogged, a bypass valve operates to pass unfiltered oil to the engine.
FWD	Front wheel drive.
Gear pump	Two meshing gears in a close fitting casing. Oil is carried from the inlet round the outside of both gears in the spaces between the gear teeth and casing to the outlet, the meshing gear teeth prevent oil passing back to the inlet, and the oil is forced through the outlet port.
Generator	Modern term for 'Dynamo'. When rotated produces electrical current.
Grommet	A ring of protective or sealing material. Can be used to protect pipes or leads passing through bulkheads.
Grubscrew	Fully threaded headless screw with screwdriver slot. Used for locking, or alignment purposes.
Gudgeon pin	Shaft which connects a piston to its connecting rod. Sometimes called 'wrist pin', or 'piston pin'.
Halfshaft	One of a pair transmitting drive from the differ ntial.
Helical	In spiral form. The teeth of helical gears are cut at a spiral angle to the side faces of the gearwheel.
Hot spot	Hot area that assists vapourisation of fuel on its way to cylinders. Often provided by close contact between inlet and exhaust manifolds.
HT	High Tension. Applied to electrical current produced by the ignition coil for the sparking plugs.
Hydrometer	A device for checking specific gravity of liquids. Used to check specific gravity of electrolyte.
Hypoid bevel gears	A form of bevel gear used in the rear axle drive gears. The bevel pinion meshes below the centre line of the crownwheel, giving a lower propeller shaft line.
Idler	A device for passing on movement. A free running gear between driving and driven gears. A lever transmitting track rod movement to a side rod in steering gear.
Impeller	A centrifugal pumping element. Used in water pumps to stimulate flow.

Journals	Those parts of a shaft that are in contact with the bearings.
Kingpin	The main vertical pin which carries the front wheel spindle, and permits steering movement. May be called 'steering pin' or 'swivel pin'.
Layshaft	The shaft which carries the laygear in the gearbox. The laygear is driven by the first motion shaft and drives the third motion shaft according to the gear selected. Sometimes called the 'countershaft' or 'second motion shaft.'
lb ft	A measure of twist or torque. A pull of 10 lb at a radius of 1 ft is a torque of 10 lb ft.
lb/sq in	Pounds per square inch.
Little-end	The small, or piston end of a connecting rod. Sometimes called the 'small-end'.
LT	Low Tension. The current output from the battery.
Mandrel	Accurately manufactured bar or rod used for test or centring purposes.
Manifold	A pipe, duct, or chamber, with several branches.
Needle rollers	Bearing rollers with a length many times their diameter.
Oil bath	Reservoir which lubricates parts by immersion. In air filters, a separate oil supply for wetting a wire mesh element to hold the dust.
Oil wetted	In air filters, a wire mesh element lightly oiled to trap and hold airborne dust.
Overlap	Period during which inlet and exhaust valves are open together.
Panhard rod	Bar connected between fixed point on chassis and another on axle to control sideways movement.
Pawl	Pivoted catch which engages in the teeth of a ratchet to permit movement in one direction only.
Peg spanner	Tool with pegs, or pins, to engage in holes or slots in the part to be turned.
Pendant pedals	Pedals with levers that are pivoted at the top end.
Phillips screwdriver	A cross-point screwdriver for use with the cross-slotted heads of Phillips screws.
Pinion	A small gear, usually in relation to another gear.
Piston-type damper	Shock absorber in which damping is controlled by a piston working in a closed oil-filled cylinder.
Preloading	Preset static pressure on ball or roller bearings not due to working loads.
Radial	Radiating from a centre, like the spokes of a wheel.

Radius rod	Pivoted arm confining movement of a part to an arc of fixed radius.
Ratchet	Toothed wheel or rack which can move in one direction only, movement in the other being prevented by a pawl.
Ring gear	A gear tooth ring attached to outer periphery of flywheel. Starter pinion engages with it during starting.
Runout	Amount by which rotating part is out of true.
Semi-floating axle	Outer end of rear axle halfshaft is carried on bearing inside axle casing. Wheel hub is secured to end of shaft.
Servo	A hydraulic or pneumatic system for assisting, or, augmenting a physical effort. See 'Vacuum Servo'.
Setscrew	One which is threaded for the full length of the shank.
Shackle	A coupling link, used in the form of two parallel pins connected by side plates to secure the end of the master suspension spring and absorb the effects of deflection.
Shell bearing	Thinwalled steel shell lined with anti-friction metal. Usually semi-circular and used in pairs for main and big-end bearings.
Shock absorber	See 'Damper'.
Silentbloc	Rubber bush bonded to inner and outer metal sleeves.
Socket-head screw	Screw with hexagonal socket for an Allen key.
Solenoid	A coil of wire creating a magnetic field when electric current passes through it. Used with a soft iron core to operate contacts or a mechanical device.
Spur gear	A gear with teeth cut axially across the periphery.
Stub axle	Short axle fixed at one end only.
Tachometer	An instrument for accurate measurement of rotating speed. Usually indicates in revolutions per minute.

TDC	Top Dead Centre. The highest point reached by a piston in a cylinder, with the crank and connecting rod in line.
Thermostat	Automatic device for regulating temperature. Used in vehicle coolant systems to open a valve which restricts circulation at low temperature.
Third motion shaft	Output shaft of gearbox.
Threequarters floating axle	Outer end of rear axle halfshaft flanged and bolted to wheel hub, which runs bearing mounted on outside of axle casing. Vehicle weight is not carried by the axle shaft.
Thrust bearing or washer	Used to reduce friction in rotating parts subject to axial loads.
Torque	Turning or twisting effort. See 'lb ft'.
Track rod	The bar(s) across the vehicle which connect the steering arms and maintain the front wheels in their correct alignment.
UJ	Universal joint. A coupling between shafts which permits angular movement.
UNF	Unified National Fine screw thread.
Vacuum servo	Device used in brake system, using difference between atmospheric pressure and inlet manifold depression to operate a piston which acts to augment brake pressure as required. See 'Servo'.
Venturi	A restriction or 'choke' in a tube, as in a carburetter, used to increase velocity to obtain a reduction in pressure.
Vernier	A sliding scale for obtaining fractional readings of the graduations of an adjacent scale.
Welch plug	A domed thin metal disc which is partially flattened to lock in a recess. Used to plug core holes in castings.
Wet liner	Removeable cylinder barrel, sealed against coolant leakage, where the coolant is in direct contact with the outer surface.
Wet sump	A reservoir attached to the crankcase to hold the lubricating oil.

INDEX

THE AUTOBOOK SERIES OF WORKSHOP MANUALS

Make				Author	Title
ALFA ROMEO					
1600 Giulia TI 1962–67	..	..	..	Ball	Alfa Romeo Giulia 1962–70 Autobook
1600 Giulia Sprint 1962–68	.,	..	..	Ball	Alfa Romeo Giulia 1962–70 Autobook
1600 Giulia Spider 1962–68	..	..	..	Ball	Alfa Romeo Giulia 1962–70 Autobook
1600 Giulia Super 1965–70	..	..	..	Ball	Alfa Romeo Giulia 1962–70 Autobook
ASTON MARTIN					
All models 1921–58	..	..	..	Coram	Aston Martin 1921–58 Autobook
AUSTIN					
A30 1951–56	..	..	..	Ball	Austin A30, A35, A40 Autobook
A35 1956–62	..	..	..	Ball	Austin A30, A35, A40 Autobook
A40 Farina 1957–67	..	..	..	Ball	Austin A30, A35, A40 Autobook
A40 Cambridge 1954–57	..	..	..	Ball	BMC Autobook Three
A50 Cambridge 1954–57	..	..	..	Ball	BMC Autobook Three
A55 Cambridge Mk 1 1957–58	..	..	..	Ball	BMC Autobook Three
A55 Cambridge Mk 2 1958–61	..	..	..	Smith	BMC Autobook One
A60 Cambridge 1961–69	..	..	..	Smith	BMC Autobook One
A99 1959–61	..	..	..	Ball	BMC Autobook Four
A110 1961–68	..	..	..	Ball	BMC Autobook Four
Mini 1959–70	..	..	..	Ball	Mini 1959–70 Autobook
Mini Clubman 1969–70	..	..	..	Ball	Mini 1959–70 Autobook
Mini Cooper 1961–70	..	..	..	Ball	Mini Cooper 1961–70 Autobook
Mini Cooper S 1963–70	..	..	..	Ball	Mini Cooper 1961–70 Autobook
1100 Mk 1 1963–67	..	..	..	Ball	1100 Mk 1 1962–67 Autobook
1100 Mk 2 1968–70	..	..	..	Ball	1100 Mk 2, 1300 Mk 1, 2, America 1968–70 Autobook
1300 Mk 1, 2 1968–70	..	..	..	Ball	1100 Mk 2, 1300 Mk 1, 2, America 1968–70 Autobook
America 1968–70	..	..	..	Ball	1100 Mk 2, 1300 Mk 1, 2, America 1968–70 Autobook
1800 Mk 1, 2 1964–70	..	..	..	Ball	1800 1964–70 Autobook
1800S 1969–70	..	..	..	Ball	1800 1964–70 Autobook
Maxi 1969	..	..	..	Ball	Austin Maxi 1969 Autobook
AUSTIN HEALEY					
100/6 1956–59	..	..	..	Ball	Austin Healey 100/6, 3000 1956–68 Autobook
Sprite 1958–70	..	..	..	Ball	Sprite, Midget 1958–70 Autobook
3000 Mk 1, 2, 3 1959–68	..	..	..	Ball	Austin Healey 100/6, 3000 1956–68 Autobook
BEDFORD					
CA Mk 1 and 2 1961–69	..	..	..	Ball	Vauxhall Victor 1, 2 FB 1957–64 Autobook
Beagle HA 1964–66	..	..	..	Ball	Vauxhall Viva HA 1964–66 Autobook
BMW					
1600 1966–70	..	..	..	Ball	BMW 1600 1966–70 Autobook
1600–2 1966–70	..	..	..	Ball	BMW 1600 1966–70 Autobook
1600TI 1966–70	..	..	..	Ball	BMW 1600 1966–70 Autobook
1800 1964–70	..	..	..	Ball	BMW 1800 1964–70 Autobook
1800TI 1964–67	..	..	..	Ball	BMW 1800 1964–70 Autobook
2000 1966–70	..	..	..	Ball	BMW 2000, 2002 1966–70 Autobook
2000A 1966–70	..	..	..	Ball	BMW 2000, 2002 1966–70 Autobook
2000TI 1966–70	..	..	..	Ball	BMW 2000, 2002 1966–70 Autobook
2000CS 1967–70	..	..	..	Ball	BMW 2000, 2002 1966–70 Autobook
2000CA 1967–70	..	..	..	Ball	BMW 2000, 2002 1966–70 Autobook
2002 1968–70	..	..	..	Ball	BMW 2000, 2002 1966–70 Autobook
CITROEN					
DS19 1955–65	..	..	..	Ball	Citroen DS19, ID19 1955–66 Autobook
ID19 1956–66	..	..	..	Ball	Citroen DS19, ID19 1955–66 Autobook

BMC3

Make				Author	Title
COMMER					
Cob Series 1, 2, 3 1960–65	..	..	..	Ball	Hillman Minx 1 to 5 1956–65 Autobook
Imp Vans 1963–68	..	..	..	Smith	Hillman Imp 1963–68 Autobook
Imp Vans 1969–71	..	..	..	Ball	Hillman Imp 1969–71 Autobook
DE DION BOUTON					
One-cylinder 1899–1907	..	..	..	Mercredy	De Dion Bouton Autobook One
Two-cylinder 1903–1907	..	..	..	Mercredy	De Dion Bouton Autobook One
Four-cylinder 1905–1907	..	..	..	Mercredy	De Dion Bouton Autobook One
DATSUN					
1300 1968–70	..	..	..	Ball	Datsun 1300, 1600 1968–70 Autobook
1600 1968–70	..	..	..	Ball	Datsun 1300, 1600 1968–70 Autobook
FIAT					
500 1957–61	..	..	..	Ball	Fiat 500 1957–69 Autobook
500D 1960–65	..	..	..	Ball	Fiat 500 1957–69 Autobook
500F 1965–69	..	..	..	Ball	Fiat 500 1957–69 Autobook
500L 1968–69	..	..	..	Ball	Fiat 500 1957–69 Autobook
600 633cc 1955–61	..	..	..	Ball	Fiat 600, 600D 1955–69 Autobook
600D, 767cc 1960–69	..	..	..	Ball	Fiat 600, 600D 1955–69 Autobook
850 Sedan 1964–70	..	..	..	Ball	Fiat 850 1964–70 Autobook
850 Coupé 1965–70	..	..	..	Ball	Fiat 850 1964–70 Autobook
850 Roadster 1965–70	..	..	..	Ball	Fiat 850 1964–70 Autobook
850 Family 1965–70	..	..	..	Ball	Fiat 850 1964–70 Autobook
850 Sport 1968–70	..	..	..	Ball	Fiat 850 1964–70 Autobook
124 Saloon 1966–70	..	..	..	Ball	Fiat 124 1966–70 Autobook
124S 1968–70	..	..	..	Ball	Fiat 124 1966–70 Autobook
FORD					
Anglia 100E 1953–59	..	..	..	Ball	Ford Anglia Prefect 100E Autobook
Anglia 105E 1959–67	..	..	..	Smith	Ford Anglia 105E, Prefect 107E 1959–67 Autobook
Anglia Super 123E 1962–67	..	..	..	Smith	Ford Anglia 105E, Prefect 107E 1959–67 Autobook
Capri 109E 1962	..	..	..	Smith	Ford Classic, Capri 1961–64 Autobook
Capri 116E 1962–64	..	..	..	Smith	Ford Classic, Capri 1961–64 Autobook
Capri 1300, 1300GT 1968–69	..	..	..	Ball	Ford Capri 1968–69 Autobook
Capri 1600, 1600GT 1968–69	..	..	..	Ball	Ford Capri 1968–69 Autobook
Classic 109E 1961–62	..	..	..	Smith	Ford Classic, Capri 1961–64 Autobook
Classic 116E 1962–63	..	..	..	Smith	Ford Classic, Capri 1961–64 Autobook
Consul Mk 1 1950–56	..	..	..	Ball	Ford Consul Zephyr, Zodiac 1, 2 1950–62 Autobook
Consul Mk 2 1956–62	..	..	..	Ball	Ford Consul, Zephyr, Zodiac 1, 2 1950–62 Autobook
Corsair V4 3004E 1965–68	..	..	..	Smith	Ford Corsair V4 1965–68 Autobook
Corsair V4 GT 1965–66	..	..	..	Smith	Ford Corsair V4 1965–68 Autobook
Corsair V4 1663cc 1969–70	..	..	..	Ball	Ford Corsair V4 1969–70 Autobook
Corsair 2000, 2000E 1966–68	..	..	..	Smith	Ford Corsair V4 1965–68 Autobook
Corsair 2000, 2000E 1969–70	..	..	..	Ball	Ford Corsair V4 1969–70 Autobook
Cortina 113E 1962–66	..	..	..	Smith	Ford Cortina 1962–66 Autobook
Cortina Super 118E 1963–66	..	..	..	Smith	Ford Cortina 1962–66 Autobook
Cortina Lotus 125E 1963–66	..	..	..	Smith	Ford Cortina 1962–66 Autobook
Cortina GT 118E 1963–66	..	..	..	Smith	Ford Cortina 1962–66 Autobook
Cortina 1300 1967–68	..	..	..	Smith	Ford Cortina 1967–68 Autobook
Cortina 1300 1969–70	..	..	..	Ball	Ford Cortina 1969–70 Autobook
Cortina 1500 1967–68	..	..	..	Smith	Ford Cortina 1967–68 Autobook
Cortina 1600 (including Lotus) 1967–68		..	..	Smith	Ford Cortina 1967–68 Autobook
Cortina 1600 1969–70	..	..	..	Ball	Ford Cortina 1969–70 Autobook
Escort 100E 1955–59	..	..	..	Ball	Ford Anglia Prefect 100E Autobook
Escort 1100 1967–70	..	..	..	Ball	Ford Escort 1967–70 Autobook
Escort 1300 1967–70	..	..	..	Ball	Ford Escort 1967–70 Autobook
Prefect 100E 1954–59	..	..	..	Ball	Ford Anglia Prefect 100E Autobook
Prefect 107E 1959–61	..	..	..	Smith	Ford Anglia 105E, Prefect 107E 1959–67 Autobook
Popular 100E 1959–62	..	..	..	Ball	Ford Anglia Prefect 100E Autobook

Make				Author	Title
Squire 100E 1955–59	..	..	..	Ball	Ford Anglia Prefect 100E Autobook
Zephyr Mk 1 1950–56	..	..	..	Ball	Ford Consul, Zephyr, Zodiac 1, 2 1950–62 Autobook
Zephyr Mk 2 1956–62	..	..	..	Ball	Ford Consul, Zephyr, Zodiac 1, 2 1950–62 Autobook
Zephyr 4 Mk 3 1962–66	..	..	..	Ball	Ford Zephyr, Zodiac Mk 3 1962–66 Autobook
Zephyr 6 Mk 3 1962–66	..	..	..	Ball	Ford Zephyr, Zodiac Mk 3 1962–66 Autobook
Zodiac Mk 3 1962–66	..	..	..	Ball	Ford Zephyr, Zodiac Mk 3 1962–66 Autobook
Zodiac Mk 1 1953–56	..	..	..	Ball	Ford Consul, Zephyr, Zodiac 1, 2 1950–62 Autobook
Zodiac Mk 2 1956–62	..	..	..	Ball	Ford Consul, Zephyr, Zodiac 1, 2 1950–62 Autobook
Zephyr V4 2 litre 1966–69	..	..	..	Ball	Ford Zephyr V4, V6, Zodiac 1966–69 Autobook
Zephyr V6 2.5 litre 1966–69	..	..	..	Ball	Ford Zephyr V4, V6, Zodiac 1966–69 Autobook
Zodiac V6 3 litre 1966–69	..	..	..	Ball	Ford Zephyr V4, V6, Zodiac 1966–69 Autobook

HILLMAN

Hunter GT 1966–70	..	..	..	Ball	Hillman Hunter 1966–70 Autobook
Minx series 1, 2, 3 1956–59	..	..	..	Ball	Hillman Minx 1 to 5 1956–65 Autobook
Minx series 3A, 3B, 3C 1959–63	..	..	..	Ball	Hillman Minx 1 to 5 1956–65 Autobook
Minx series 5 1963–65	..	..	..	Ball	Hillman Minx 1 to 5 1956–65 Autobook
Minx series 6 1965–67	..	..	..	Ball	Hillman Minx 1965–67 Autobook
New Minx 1500, 1725 1966–70	..	..	..	Ball	Hillman Minx 1966–70 Autobook
Imp 1963–68	..	..	..	Smith	Hillman Imp 1963–68 Autobook
Imp 1969–71	..	..	..	Ball	Hillman Imp 1969–71 Autobook
Husky series 1, 2, 3 1958–65	..	..	..	Ball	Hillman Minx 1 to 5 1956–65 Autobook
Husky Estate 1969–71	..	..	..	Ball	Hillman Imp 1969–71 Autobook
Super Minx Mk 1, 2, 3 1961–65	..	..	..	Ball	Hillman Super Minx 1, 2, 3 1961–65 Autobook
Super Minx Mk 4 1965–67	..	..	..	Ball	Hillman Minx 1965–67 Autobook

HUMBER

Sceptre Mk 2 1965–67				Ball	Hillman Minx 1965–67 Autobook
Sceptre 1967–70	..	..	..	Ball	Hillman Hunter 1966–70 Autobook

JAGUAR

XK 120 1948–54	..	..	..	Ball	Jaguar XK120, 140, 150 Mk 7, 8, 9 1948–61 Autobook
XK 140 1954–57	..	..	..	Ball	Jaguar XK 120, 140, 150 Mk 7, 8, 9 1948–61 Autobook
XK 150 1957–61	..	..	..	Ball	Jaguar XK 120, 140, 150 Mk 7, 8, 9 1948–61 Autobook
XK 150S 1959–61	..	..	..	Ball	Jaguar XK 120, 140, 150 Mk 7, 8, 9 1948–61 Autobook
Mk 7, 7M, 8, 9 1950–61	..	..	..	Ball	Jaguar XK 120, 140, 150 Mk 7, 8, 9 1948–61 Autobook
2.4 Mk 1, 2 1955–67	..	..	..	Ball	Jaguar 2.4, 3.4, 3.8 Mk 1, 2 1955–69 Autobook
3.4 Mk 1, 2 1957–67	..	..	..	Ball	Jaguar 2.4, 3.4, 3.8 Mk 1, 2 1955–69 Autobook
3.8 Mk 2 1959–67	..	..	..	Ball	Jaguar 2.4, 3.4, 3.8 Mk 1, 2 1955–69 Autobook
240 1967–69	..	..	..	Ball	Jaguar 2.4, 3.4, 3.8 Mk 1, 2 1955–69 Autobook
340 1967–69	..	..	..	Ball	Jaguar 2.4, 3.4, 3.8 Mk 1, 2 1955–69 Autobook
E. Type 3.8 1961–65	..	..	..	Ball	Jaguar E Type 1961–70 Autobook
E Type 4.2 1964–69	..	..	..	Ball	Jaguar E Type 1961–70 Autobook
E Type 4.2 2+2 1966–70	..	..	..	Ball	Jaguar E Type 1961–70 Autobook
E Type 4.2 Series 2 1969–70	..	..	..	Ball	Jaguar E Type 1961–70 Autobook
S Type 3.4 1963–68	..	..	..	Ball	Jaguar S Type and 420 1963–68 Autobook
S Type 3.8 1963–68	..	..	..	Ball	Jaguar S Type and 420 1963–68 Autobook
420 1963–68	..	..	..	Ball	Jaguar S Type and 420 1963–68 Autobook
XJ6 2.8 litre 1968–70	..	..	..	Ball	Jaguar XJ6 1968–70 Autobook
XJ6 4.2 litre 1968–70	..	..	..	Ball	Jaguar XJ6 1968–70 Autobook

JOWETT

Javelin PA 1947–49	..	..	..	Mitchell	Jowett Javelin Jupiter 1947–53 Autobook
Javelin PB 1949–50	..	..	..	Mitchell	Jowett Javelin Jupiter 1947–53 Autobook
Javelin PC 1950–51	..	..	..	Mitchell	Jowett Javelin Jupiter 1947–53 Autobook
Javelin PD 1951–52	..	..	..	Mitchell	Jowett Javelin Jupiter 1947–53 Autobook
Javelin PE 1952–53	..	..	..	Mitchell	Jowett Javelin Jupiter 1947–53 Autobook
Jupiter Mk 1 SA 1949–52	..	..	..	Mitchell	Jowett Javelin Jupiter 1947–53 Autobook
Jupiter Mk 1A SC 1952–53	..	..	..	Mitchell	Jowett Javelin Jupiter 1947–53 Autobook

Make					Author	Title

LANDROVER

Series 1 1948–58	..	..	..	..	Ball	Landrover 1, 2 1948–61 Autobook
Series 2 1997 cc 1959–61	..	..	..		Ball	Landrover 1, 2 1948–61 Autobook
Series 2 2052 cc 1959–61	..	..	..		Ball	Landrover 1, 2 1948–61 Autobook
Series 2 2286 cc 1959–61	..	..	..		Ball	Landrover 2, 2A 1959–70 Autobook
Series 2A 2286 cc 1961–70	..	..	..		Ball	Landrover 2, 2A 1959–70 Autobook
Series 2A 2625 cc 1967–70	..	..	..		Ball	Landrover 2, 2A 1959–70 Autobook

MG

TA 1936–39	..	..	..	..	Ball	MG TA to TF 1936–55 Autobook
TB 1939	..	..	..	..	Ball	MG TA to TF 1936–55 Autobook
TC 1945–49	..	..	..	..	Ball	MG TA to TF 1936–55 Autobook
TD 1950–53	..	..	..	..	Ball	MG TA to TF 1936–55 Autobook
TF 1953–54	..	..	..	..	Ball	MG TA to TF 1936–55 Autobook
TF 1500 1954–55	..	..	..	..	Ball	MG TA to TF 1936–55 Autobook
Midget 1961–70	..	..	..	..	Ball	Sprite, Midget 1958–70 Autobook
Magnette ZA, ZB 1955–59	..	..	..		Ball	BMC Autobook Three
Magnette 3, 4 1959–68	..	..	..		Smith	BMC Autobook One
MGA 1500, 1600 1955–62	..	..	..		Ball	MGA, MGB 1955–68 Autobook
MGA Twin Cam 1958–60	..	..	..		Ball	MGA, MGB 1955–68 Autobook
MGB 1962–68	..	..	..	..	Ball	MGA, MGB 1955–68 Autobook
MGB 1969–70	..	..	..	..	Ball	MG MGB 1969–70 Autobook
1100 Mk 1 1962–67	..	..	..	..	Ball	1100 Mk 1 1962–67 Autobook
1100 Mk 2 1968	..	..	..	..	Ball	1100 Mk 2, 1300 Mk 1, 2, America Autobook
1300 Mk 1, 2 1968–70	..	..	..		Ball	1100 Mk 2, 1300 Mk 1, 2, America 1968–70 Autobook

MERCEDES BENZ

190B 1959–61	..	..	..	..	Ball	Mercedes-Benz 190B, C, 200 1959–68 Autobook
190C 1961–65	..	..	..	..	Ball	Mercedes-Benz 190B, C, 200 1959–68 Autobook
200 1965–68	..	..	..	..	Ball	Mercedes-Benz 190B, C, 200 1959–68 Autobook
220B 1959–65	..	..	..	..	Ball	Mercedes-Benz 220 1959–65 Autobook
220SB 1959–65	..	..	..	..	Ball	Mercedes-Benz 220 1959–65 Autobook
220SEB 1959–65	..	..	..	..	Ball	Mercedes-Benz 220 1959–65 Autobook
220SEBC 1961–65	..	..	..	..	Ball	Mercedes-Benz 220 1959–65 Autobook

MORGAN

Four wheelers 1936–69	..	..	..		Clarke	Morgan 1936–69 Autobook

MORRIS

Oxford 2, 3 1956–59	..	..	..	..	Ball	BMC Autobook Three
Oxford 5, 6 1959–69	..	..	..	..	Smith	BMC Autobook One
Minor series 2 1952–56	..	..	..		Ball	Morris Minor 1952–70 Autobook
Minor 1000 1957–70	..	..	..	..	Ball	Morris Minor 1952–70 Autobook
Mini 1959–70	..	..	..	..	Ball	Mini 1959–70 Autobook
Mini Clubman 1969–70	..	..	..		Ball	Mini 1959–70 Autobook
Mini Cooper 1961–70	..	..	..		Ball	Mini Cooper 1961–70 Autobook
Mini Cooper S 1963–70	..	..	..		Ball	Mini Cooper 1961–70 Autobook
1100 Mk 1 1962–67	..	..	..	..	Ball	1100 Mk 1 1962–67 Autobook
1100 Mk 2 1968–70	..	..	..	..	Ball	1100 Mk 2, 1300 Mk 1, 2, America 1968–70 Autobook
1300 Mk 1, 2 1968–70	..	..	..		Ball	1100 Mk 2, 1300 Mk 1, 2, America 1968–70 Autobook
1800 Mk 1, 2 1966–70	..	..	..		Ball	1800 1964–70 Autobook
1800S 1968–70	..	..	..	..	Ball	1800 1964–70 Autobook

OPEL

Kadett 993 cc 1962–65	..	..	..		Ball	Opel Kadett 1962–70 Autobook
Kadett 'B' 1965–70	..	..	..		Ball	Opel Kadett 1962–70 Autobook

PEUGEOT

404 1960–69	..	..	..	..	Ball	Peugeot 404 1960–69 Autobook

Make					Author	Title

PORSCHE

356A 1957–59	..	..	..	..	Ball	Porsche 356A, 356B, 356C 1957–65 Autobook
356B 1959–63					Ball	Porsche 356A, 356B, 356C 1957–65 Autobook
356C 1963–65					Ball	Porsche 356A, 356B, 356C 1957–65 Autobook
911 1964–67	..	..	..	..	Ball	Porsche 911 1964–69 Autobook
911L 1967–68					Ball	Porsche 911 1964–69 Autobook
911S 1966–69					Ball	Porsche 911 1964–69 Autobook
911T 1967–69	..	..	..	..	Ball	Porsche 911 1964–69 Autobook
911E 1968–69					Ball	Porsche 911 1964–69 Autobook

RENAULT

R4L 748cc, 845cc 1961–65	..	·	..	..	Ball	Renault R4, R4L, 4 1961–70 Autobook
R4 845cc 1962–66					Ball	Renault R4, R4L, 4 1961–70 Autobook
4 845cc 1966–70	..	..	..	..	Ball	Renault R4, R4L, 4 1961–70 Autobook
6 1968–70	..	..	..	..	Ball	Renault 6 1968–70 Autobook
R8 956cc 1962–65					Ball	Renault 8, 10, 1100 1962–70 Autobook
8 956cc, 1108cc 1965–70					Ball	Renault 8, 10, 1100 1962–70 Autobook
8S 1108cc 1968–70					Ball	Renault 8, 10, 1100 1962–70 Autobook
1100, 1108cc 1964–69					Ball	Renault 8, 10, 1100 1962–70 Autobook
R10 1108cc 1967–69					Ball	Renault 8, 10, 1100 1962–70 Autobook
10 1289cc 1969–70					Ball	Renault 8, 10, 1100 1962–70 Autobook
16 1470cc 1965–70					Ball	Renault R16 1965–70 Autobook
16TS 1565cc 1968–70					Ball	Renault R16 1965–70 Autobook

RILEY

1.5 1957–65	..			..	Ball	BMC Autobook Three
4/68 1959–61	..			..	Smith	BMC Autobook One
4/72 1961–69	..			..	Smith	BMC Autobook One
Elf Mk 1, 2, 3 1961–70					Ball	Mini 1959–70 Autobook
1100 Mk 1 1965–67	..				Ball	1100 Mk 1 1962–67 Autobook
1100 Mk 2 1968					Ball	1100 Mk 2, 1300 Mk 1, 2, America 1968–70 Autobook
1300 Mk 1, 2 1968–70					Ball	1100 Mk 2, 1300 Mk 1, 2, America 1968–70 Autobook

ROVER

60 1953–59	..	..		..	Ball	Rover 60–110 1953–64 Autobook
75 1954–59	..	..		..	Ball	Rover 60–110 1953–64 Autobook
80 1959–62	..	..		..	Ball	Rover 60–110 1953–64 Autobook
90 1954–59	..	..		..	Ball	Rover 60–110 1953–64 Autobook
95 1962–64					Ball	Rover 60–110 1953–64 Autobook
100 1959–62	..	..		..	Ball	Rover 60–110 1953–64 Autobook
105R 1957–58					Ball	Rover 60–110 1953–64 Autobook
105S 1957–59					Ball	Rover 60–110 1953–64 Autobook
110 1962–64	..	..		..	Ball	Rover 60–110 1953–64 Autobook
2000 SC 1963–69					Ball	Rover 2000 1963–69 Autobook
2000 TC 1963–69					Ball	Rover 2000 1963–69 Autobook
3 litre Saloon Mk 1, 1A 1958–62					Ball	Rover 3 litre 1958–67 Autobook
3 litre Saloon Mk 2, 3 1962–67					Ball	Rover 3 litre 1958–67 Autobook
3 litre Coupé 1965–67					Ball	Rover 3 litre 1958–67 Autobook
3500, 3500S 1968–70					Ball	Rover 3500, 3500S 1968–70 Autobook

SIMCA

1000 1961–68					Ball	Simca 1000 1961–70 Autobook
1000 GL 1963–70	..	..	..	..	Ball	Simca 1000 1961–70 Autobook
1000 GLS 1964–70					Ball	Simca 1000 1961–70 Autobook
1000 GLA 1966–70					Ball	Simca 1000 1961–70 Autobook
1100 LS 1967–70	..			..	Ball	Simca 1100 1967–70 Autobook
1100 GL, GLS 1967–70					Ball	Simca 1100 1967–70 Autobook
1200 1970	..	..	..	..	Ball	Simca 1100 1967–70 Autobook

Make	Author	Title

SINGER

	Author	Title
Chamois 1964–68	Smith	Hillman Imp 1963–68 Autobook
Chamois 1969–70	Ball	Hillman Imp 1969–71 Autobook
Chamois Sport 1964–68	Smith	Hillman Imp 1963–68 Autobook
Chamois Sport 1969–70	Ball	Hillman Imp 1969–71 Autobook
Gazelle series 2A 1958	Ball	Hillman Minx 1 to 5 1956–65 Autobook
Gazelle 3, 3A, 3B, 3C 1958–63	Ball	Hillman Minx 1 to 5 1956–65 Autobook
Gazelle series 5 1963–65	Ball	Hillman Minx 1 to 5 1956–65 Autobook
Gazelle series 6 1965–67	Ball	Hillman Minx 1965–67 Autobook
New Gazelle 1500, 1725 1966–70	Ball	Hillman Minx 1966–70 Autobook
Vogue series 4 1965–67	Ball	Hillman Minx 1965–67 Autobook
New Vogue 1966–70	Ball	Hillman Hunter 1966–70 Autobook

SKODA

	Author	Title
440, 445, 450 1957–69	Skoda	Skoda Autobook One

SUNBEAM

	Author	Title
Alpine series 1, 2, 3, 4 1959–65	Ball	Sunbeam Rapier Alpine 1955–65 Autobook
Alpine series 5 1965–67	Ball	Hillman Minx 1965–67 Autobook
Alpine 1969–70	Ball	Hillman Hunter 1966–70 Autobook
Rapier series 1, 2, 3, 3A, 4 1955–65	Ball	Sunbeam Rapier Alpine 1955–65 Autobook
Rapier series 5 1965–67	Ball	Hillman Minx 1965–67 Autobook
Rapier H.120 1967–70	Ball	Hillman Hunter 1966–70 Autobook
Imp Sport 1963–68	Smith	Hillman Imp 1963–68 Autobook
Imp Sport 1969–71	Ball	Hillman Imp 1969–71 Autobook
Stilletto 1967–68	Smith	Hillman Imp 1963–68 Autobook
Stilletto 1969–71	Ball	Hillman Imp 1969–71 Autobook

TOYOTA

	Author	Title
Corona 1500 Mk 1 1965–70	Ball	Toyota Corona 1500 Mk 1 1965–70 Autobook
Corona 1900 Mk 2 1969–70	Ball	Toyota Corona 1900 Mk 2 1969–70 Autobook

TRIUMPH

	Author	Title
TR2 1952–55	Ball	Triumph TR2, TR3, TR3A 1952–62 Autobook
TR3, TR3A 1955–62	Ball	Triumph TR2, TR3, TR3A 1952–62 Autobook
TR4, TR4A 1961–67	Ball	Triumph TR4, TR4A 1961–67 Autobook
TR5 1967–69	Ball	Triumph TR5, TR250, TR6 1967–70 Autobook
TR6 1969–70	Ball	Triumph TR5, TR250, TR6 1967–70 Autobook
TR250 1967–69	Ball	Triumph TR5, TR250, TR6 1967–70 Autobook
1300 1965–70	Ball	Triumph 1300 1965–70 Autobook
1300TC 1967–70	Ball	Triumph 1300 1965–70 Autobook
2000 1963–69	Ball	Triumph 2000 1963–69 Autobook
Herald 948 1959–64	Smith	Triumph Herald 1959–68 Autobook
Herald 1200 1961–68	Smith	Triumph Herald 1959–68 Autobook
Herald 1200 1969–70	Ball	Triumph Herald 1969–70 Autobook
Herald 12/50 1963–67	Smith	Triumph Herald 1959–68 Autobook
Herald 13/60 1967–68	Smith	Triumph Herald 1959–68 Autobook
Herald 13/60 1969–70	Ball	Triumph Herald 1969–70 Autobook
Spitfire 1962–68	Smith	Triumph Spitfire Vitessse 1962–68 Autobook
Spitfire Mk 3 1969–70	Ball	Triumph Spitfire Mk 3 1969–70 Autobook
Vitesse 1600 and 2 litre 1962–68	Smith	Triumph Spitfire Vitesse 1962–68 Autobook
Vitesse 2 litre 1969–70	Ball	Triumph GT6, Vitesse 2 litre 1969–70 Autobook
GT Six 2 litre 1966–68	Smith	Triumph Spitfire Vitesse 1962–68 Autobook
GT Six 1969–70	Ball	Triumph GT6, Vitesse 2 litre 1969–70 Autobook

VANDEN PLAS

	Author	Title
3 litre 1959–64	Ball	BMC Autobook Four
1100 Mk 1 1963–67	Ball	1100 Mk 1 1962–67 Autobook
1100 Mk 2 1968	Ball	1100 Mk 2, 1300 Mk 1, 2, America 1968–70 Autobook
1300 Mk 1, 2, 1968–70	Ball	1100 Mk 2, 1300 Mk 1, 2, America 1968–70 Autobook

Make	Author	Title

VAUXHALL

Make	Author	Title
Victor 1 1957–59	Ball	Vauxhall Victor 1, 2 FB 1957–64 Autobook
Victor 2 1959–61	Ball	Vauxhall Victor 1, 2 FB 1957–64 Autobook
Victor FB 1961–64	Ball	Vauxhall Victor 1, 2 FB 1957–64 Autobook
VX4/90 FBH 1961–64	Ball	Vauxhall Victor 1, 2 FB 1957–64 Autobook
Victor FC 101 1964–67	Ball	Vauxhall Victor 101 1964–67 Autobook
VX 4/90 FCH 1964–67	Ball	Vauxhall Victor 101 1964–67 Autobook
Victor FD 1599 cc 1967–69	Ball	Vauxhall Victor FD 1600, 2000 1967–69 Autobook
Victor FD 1975 cc 1967–69	Ball	Vauxhall Victor FD 1600, 2000 1967–69 Autobook
Velox, Cresta PA 1957–62	Ball	Vauxhall Velox Cresta 1957–70 Autobook
Velox, Cresta PB 1962–65	Ball	Vauxhall Velox Cresta 1957–70 Autobook
Cresta PC 1965–70	Ball	Vauxhall Velox Cresta 1957–70 Autobook
Viscount 1966–70	Ball	Vauxhall Velox Cresta 1957–70 Autobook
Viva HA (including 90) 1964–66	Ball	Vauxhall Viva HA 1964–66 Autobook
Viva HB (including 90 and SL90) 1966–69	Ball	Vauxhall Viva HB 1966–69 Autobook

VOLKSWAGEN

Make	Author	Title
1200 Beetle 1954–67	Ball	Volkswagen Beetle 1954–67 Autobook
1200 Beetle 1968–70	Ball	Volkswagen Beetle 1968–70 Autobook
1200 Karmann Ghia 1955–65	Ball	Volkswagen Beetle 1954–67 Autobook
1200 Transporter 1954–64	Ball	Volkswagen Transporter 1954–67 Autobook
1300 Beetle 1965–67	Ball	Volkswagen Beetle 1954–67 Autobook
1300 Beetle 1968–70	Bell	Volkswagen Beetle 1968–70 Autobook
1300 Karmann Ghia 1965–66	Ball	Volkswagen Beetle 1954–67 Autobook
1500 Beetle 1966–67	Ball	Volkswagen Beetle 1954–67 Autobook
1500 Beetle 1968–70	Ball	Volkswagen Beetle 1968–70 Autobook
1500 1961–65	Ball	Volkswagen 1500 1961–66 Autobook
1500N 1963–65	Ball	Volkswagen 1500 1961–66 Autobook
1500S 1963–65	Ball	Volkswagen 1500 1961–66 Autobook
1500A 1965–66	Ball	Volkswagen 1500 1961–66 Autobook
1500 Karmann Ghia 1966–67	Ball	Volkswagen Beetle 1954–67 Autobook
1500 Transporter 1963–67	Ball	Volkswagen Transporter 1954–67 Autobook
1500 Karmann Ghia 1968–70	Ball	Volkswagen Beetle 1968–70 Autobook

VOLVO

Make	Author	Title
121, 131, 221 1962–68	Ball	Volvo P120 1961–68 Autobook
122, 132, 222 1961–68	Ball	Volvo P120 1961–68 Autobook
123 GT 1967–68	Ball	Volvo P120 1961–68 Autobook

WOLSELEY

Make	Author	Title
1500 1959–65	Ball	BMC Autobook Three
15/50 1956–58	Ball	BMC Autobook Three
15/60 1958–61	Smith	BMA Autobook One
16/60 1961–69	Smith	BMC Autobook One
6/99 1959–61	Ball	BMC Autobook Four
6/110 1961–68	Ball	BMC Autobook Four
Hornet Mk 1, 2, 3 1961–70	Ball	Mini 1959–70 Autobook
1100 Mk 1 1965–67	Ball	1100 Mk 1 1962–67 Autobook
1100 Mk 2 1968	Ball	1100 Mk 2, 1300 Mk 1, 2, America 1968–70 Autobook
1300 Mk 1, 2 1968–70	Ball	1100 Mk 2, 1300 Mk 1, 2, America 1968–70 Autobook
18/85 Mk 1, 2 1967–70	Ball	1800 1964–70 Autobook
18/85S 1969–70	Ball	1800 1964–70 Autobook

NOTES

NOTES